A Volume in *The Life of Science Library* (No. 24)

THE HISTORY OF ASTRONOMY

the history of astronomy

Giorgio Abetti: TRANSLATED
FROM THE ITALIAN *STORIA DELL'ASTRONOMIA*
BY BETTY BURR ABETTI

ABELARD-SCHUMAN
London — New York

preface to the American edition

THE HISTORY OF ASTRONOMY IS PERHAPS
one of the most fascinating and interesting in the development of
scientific thought. Born from man's admiration and veneration of
grandiose phenomena, both natural and universal, and his need to
understand them, at first very slowly and then very rapidly with the
invention of optical means, astronomy has achieved goals which
might have seemed impossible.

In astronomical literature we cannot say that the history of astronomy has been overlooked, but we can say that it is not so rich as
the subject demands and that the histories are not numerous enough
to give a general idea of the great development. In the beginning
this development consisted of the work of a few famous pioneers
whose history is generally well known, but as we approach modern
times individual work loses itself more and more in collective work.
Although exceptional personalities always appear, nevertheless new
discoveries and results are often obtained from the work and contributions of many astronomers and by international co-operation.

Furthermore it is very helpful, I would say almost necessary, that
history not be written in one country alone. Linguistic differences
and other obvious difficulties, as for example that of the priority of
discoveries and inventions which often mature almost instantaneously
in several places, lead to different evaluations. Although he tries to
be objective, each person often writes his "own" history.

This history which we now present to English-speaking readers was written originally in Italian, and it is therefore evident why I have lingered more, in the course of its development, on the Italian personalities and on their contributions to astronomical progress. In truth these contributions, perhaps because the Italian language is not so widespread as other more universally spoken languages, often are not well known. Thus it may be helpful to record them and explain them with somewhat greater detail. Then by comparison with similar historical discussions originating in other countries, the reader may obtain a more complete and comprehensive picture of the history and development of astronomy.

I think that one cannot know astronomy really well without knowing its history and without considering the fact that this precise and elaborate science of the sky has been built up little by little from empiricism. Really marvelous results which could not have been hoped for or foreseen have been attained in relatively few years. The motions of the celestial bodies which seemed so mysterious and complicated and apparently contrary to every law have been clarified. For example, today we can determine, with the greatest precision, the positions of the components of the solar system for any instant in the past and future. Furthermore, we are about to unveil of what material the celestial bodies are constituted and in what physical conditions they exist. We are approaching the conception of "a harmony of creation," as Kepler says, and of a unity of matter in all the visible world. Everyone can see how much importance such a conception has for humanity in science, in philosophy, and in religion. This conception must not be ignored either as a whole or in its particulars, which are as interesting as in all the other sciences—we might say the more earthly sciences, which at first glance might seem more important for practical applications.

We say that astronomy sprang from man's need either to regulate his life with the change of time corresponding to the positions of the sun and the moon, or to satisfy his religious sentiments, or to interpret his superstitions regarding the influence of celestial bodies on human events and human health; and we may certainly maintain that astronomy, developing through error and understandable retrogression (common also to other sciences), has gradually raised itself above all the other sciences in dignity and magnificence, both as to the ends achieved and those sought.

Another inestimable value of astronomy is that which has been so nobly expressed by Sir David Gill, Astronomer Royal at the Cape of Good Hope. At the conclusion of his monumental studies to determine the distance of the sun from the earth and the mass of the moon by observations of the planetoids, Iris, Victoria, and Sappho, which he carried out in collaboration with the observations at Yale University, Leipzig, Göttingen, Bamberg (Germany), and Radcliffe (Oxford, England) in the years 1888-1889, he wrote:

> The following work is the outcome of co-operation on part of many astronomers and many observatories, to determine some of the fundamental constants of astronomy with a higher accuracy than had hitherto been attained. The wide-felt scientific need of such an undertaking may be assumed to be demonstrated by the fact that almost every astronomer who was appealed to entered with heart and soul into his allotted share of the work, and probably no similar astronomical undertaking has ever before received such universal and powerful co-operation. Such co-operation proves, if proof is necessary, that science knows no nationality, and that the common pursuit of truth for truth's sake affords "one touch of nature" which "makes the whole world kin."

The importance of international collaboration for the study of the sky has become more manifest in other enterprises in which observatories and astronomers all over the world have taken part. In 1922 the International Astronomical Union was established, and from the time of its foundation to the present it has developed, as we shall see in the course of this history, an intensive program of work and has achieved extraordinary results.

We remind the reader of this history that it can be nothing but a summary of the vast amount of material which only a complete history could adequately present. Astronomy in its various branches— theoretical, observational, experimental (which it comprises especially in modern research)—continuously broadens its field of action and more and more makes use of and co-operates with the related sciences. I only hope that the more essential and fundamental facts have been recorded here and may be a guide to those who wish to widen their knowledge in this field.

What the future story of astronomy will be is very difficult to predict, but it is certain that the enormous progress in the theory, in the technical means, and in the connection with the related sciences promises an ever more interesting future rich in achievement.

Arcetri–Florence, Italy   GIORGIO ABETTI
July, 1951

contents

illustrations

17. French Universal Ring Dial made by Chapotot, Paris, about 1600.

18. Quadrant, Tyrolean, date about 1600.

19. Hevelius with a quadrant, one of his 17th century observing instruments.

20. Hevelius and his wife measuring stellar altitudes.

21. Isaac Newton.

22. Eichner model of Newtonian telescope.

23. Lord Rosse's Great Telescope.

24. A view of The Inhabitants of The Moon as seen through the telescope of Sir John Herschel.

25. William Herschel.

26. Sir William Herschel's 40 ft. reflecting telescope.

27. Giovanni Virginio Schiaparelli, famous Italian Astronomer.

28. Halley's Comet, 1910; May 12th and 15th.

29. Albert Einstein.

30. A. S. Eddington.

31. A Giant Bolide or Meteor, Prague, Czechoslovakia.

32. Spectograph attached to the 100″ telescope at Mount Wilson Observatory.

33. Dome of the 72″ reflection telescope, Dominion Observatory, Victoria, B.C.

34. The 72″ reflection telescope, Dominion Observatory, Victoria, B.C.

35. The Dome of the 26″ telescope of The Naval Observatory, Washington, D.C.

36. The 48″ Schmidt telescope.

37. The 60 ft. dome, and 150 ft. tower telescopes from the balcony of the Hooker Telescope Dome.

38. The 200″ Hale telescope.

39. The 200″ Hale telescope pointing to zenith.

40. A Miniature model of the 200″ Hale telescope.

41. The Dome of the 200″ Hale reflector showing entrance.

I : FROM THE BEGINNING TO COPERNICUS

1 : primeval times

MAN, CREATED BY GOD TO DWELL UPON THE
earth, can easily and comfortably, because of his upright posture, turn
his eyes to the sky. In the primeval ages, before any glimmer of civilization existed, he surely must have admired and enjoyed the spectacle
of the heavens, the daily journey of the sun, its rising and setting, the
appearance and disappearance of the stars, their twinkling, the shim-
mering of the Milky Way during a moonless night, the changing
phases of the moon and the glory of her fullness.

Aside from this contemplation of the natural wonders of creation,
the succession of day and night, of the lunar phases, and of the seasons must have led man to some sort of crude computation of time.
He needed to fit his farming, his hunting, or his animal husbandry
into the natural periods of time. Paleolithic man, who may have tried
to determine the length of the seasons or of the lunar months, or
have mentally pictured beings among the constellations, or have followed the planets' path across the heavens, blazed the trail for that
science which was afterward called *astronomy*.

In prehistoric times, because of the impossibility or difficulty of
communication, cultural centers were formed independently in the
various regions of the earth, each one according to the conditions of
its people, the traditions and customs, and even the climate. Therefore there is little sense in speaking of the origin or invention of
astronomy, and still less in localizing it in this or that place.

In the minds of all peoples astronomy, the science of the heavens, has always been closely connected with religious tradition, so closely that astronomical phenomena were often confused with religious events, the one confirming or even predicting the other. Sometimes these predictions were based on observation and calculation, sometimes on empirical and purely false assumptions. Thus among the primitive peoples, even until the late Middle Ages, pure astronomy was confused with her empirical sister cult, *astrology*. This was a dangerous relationship, and only the most thoughtful minds could truly distinguish pure science from empiricism. Yet the impulse which astronomy received from the priests in their search for supernatural causes and in their predictions of the future contributed greatly toward its general development. In the course of time faith and science have interfered less and less with each other, though the fundamental fact remains that astronomy is the science most closely allied to religion. Although it has shown the earth to be an insignificant part of the universe, still it has magnified the glory of the whole universe; it has taught us respect for the unity of matter and the immeasurable quantity of energy, all existing in a sublime harmony of space, time, and motion. Thus the human mind is led, through such study, to admire all the more the great mystery of creation.

Though precise documents are lacking, traditions and fundamental human necessities can lead us to imagine what were the first attempts to understand the laws of apparent motion of the celestial bodies. In most of the earth's regions, the periods of the moon afforded the basis for a computation of time, easily determined by the regular and rapid succession of her phases. But in high latitudes, within the polar circle, the continuous presence of the sun above the horizon, making a perpetual day for six months of the year, must have made it difficult for the primitive polar inhabitants to calculate a lunar month. However, during the long winter nights, by its return to the same point above the horizon, the moon defined another period, somewhat longer than that defined by the sun. It is known, for example, that the Greenlanders counted their years from the beginning of the winter, when the sun disappeared, leaving them in perpetual night. The Greenlanders also reckoned the full moons, the position of the Big Dipper, the variable positions of shadows as the sun rose, and the maximum length of the shadows as the sun rounded the pole. The migration of animals must have given these peoples, then as today, another division of time.

In the Torrid Zone the apparent daily course of the sun is easier to define, since the sun culminates at noon always at a high altitude above the horizon. On the other hand, it is more difficult to calculate the length of the year without systematic observations. The people of the Torrid Zone preferred rather to rely on meteorological conditions, such as the periodic rains. Moreover, the division of time based on the course of the moon presented to them a most natural and simple way to tell time. Time was counted by moons and by dozens of moons, improperly called "years." This was the first attempt (made by the Arabs) to correlate the lunar month with the seasons and with the period of the sun. This imperfect calendar was used from time immemorial by the sons of the desert. They had no need of greater accuracy, since they carried on no important agriculture and relied little upon seasonal changes. In the tropical islands we have even found that computations of time were based exclusively on moon counting. At every moon one of thirty knots on a rope was untied.

In the Americas, lunations served in the ancient days as divisions of time. The Peruvians and Araucans employed a conventional month of thirty days, like that of the ancient Egyptians, probably derived from the moon. Actually, the peoples of central America were more advanced in astronomical matters than were other peoples.

In the early days of astronomy and among primitive peoples, the computation of time by days and lunar months, defined by the interval between two consecutive new moons or two consecutive full moons, was adopted spontaneously in various regions of the earth at various times. Time could thus be fixed within one or two days. However, the establishment of a "calendar," co-ordinating the course of the sun with that of the moon, required a more advanced civilization, since it was first of all necessary to know the exact number of days in a solar year. To obtain this knowledge it is necessary to observe the celestial phenomena dependent upon the apparent motion of the sun among the stars. Another means of determining the sun's position in the sky is a "gnomon"—a shadow indicator—in its simplest form just a stick fixed on a horizontal plane. From the length of the stick and of its shadow the apparent altitude of the sun may be calculated. A different form of gnomon is simply a hole through which the sun's rays pass and are gathered into a horizontal plane. Another simple method used by primitive peoples to establish the course of the seasons, and thus to define a sufficiently precise calendar, was to note the position of the stars just before sunrise or just after sunset, that is, the "heliacal" rising and setting.

Thus many points of reference, useful for everyday living, were obtained within the course of the year. The Egyptians and Indian Aryans made particular use of the heliacal method. Hesiod speaks of it as being well known among the Greeks for agriculture and navigation. Sirius, the brightest star in the Northern Hemisphere, was especially observed, since it was the first to appear after sunset and the last to disappear before sunrise. The division of the day was made by estimating at various seasons that part of the diurnal arc included between the points on the horizon of the rising and setting of the sun. Some characteristic of the horizon or some rudimentary measures were used as reference. In this way it was possible with a little practice to obtain an accuracy of within twenty to thirty minutes; then it seemed easy and convenient to divide the day into four or six parts.

The problem of orientation, as they went from one place to another and returned, must have interested the primitive peoples, most especially those who depended upon navigation for a living. The cardinal points were easily determined by the apparent motion of the sun and stars. East was considered the most fundamental direction, for there is born the star which gives light and life to the earth. Among many peoples east thus assumed a ritual and holy character; among the early Italian peoples, particularly the Etruscans, the temples were built in an east-west direction. East was considered the front part of the world, west the back, south the right part, and north the left. The almost imperceptible motion of the stars near the pole, as well as the motion of the circumpolar stars, gave primitive peoples an easy determination of north. For instance, the Phoenicians used the Little Dipper, in their times close enough to the pole to give a northern direction sufficiently accurate for short voyages. For longer voyages, when the mainland was out of sight, other information was necessary. Therefore the Polynesians, for instance, had to study very carefully the position of the stars and the course of the sun. Since the customs and languages of all the islands scattered in that great expanse of ocean are closely allied, we may suppose that these islands were connected by sea trade which required astronomical navigation, even if very primitive. Since the polar star was not visible to these islanders, they had to rely on other principal stars and the parts of the sky where they happened to appear at the different seasons. Around the celestial equator, the points on the horizon at which a given star rises or sets do not vary much for close latitudes. Therefore, in the absence of the compass, these points could offer a simple method of orientation.

A first "uranography," or mapping of the heavens, was thus established for conspicuous groups of stars, but we know little about it. The configurations and representations of animals or terrestrial objects vary considerably with different peoples. But sometimes we find similarities, especially in a well-defined constellation, such as the Big and Little Dippers, Orion, or the Pleiades.

Of the planets, the wandering stars, we have no record of any particular observations. Venus is the most mentioned, considered in the evening and in the morning as two different stars, Hesper and Lucifer. We do know, however, that the Peruvians and the Mexicans considered them the same star. Moreover, the Indians of the Orinoco region (South America) had noticed that Venus never went beyond certain limits away from the sun, and therefore they called her the "wife" of the sun.

From these first steps in the study of the sky in connection with the necessities of life or purposes of religion, the peoples of the earth had far to come. More difficult concepts were possible only for a more advanced civilization. With the progress of time, astronomy assumed always greater importance and employed more rigorous methods both as a pure science and as an applied science.

2 : historical periods of astronomy

THE HISTORY OF ASTRONOMY MAY BE ARRANGED into three great periods corresponding to the history and civilization of the peoples of the earth: Ancient Astronomy, Medieval Astronomy, and Modern Astronomy. Between the latter two periods the study of astronomy underwent a basic reform, and thus in four centuries Modern Astronomy has accomplished enormous progress such as could not even have been imagined in the preceding centuries.

We assume Ancient Astronomy to begin at the time when, through tradition or the advent of some rare document, the most ancient peoples are believed to have had some cognizance of astronomical phenomena. Such an epoch seems to have arisen about forty centuries before Christ among a people in Asia, who built a high civilization that spread throughout Asia, into Europe, Egypt, and most probably even to central America. From this astronomy we pass to that of the Egyptians and the Indians, thirty centuries before Christ, and on to that of the Babylonians and the Jews up until Alexander. We have some suspicion of a primitive Chinese astronomy and of one derived by the Greeks at the time of Homer and Hesiod. The Greek school, which raised astronomy to real scientific importance, developed with the astronomer-physicists of Ionia, Thales, and Anaximander, then Pythagoras, Plato, and Aristotle. In its greatest glory the school of Alexandria counted among its members Aristarchus of Samos and Eratosthenes, who were followed in Magna Graecia by Archimedes. Meanwhile, along with the foundation of Alexandria, in the third century before Christ arose the great scientific center which made considerable astronomical progress with Hipparchus, the greatest astronomer of antiquity. The works of Hipparchus were preserved and were completed three centuries later by Ptolemy. With Ptolemy and then with the decline of the Alexandrian school about 650 A.D. we can close, according to Schiaparelli, the period of Ancient Astronomy.

Medieval Astronomy, which comprises the period from 500 to 1500 A.D., is the astronomy of the Romans, actually not very important, and that, much more important, of the Arabs, with the schools of Bagdad, Cairo, Persia, and Mongolia. But the astronomy of these peoples, as also of the western Latins until Copernicus, is essentially nothing but a repetition of the *Almagest* of Ptolemy. During the Renaissance Purbach and Regiomontanus do nothing but explain and comment on this famous book.

Copernicus himself may be considered as continuing in the Greek school, because he developed the fundamental idea of Aristarchus, applying to it the geometric methods of Hipparchus and Ptolemy. With him and Tycho Brahe, with Kepler, Galileo, and Newton, began really a new era which may be considered as the reformation of astronomy. Through the work of these great men, astronomy was launched on new and unthought-of paths to numerous and important conquests.

The Modern Era follows directly after Newton. Thereafter the celestial bodies were considered in a unit frame, subject to the same physical and mechanical laws. These laws could be applied to the study of the shape and movements of the planets, satellites, and comets, as well as to the study of the position and distribution of the stars in the Milky Way.

Another tremendous step forward was made by "spectrum analysis" of the physical and chemical constitution of celestial bodies, beginning with the date of Kirchhoff's discovery (1859). With this analysis, and indeed with all the most recent methods discovered by experimental and theoretical physicists, enormous progress has been made in the determination of the surface and internal constitution of the stars, and the structure of the universe, inside and outside our galaxy as far as our modern instruments can observe. We are now in that period foreseen by Schiaparelli when he was writing his masterpieces on the history of astronomy: "Happy are those who will live in such times." This period, despite the many sad events in the world today, is in full development, and it prompted George Hale, some thirty-five years ago, to write:

> . . . thanks to observatories in all quarters of the earth, the picture of the universe still continues to unfold and to influence progress in every field of thought. We are happily in a period of unprecedented progress, when the empirical conceptions of an earlier time are rapidly giving place to well-grounded views. The privilege of aiding in this advance, at a time when the pioneer stage has not yet been passed, will be appreciated by those who reflect on the true meaning and influence of astronomical discovery.

3 : ancient astronomers other than Greek

MESOPOTAMIA

THE REFERENCES TO THE ASTRONOMY OF THE
Mesopotamians are few and incomplete. They inhabited the vast
plains between the Tigris and Euphrates rivers, and their history,
according to Simplicius, is thought to have begun about forty centuries before Christ. Theirs is the history of the Babylonians and
Assyrians, recorded on thousands of clay tablets, which have been
excavated in various parts of Mesopotamia. The interpretation of
these documents, written in a dead language and with strange char-
acters, has been a difficult enterprise, which, however, has resulted in
very important disclosures.

The caste of the Babylonian priests were distinguished for their
profound knowledge of astronomy, on account of which their religious
activities became largely astrological.

On the clay tablets are found observations and calculations of the
positions and motions of the planets. These data had been accumulated in the course of many centuries before the destruction of
Nineveh, in order to establish and verify astrological predictions at
short range. It does not appear that the Assyro-Babylonian astronomers had reached a sure and consistent computation of time before
the so-called "era of Nabonassar" (eighth century B.C.), and this
computation became public usage only many years later. The Chaldeans never made the progress in astronomy later achieved by the
Greeks, though in some discoveries they did precede them. For in-

stance, the Chaldeans were able to predict, with a certain degree of accuracy, the apparent motions of the planets, with their stations and retrogradations, their heliacal rising and setting, and their conjunctions with the principal stars. They were able also to calculate new moons and to predict eclipses.

On the basis of archeological discoveries we can divide the history of Babylonian astronomy into two periods: (1) the ancient period extending from remote antiquity to the destruction of Nineveh (607 B.C.); and (2) from the destruction of Nineveh and the founding of the Neo-Babylonian empire to the birth of Christ.

Of the first period little is known. The astronomy was for the most part connected with astrology and was concerned with religious worship. In the second period it was already a true science which, though always studied for the purpose of predictions, was also studied for its own sake.

The oldest astronomical documents which have come down to us from Mesopotamia are the so-called "astrolabes." These are clay tablets on which are engraved three concentric circles divided by twelve radii into twelve sections. In each of the resulting thirty-six fields we find the name of a constellation and simple numbers, the significance of which has not yet been explained. But it seems evident that the representation constitutes a kind of schematic celestial map wherein the sky is divided into three regions of twelve fields each, and characteristic numbers are attributed to each constellation. These numbers increase and decrease in arithmetic progression and are undoubtedly connected with a corresponding month in the schematic calendar of twelve months. It is evident that we have here a kind of simple astronomical calendar similar to that of the Egyptians. These calendars of the Mesopotamians and Egyptians are of great interest to us for the determination of the relative positions of the constellations and of their ancient names.

The calendar was based on the periodic return of the "apparent new moon," that is, on the days when the moon, after having disappeared in the light of the sun, reappeared in the western sky after sunset. In this way a lunar month was obtained. It was necessary, in the interests of practical life, that this lunar month should stand in some relation to the solar year so that the seasons would come at the same time every year. To meet such a requirement, the Babylonians devised a "lunisolar" calendar, which was used in the regions of Sumer and Akkad. This calendar had a year of twelve moons, to which a thirteenth had to be added once in a while in order that the same months should always be in the same seasons. At first, the thirteenth month was added empirically, according to the number of moons, twelve or thirteen, in a year. But later the Babylonians noticed that the length of the year could be determined more accurately by the heliacal rising of one or more stars. The heliacal rising may be considered as a fixed epoch, in relation to the movement of the sun and the passing of the seasons. If the heliacal rising of the stars under observation fell in the assigned month, the calendar was in order; otherwise the Chaldean astronomers inserted a thirteenth month. Naturally they had to choose very bright stars, stars which could be seen at dawn just before sunrise; and it was not possible to find such stars for every month. Thus we find uncertainties and irregularities in the years containing intercalated months.

The Babylonians used also, though not generally, some kind of week. The 7th, 14th, 21st, and 28th days of every moon were considered of ill omen, when it was forbidden to certain persons to do certain things, or else they had to observe certain rituals. The instant of sunrise marked for the Babylonians the beginning of the day, which was divided into twelve intervals called "kaspu." In celestial observations they used the solar "kaspu," that is, the span of 30° which the sun traverses in two hours of its apparent daily motion. In the Babylonian astronomical tablets of the period after Alexander the Great, we find the arc of one degree used as a unit of space, just as today. As a unit of time they used the "time degree," corresponding to four of our minutes, which is approximately the path of the sun in one day of its apparent yearly revolution around the earth. Thus originated the division of the circle into 360°, which was adopted later by the Greeks and is still in use today.

The exact computation of rather long intervals of time, indispensable for astronomical observations, constituted one of the greatest difficulties for the ancient astronomers, since they had no measuring instruments of sufficient accuracy. From the times of Nabonassar, celestial phenomena were observed systematically, so that the Babylonians were able to predict certain celestial phenomena, for instance eclipses, on the basis of their calculations. The earliest eclipse which they observed with great care at the instant of beginning and end was the eclipse of March 19, 721 B.C.

This and other Chaldean observations of eclipses are used even today for calculations in the modern theories concerning lunar motions.

The motions of the planets among the stars were systematically observed in their direct, stationary, and retrograde phases. The heliacal rising of the stars, as we have already said, was carefully observed, to indicate the months. Comets, which even in those times were considered very important for their astrological effects, and the most luminous shooting stars, or meteors, were followed and recorded. The apparent yearly path of the sun around the earth had been carefully determined, and this path, which we call the "zodiac" or "ecliptic," had been divided into four parts corresponding to the four seasons. Since we find that the Babylonian astronomers had tried to establish in what proportion the length of the day and night varied during the different seasons, we must surmise that they used instruments for measuring time, probably based on the flow of water from special containers.

The Babylonians knew well that a lunation (the period between two successive new moons) is a little longer than 29.5 days, and they were very accurate in their predictions of new moons. They then foretold good or bad tidings according to the agreement of observation with prediction. In such matters solar eclipses were the most important for astrological purposes. It seems that the astronomers in Nineveh and Babylonia, before they had any contact with the Greeks, and although they had no accurate representation of the complicated lunar motions, had devised some sufficiently reliable means of prediction, based on long sets of lunar eclipses. In the reports of the court astronomer-astrologers of Nineveh we can read such predictions, limited, naturally, to the day of the month. For example: "On the 14th of the month an eclipse will take place; misfortune for the lands of Elam and Syria, good fortune for the king; let the king be at ease. Venus will not be present, but I say to my lord there shall be an eclipse. Irassihe senior, servant to the king." And also: "To the king my lord I have written: an eclipse will take place. This eclipse has taken place; it did not fail. This is a sign of peace for the king my lord."

To the Chaldeans is generally attributed the discovery of the "saros," a period of 223 lunations or 18 solar years, wherein the moon returns to the same position with respect to its nodes, to its perigee, and to the sun; the eclipses of the preceding cycle are then repeated in the same order. Schiaparelli observes that the "saros" was erroneously named by the moderns, and that it is improbable that the Babylonians ever determined such a period. Even with a long set of observations, missing a few, through bad weather or other reasons, would be enough to distort the sequence of the cycle. Perhaps the Chaldeans employed a much simpler method. In any case, they noticed that every lunar eclipse is part of a set of eclipses which take place at equal time intervals. Each set generally includes five or six eclipses, and the sets are separated by long intervals of 17 lunations during which there are no eclipses. Since the Babylonian calendar was based on lunar months, once a series of eclipses had begun, it was possible to predict lunar eclipses at six-month intervals, when the full moon was visible. A new series began when, after a visible full moon, a full moon with eclipse appeared. Then for four or five times, every six months, every full moon would be eclipsed.

The prediction of solar eclipses in those times was more difficult. Although solar eclipses occur in sets analogous to those of the moon, one greater difficulty exists in relation to the former, aside from cloudy weather and the location of the moon beneath the horizon. This difficulty is the limited cone of shadow on the surface of the earth, which makes an eclipse visible only in particular and narrow regions. An observer in a given location may miss five out of six eclipses. For the Babylonians, the prediction of the regions where the eclipse would be visible was too complicated. No one knew the shape and the size of the earth, or had any idea of the effect of the lunar parallax. Only later, with the advanced geometry of the Greeks, did this calculation become possible.

In the Babylonian astrological tables are often mentioned the five major planets: their presence on the horizon, their heliacal rising and setting, their position relative to the moon and the stars, indicating the months, also their direct and retrograde motion along the ecliptic. For example, an opposition of Mars is described as follows, in a tablet found among the ruins of Nineveh: "When the star of Mars becomes powerful its brightness increases: seven days, fourteen days, twenty-one days it journeys backwards, and then it continues on its prescribed course." Schiaparelli gives a translation of this excerpt in modern terms: "Mars at its greatest power becomes very bright and remains so for several weeks; then its motion becomes retrograde for several weeks, after which it resumes its usual direct motion." Thus the planet traverses the same path two or three times. All this is sufficiently close to the truth, since the maximum length of the retrograde motion is eleven weeks, and the least is nine. Numerous observations of Venus have been found, extending through 24 appearances and disappearances. To each observation is attached its proper astrological significance, and from these we can determine a good value for the synodic revolution of the planet.

The famous seven-story tower erected by the biblical Nebuchadnezzar (604 B.C.) in Borsippa, a suburb of Babylon, may be considered an astronomical monument to the seven celestial bodies, the sun, moon, and five major planets, which move through the zodiac. Schiaparelli thinks that it is rather a symbol of the seven divisions of heaven and earth: that is, the inhabited earth, surrounded by four regions corresponding to the four points of the compass, the summit of the sky above the earth, and the kingdom of the dead in the lowest regions beneath the earth.

Astrology, as we said before, was the main goal of the Babylonian astronomers. They have the great merit of not having relied upon pure fantasy or simple deception, as did other peoples later in the Middle Ages, but upon accurate and systematic celestial observations extending throughout many years. These observations were made mainly to investigate the periodicity and prediction of phenomena which, considered as supernatural, must have influence upon human beings and their earthly existence. This idea has always been believed and cultivated in various forms by primitive peoples. And it has reason to exist, aside from religion and superstition, because of the greatness of natural phenomena, which are beyond the control of man, and which do exert an influence upon the earth. Such an influence— exerted not upon a single individual but upon all mankind, so to say, collectively—is the daily and annual motion of the sun which influences the growth and development of the animals and plants and indeed all our life, or the motion of the moon which influences the tides and other phenomena. That the astronomer-astrologers of Babylonia proceeded in their applications of astronomy to astrology with sure faith is proved by the existence of their large indices and rules handed down from one generation to another during the various centuries. Having succeeded in predicting fairly accurately the eclipses of the moon, they understood all the more how much importance their observations and researches assumed, while on the other hand their fame increased, as well as the consideration given them by their rulers and by their people.

They did not, however, have any knowledge of geometry and trigonometry, which would have permitted more rigorous solutions of various astronomical problems. This weakness makes Babylonian astronomy essentially inferior to the Greek.

PEOPLES OF CENTRAL AMERICA

From monuments and inscriptions which archeologists have found in the central part of the Americas we must conclude that certain peoples of Mexico had reached a degree of civilization not much inferior to that of the Babylonians, Assyrians, and Egyptians, and indeed had made considerable progress in astronomy. Though they recognized neither the shape nor the motions of the earth, they knew the causes of the eclipses, the use of the gnomon, and the calcu-lation of the solstices and equinoxes. A complicated calendar which the priests had devised from some celestial phenomena, must have served well both religious purposes and everyday functions. In addi-tion to the solar year, these peoples used the year of Venus, deter-mined by the synodic revolution of the planet. They had distin-guished the planets and knew the Milky Way to be a great cluster of stars. They believed the sun to be the throne of the blessed, and thus deified it; likewise the moon. All this was part of their religious belief and superstition, with which were mixed phenomena and facts, observed and discussed.

But it seems that the Mayan people, who inhabited Guatemala and the peninsula of Yucatan, had developed true astronomical science more seriously. They are the only ancient people of central America who have left inscriptions in stone, in complicated hieroglyphics which are difficult to decipher. However, we are able to interpret those parts which relate to the calendar. It is clear that the Mayas possessed a very elaborate computation of time, as well as tables for the prediction of lunar and solar eclipses. Therefore we must admit that they achieved really noteworthy astronomical progress. Their year encompassed 365 days, divided into 18 months of 20 days each and a short additional month of 5 days. Each month had its own name, and the days therein were counted respectively from 0 to 19 and from 0 to 4.

The Mayan astronomers had particular regard for those points in the sky where the ecliptic intersects the Milky Way. The ephemerides of celestial phenomena were referred to these points, especially those of the planets. Such indications are found in inscriptions which must date from the fourth or fifth century of the Christian Era. These astronomical data imply observations extending over a long interval of time. We believe, on the basis of the beginning of the era adopted by the Mayas, that they date back to a time several centuries B.C. It is possible that the Mayas came into such vast astronomical knowledge through another people, but archeological research does not generally admit of such a civilization in central America in such ancient times. At any rate, there seems to be no doubt that the computation of the days adopted by the Mayas extends back to the fifth century B.C. No computation as involved has been found in any other region of the earth prior to modern times. It could not, therefore, have been elaborated by a primitive people, despite the archeological difficulties which are met in assuming a civilization so advanced.

EGYPTIANS

The Egyptians, like the Babylonians, are held in high repute for their knowledge in the astronomical field. It is not improbable that European astronomy is derived from the banks of the Nile, and it is certain that the first Greek philosophers came to Egypt to learn astronomy. Perhaps the reputation of the Egyptians has been somewhat exaggerated by the Greeks, for we really cannot say that the Egyptians made noteworthy progress in the astronomical sciences. The priests, in Egypt also, were concerned with astronomy. They tried jealously to keep hidden from the public at large their doctrines and results acquired from observations, in order to use them later for their own astrological deductions.

The periodic overflowing of the Nile, an event of prime importance for the life of the Egyptians, must have led to investigations of the reasons for the periodic renewal of the seasons. These could be found from a study of the motion of the sun and stars, especially with a view to establishing a sufficiently exact calendar. The solar year of 365 days seems to have been adopted by the Egyptians about 3000 B.C.; but they must have soon noticed that this was too short, since the year would have lacked one day every 4 years and almost a month in 120 years. The subdivisions of such a so-called "wandering year" could not have any fixed relation with the epochs determined by the course of the sun. It was therefore necessary to have recourse to a fixed calendar, in order to calculate for each wandering year the dates in which certain phenomena would take place, the most important being the overflowing of the Nile. As other primitive peoples had done, the Egyptians adopted as a starting point for their fixed year the heliacal rising of Sirius. For the Egyptians this was a most happy choice, since not only was Sirius the brightest star in the Northern Hemisphere, but the swelling of the waters of the Nile began just when the sun, receding from it, permitted it to be seen in the morning twilight. Probably the Egyptians saw in this coincidence something supernatural, and for this reason they often identified Sirius with the goddess Isis. The Egyptian year, at the beginning of which the overflowing of the Nile recurred, was determined, therefore, by the morning appearance of Sirius, and its length was the interval between two successive apparitions. As yet they had no knowledge of "precession."

Having observed the loss of one day in four years, the Egyptian priests were able to correlate the wandering year with the year adopted, for all past and future times. They established the fact that the beginning of the wandering year coincides with the beginning of the fixed year after 1461 wandering years, or 1460 years of Sirius. This is the so-called "Great Year" or "Sothic cycle," (from Sothis, Egyptian name for Sirius), or also "Year of the Gods."

The civil and religious year used by the Egyptians in the times of the Pharaohs from 2782 B.C., the first year of a Sothic cycle, until the Roman Conquest, seems probably to have been a wandering year, on the basis of documents and investigations. In contrast to our complicated calendars, this type of year had the advantage of simplicity. Ptolemy, in fact, preferred the wandering year to the complicated computations of the Greeks, just because of its simplicity and uniformity. Its anticipation of the solar year did not become noticeable during the life span of a man. After the real length of the year had been discovered, the great Sothic period was found, interpreted by the priests as a divine arrangement whereby all the seasons were equally holy, since the fixed religious festivals of the wandering year passed through all the seasons.

The Egyptians believed the stars to be fires emanating from the earth and ascending toward the sky. According to Cicero, they discovered the revolution of Mercury and Venus around the sun. They had entirely erroneous impressions of the distances of the sun, moon, and planets, whose courses they noted only for astrological purposes. It seems that we owe to the Egyptians the names of the days of the week, which are so ordered because the Egyptians set the first hour of each day under the protection of some planet.

JEWS

Despite their contacts with the Babylonians, the Jews remained essentially outside the astronomical field. They had only an imperfect calendar, and the Old Testament mentions only a few constellations. Probably they avoided the study of the sky for religious reasons. The neighboring nations of Mesopotamia were concerned with astronomy for astrological purposes, which developed into "astrolatry," the worship of the sun, the moon, and the "whole army of the heavens," a worship which the prophets denounced with the most terrible threats. We must not wonder then that the astronomy of the Jews remained in a primitive state. Their theories regarding the creation of the universe reflect this attitude; witness their conception of the position and shape of the earth, the depths of space, the firmament. Observation of the sun and the moon, and of their courses, even of eclipses and planets, are rare. The Book of Job mentions only a few constellations, probably the Big Bear, the Little Bear, the Hyades with Aldebaran, Orion, and the Pleiades.

The civil day began for the Jews in the evening. We do not believe that they divided the day into equal parts, that is, "hours." Perhaps they had imported a solar timekeeper from Babylonia, but only in the time of Christ, following the example of the Greeks, did they divide the interval between sunrise and sunset into twelve parts and then, following the example of the Romans, also divide the night into four *vigiliae* or night-watches.

At all times the Jews regulated the months and the calendar of festivals according to the phases of the moon. Without disturbing the ritual of their festivities, they gradually adopted the names of the Babylonian months, first for civil use, then for religious use, and consecrated them finally in the calendar which for fifteen centuries has been used in all synagogues. In this calendar the year commenced with autumn, at the time of the new moon, when the seventh Babylonian month began. In order to prevent the year from deviating too much from the course of the sun, it was necessary to add an intercalated month at the thirteenth moon. This inserted month determined the duration and the succession of the years and fixed the solar year with regard to its seasons and the renewal of agricultural labors. The calendar of the Jews was then lunisolar, like the calendar of the Babylonians, Syrians, and Greeks.

In later eras the year began in the spring, and a very simple

empirical procedure must have been adopted to keep the months
from falling out of season—a procedure particularly appropriate for
an essentially agricultural people. The beginning of the year must
have been at the first, sometimes the second, new moon after the
vernal equinox, at the time when wheat, barley, and grapes are rip-
ening in Palestine. Such a computation of the year is understand-
ably quite imperfect. Only the Jews of Babylonia, descendants of the
ancient exiles who had emigrated there with Nebuchadnezzar, could
give a sound basis for calculations of the dates of festivals and the
observance of rituals.

In the first half of the third century astronomy was cultivated and
taught at the schools of Nahardea and Sara by renowned professors,
like Rabbi Samuel and Rabbi Adda. They possessed not only exact
elements concerning the motion of the sun and moon, but they
even knew of the "Metonic cycle" (discovered by Meton about 433
B.C.). These masters had made precise calculations of the new moons
and the equinoxes, thus establishing the basis of the true Jewish
calendar, which was definitively adjusted by Rabbi Hillel toward
the end of the fourth century A.D. The Jews, like other peoples in
early history, adopted cycles which encompassed a small number of
days, aside from the cycles of the year and the month. Since the
duration of a lunation is approximately 29.5 days, the number of days
closest to one quarter is 7 days. From the beginning of the month
or from the new moon they counted successively 7, 14, 21, 28 days,
leaving at the end a remainder of one or two days, until the counting from the next new moon. The establishment of the week is
certainly among the most ancient records of the Jewish people, and
the "sabbath" is mentioned as the day of compulsory rest in their
most ancient monuments of law. It is possible that the origin of the
week dates back to the origin of the Jewish people, perhaps even
before Moses. This cycle of seven days, so useful and convenient
for timekeeping, was spread abroad by the Jews when they were
scattered throughout the world; it was adopted by the Chaldean
astrologers for their divinations, by the Christians, and by the Moslems, and it is at present embraced in the whole world.

PHOENICIANS

The Phoenicians adored rather than studied the heavenly
bodies, so that their conception of astronomy is more a worship than

a science. Heliopolis was celebrated as the city of sun-worship. The horses and chariots of the sun, mentioned in the Bible, were, so to speak, the emblems of Phoenicia. The worship of the moon accompanied that of the sun, and according to the phases of the moon different influences were attributed to the sun. Solemn festivals were held at every new moon. The planets represented divinities inferior to the sun, who gives them their light, warmth, and life. In a Phoenician colony a temple was even erected in honor of Venus.

The Phoenician inscriptions help to give some indication of their calendar, which is the oldest Jewish calendar. In the inscriptions of Cyprus, Malta, and Carthage are found the names of some of the months, one of which is interpreted as the month of "healing," perhaps the month when the people attended to their health and took care of their bodies, and rested from the labors of agriculture and navigation. We do not know, however, how the months were arranged.

Generally speaking, no true astronomical investigations have been noted among the Phoenicians, although with their long navigations they must certainly have studied and developed methods for orientation at sea. According to tradition, often repeated by the classical poets, they directed themselves on the high seas by day with the sun, by night with the Little Bear. Between 1500 and 500 B.C. the Little Bear afforded a more accurate orientation than the Big Bear and was called the "tail of the dog." Other than this we have no information.

HINDUS

The astronomical knowledge which we should like to attribute to the Hindus is largely legendary. These people had a philosophy of the creation and destruction of the world rather than true and systematic observations from which conclusions could be derived. Among the ruins of the cities of Hindustan, no traces of observatories are found, as in Babylonia. The science of the Hindus, then, must have been purely inspiration and imagination. However, they had supposed the earth to be round, immobile in space and supported by its own power, and surrounded by the planets. The Buddhists supposed that the earth was falling constantly without anyone being able to notice it. This concept seems to have come to the Hindus from the Greeks through the Arabs. In a book which contains the principles of Indian astronomy, the armillary sphere which divided the zodiac into parts is hardly mentioned.

One of the best-known astronomers in the history of Greco-Indian astronomy was the celebrated Aryabhatta, born in Pataliputra on the Ganges River. We do not know the precise period in which he lived, but it seems to date back as far as the fifth century of the Christian Era. Around 628 A.D. lived Brahmagupta, who wrote an astronomical treatise wherein he states what Aryabhatta thought about the rotation of the earth: "The sphere of the stars is immobile; the earth through one rotation produces the daily rising and setting of the stars and the planets." Brahmagupta observes on his own account: "If the earth moves one minute in a prana (four seconds of sidereal time), from where is it coming and where is it going?" Another Indian astronomer of those times answers these queries: "The opinion of Aryabhatta seems quite satisfactory, because the planet cannot have two simultaneous motions; the reason why objects above us do not fall down is explained by thinking that what is above the earth is also below. Since we are on the surface of the earth this is (for us) the highest place."

It is probable, as Schiaparelli thinks, that these ideas of the Indian astronomers were derived from a Greek source. The speculations of Heraclides Ponticus, after having traveled as far as the Tigris, may well have reached the Ganges.

CHINESE

A legend of a very advanced astronomical science, even in earliest times, is also very widespread among the Chinese. There are few documents which inform us with any reliability of their true advancement. We believe that the Chinese calculated a series of eclipses as far back as 4000 B.C. In 2608 B.C. the emperor Hoang-Ti had an observatory built mainly for the purpose of correcting the calendar, which had fallen into great confusion. He entrusted this task to various astronomers who were to follow the course of the sun, the moon, the planets, and the stars. They may have discovered that, in order to bring the solar calendar in agreement with the lunar calendar, it was necessary to intercalate seven lunations in an interval of 19 years. Thus they may have discovered the "Metonic cycle" before the Greeks.

In the reign of Hoang-Ti a mathematical tribunal was instituted to promote the astronomical sciences, especially the prediction of eclipses. The members of the tribunal were responsible with their lives for the accuracy of their predictions. In fact, if a celestial phenomenon had been erroneously predicted, or if the phenomenon had not been foreseen in time, the negligence of the astronomers would be punished by death. Such is the story of the two mathematicians Ho and Hi, in the reign of Tchong-Kang, who fell victims to this bloody law because an eclipse took place which they did not foresee in time. The study of astronomy received new impetus under the emperor Yao, who lived about 2317 B.C. The zodiac was divided into 28 "houses," the beginning of a division of the sky according to constellations. The year had 365¼ days. The circle was divided into 365¼ parts, so that the sun in its daily orbit described an arc of one Chinese degree. It seems that around 1100 B.C. the Chinese had accurately established the obliquity of the ecliptic and the position of the winter solstice in the sky. After the fifth century B.C., the study of astronomy was abandoned in China and many of its findings were even destroyed. All the later modern conceptions were afterward imported from the Arabs and the Europeans.

Father Matteo Ricci, Jesuit Missionary, during his stay in China had to concern himself with the "imperial calendar," which was so important for the life of the nation. Two other missionaries, along with him, were ordered to find an agreement between the lunar and the solar calendar. In the official history of the Ming dynasty: "In the tenth moon of the same year—1610—a solar eclipse took place in the calculation of which the Chinese astronomers made a serious error; therefore two Europeans, the missionaries de Pantoja and de Ursis, were elected to calculate eclipses according to the current method used in Europe, but at present unknown in China." De Ursis calculated the longitude of Peking by means of a comparative study of lunar eclipses visible not only in China but also in India and Europe. De Pantoja determined the latitude of the principal cities, Canton and Peking. Several years later other missionaries had to introduce new reforms for the solar year. Many missionaries of that time wrote extensive treatises on astronomy. The Jesuit Ferdinand Verbiest in 1668 published his "Astronomical Observations," also for the improvement of the calendar, and much later his magnum opus, a complete handbook of astronomy in 32 volumes. Finally he wrote the *Liber Organicus Astronomiae Europeae apud Sinas Restitutae sub Imperatore Tartarico Cam-hy Appellat*, (Systematic Treatise on European Astronomy as Revived among the Chinese under the Tatar Emperor Named Cam-hy), illustrated with 125 tables with explanations in Chinese. In 1673 Verbiest erected new instruments in the old observatory built in 1279 by Ko Show.

4 : early Greek astronomers

THALES AND ANAXIMANDER

THE FIRST FOUNDATIONS OF GREEK ASTRON-
omy seem to date back to Thales, the head of the Ionian school,
who was born in Miletus, 640 B.C. He taught that the stars were made
of fire, that the moon received its light from the sun and was invisible during conjunction because it was hidden in the solar rays, and
that the earth, the center of the universe, was round. He knew of
the fundamental planes, the ecliptic and the equator. According to
Herodotus, he predicted the famous eclipse which ended the war
between the Medes and the Lydians. It seems that he determined
the position of the stars in the Little Bear, which were used by the
Phoenicians in their voyages. Anaximander succeeded him in the
Ionian school. To him is attributed the recognition of the zodiac
and the invention of the gnomon, an instrument which he erected
in Lacedaemon to observe the solstices and the equinoxes. Anaximander also drew geographical maps.

ASTRONOMERS OF THE PYTHAGOREAN SCHOOL

The first ideas of the motion of the earth, both its rotation
about its axis and its revolution around the sun, are often attributed
to Pythagoras. Actually they stem from Philolaus and from some
other later philosophers of the Pythagorean school, though in their
times the school, as a philosophic-religious order, had been extin-

guished and scattered. Pythagoras lived about 550 B.C., around forty years after Anaximander, who was the most celebrated astronomer of the Ionian school. Since traditionally Pythagoras and his disciples did not record their doctrines in writing, in order to keep them secret, many legends have arisen, for instance, that Pythagoras was a forerunner of Copernicus.

A better known cosmic system of the Pythagorean school is the one attributed to Philolaus, which was in use almost to the time of Aristotle. Philolaus, a native of Tarentum, lived around 450 B.C., and moved from Italy to Thebes in Boeotia. Following the Pythagoreans, he sets the creation and origin of the world in harmony with the center, which is the "heart of the universe" or the "seat of Jove," where cosmic activity has its source. The world is bounded externally by Olympus, beyond which lies the indeterminate. Between the sphere of Olympus and the heart of the universe revolve ten heavenly bodies; the first and outermost, the sphere which holds the fixed stars; then the five planets; next the sun, the moon, and the earth; and finally, close to the central fire, the "anti-earth."

This last had been imagined, in order to complete the number of ten spheres, a sign of perfection; and along with the other celestial bodies, it was constantly directed toward the central fire. The earth, on the contrary, always faced toward Olympus, that is, to the outside. This fact explained why the anti-earth could never be seen from the earth, for the antipodes were not yet known. The revolution of the earth around the central fire was accomplished in one day. Since the face of the earth was always turned outward, we have the succession of day and night as well as the apparent diurnal revolution of all the stars, including the sun and the moon. Since outside the center of the universe there could exist no other source of activity or life-giving force, Philolaus thought that the sun could not be luminous by itself, but that it was a vitreous and porous body which absorbed the invisible light of Olympus and of the central fire and made it sensible to us by materializing it.

From these indications we see that the cosmic system of Philolaus is far from representing anything like the Copernican, as was often believed, especially after the death of Copernicus, when the fight began between the Copernicans and their adversaries concerning the motion of the earth. Nor must we think that this system was devised by Philolaus alone, but rather it represented an opinion widespread among the Italian Pythagoreans at that time.

PLATO AS AN ASTRONOMER

Of the numerous allusions to astronomy which are found in Plato's (429-347 B.C.) writings, there could be many interpretations because of their mystic and semipoetic character. Some credit the Greek philosopher with the invention of the epicycles, or even of the Copernican system. Schiaparelli, in his well-known writings on ancient astronomy, discusses thoroughly some of Plato's passages and shows how they must be interpreted. Plato expresses himself as follows, in explaining the form given by God to the universe:

> Therefore he made the world in the form of a globe; round as from a lathe, having its extremes in every direction equidistant from the center, the most perfect and the most like itself of all figures; for he considered that the like is infinitely fairer than the unlike. This he finished off, making the surface smooth all around for many reasons . . . ; but the movement suited to his spherical form was assigned to him, being of all the seven that which is most appropriate to mind and intelligence.

The seven motions are the rotary motion about the axis, and the motions up and down, right and left, back and forth. Plato then continues:

> and it was made to move in the same manner and the same spot, within his own limits revolving in a circle. All the other six motions were taken away from him. . . . And in the center he put the soul which he diffused throughout the body, making it also to be the exterior environment of it; and he made the universe a circle moving in a circle, one and solitary . . . .*

Plato then defines the diurnal motion of the world, of the planets, and of the stars (also the lunar month and the solar year), while the earth, remaining immobile in its opaque mass, produces and establishes in an invariable manner the succession of night and day. It must be noted that Aristotle, disciple and friend of Plato in the last years of Plato's life, maintains in the second book of his *De Caelo* the interpretation by which the earth, though being the center, rotates about its axis which pierces the world, affirming that this is

* Translator's note: *Timaeus,* from the B. Jowett translation of the "Dialogues" of Plato.

written in the *Timaeus.* There is only one passage which could be
so interpreted; all the others imply the immobility of the earth. To
explain this contradiction, Schiaparelli offers proof that Plato, in
the later years of his life, really believed in the motion of the earth.
In fact, Plutarch narrates that Plato having become old "was very
sorry that he had located the earth in the center of the universe, in a
place not fitting for it . . . , since the central and most noble place
should be reserved for something more worthy." Probably Plato,
during his trips in Sicily, had heard of the doctrine of the central
fire, and by adopting it, he admitted the diurnal rotation of the
earth, if not about its axis, at least around the central fire.

Thus Plato, who in his first writings imagined that the Gods drove
across the celestial dome in their chariots, and in the *Phaedo* won-
dered whether the earth was flat or round, afterward confirmed this
second conjecture of a convex body of spherical form, or little different from spherical. In the "Republic" and in the *Timaeus* he illustrated a geocentric system like the one which, perfected at the
school of Alexandria, held the field for many centuries. Having
learned of the Pythagorean doctrines, Plato began to understand
that the rotating motion of the earth (according to Aristotle) or the
revolving motion (as follows from Theophrastus) are better able
to explain celestial phenomena. He even went so far as to declare that
the contrary opinion was displeasing to the Gods, and that the weakness of those persons who did not participate in the divine intelligence was scarcely pardonable. Soon after Plato, the Pythagorean
school collapsed and with it the hypothesis of a central fire and
anti-earth, which became always more inadmissible as geographical
knowledge progressed.

THE "HOMOCENTRIC SPHERES" OF EUDOXUS

It fell to Eudoxus of Cnidus, a disciple of Plato, to improve
the system of his master with the theory of the "homocentric
spheres," an ingenious construction of ancient geometry. As completed by Aristotle and Calippus, this theory was generally adopted
until Hipparchus made way for the theory of eccentrics and epicycles.
However, the homocentric spheres were not abandoned entirely, for
in the Middle Ages they formed the basis of the astronomy of the
scholastics and the frame of Dante's "Paradise."

Eudoxus of Cnidus (409-356 B.C.), an able geometer, directed a school in which he sought to solve the cosmic problem by describing concentric spheres symmetrically about the earth, which were later called "homocentric spheres." In the complicated but ingenious construction originated by him and successively modified by Calippus, Aristotle, and Aristotle's pupils, it was necessary to introduce a great number of spheres. These spheres are still used nowadays, as Schiaparelli acutely observes, in our epicyclic planetary theories, hidden under the name of "periodic terms of infinite series." The system of Eudoxus hinged primarily on that elegant "spherical epicycloid," called by Eudoxus *hippopede*. Until the times of Philolaus and Plato, no attempt had been made to explain the stationary and retrograde motions of the planets, inasmuch as none of the hypotheses proposed before them could altogether explain the observed phenomena. Eudoxus went to study in Egypt and had a teacher there, a priest from Heliopolis, from whom he must have learned the results of the planetary observations made by the Egyptians over many years, but not reduced to any geometrical terms.

The principal characteristic of the system of Eudoxus is the complete elimination of all translatory motion. He resorted to combinations of rotary motion and found a solution which had no equal until the time of Kepler. Eudoxus imagined therefore, just like Plato before him, that every celestial body was carried around by a rotating sphere, so that it described during its revolution a great circle whose plane was perpendicular to the axis of rotation of the sphere. To explain the different speeds of the planets in their orbits, their stationary positions, their retrograde motions, and their variations in latitude, it was necessary to suppose that the planet had several motions, which, when combined together, produced the single observed motion which is apparently irregular. Then Eudoxus conceived the idea that the poles of the sphere which carried the planet were not stationary, but were carried by a larger sphere concentric to the first, which rotated with its own uniform motion and velocity around two poles, different from the poles of the first sphere. This hypothesis was still not sufficient to explain the apparent peregrinations of the seven wandering bodies. Then Eudoxus added other spheres, three or four, always concentric, which carried in succession the poles of the other spheres and which rotated with their own velocity about their own poles. By choosing a convenient position for the poles and a convenient velocity of rotation he represented quite well the motion of the sun and moon with three spheres. He needed four for each of the other planets. The carrier spheres of each body were entirely independent of the spheres which carried the other bodies. For the stars only one sphere was needed to produce the diurnal rotation of the sky.

Just as Plato also had supposed, Eudoxus imagined the following order of the planets, each having the number of moving spheres indicated:

(1)	Saturn, 4	(5)	Venus, 4
(2)	Jupiter, 4	(6)	Sun, 3
(3)	Mars, 4	(7)	Moon, 3
(4)	Mercury, 4		

There was one moving sphere for the fixed stars, making a total of 27.

Schiaparelli demonstrated how a point, subject to the combined motion of four homocentric spheres, describes a curve to which he gives the name "spherical lemniscate." To the curve described by a point (that is, a planet), resulting from its simultaneous motion on the third and on the fourth sphere, Eudoxus, as noted above, gives the name *hippopede*. This name is derived from the fact that the curve resembles the course followed by horses in riding-school exercises; the *hippopede* has the form and properties of a spherical lemniscate.

REFORMS OF CALIPPUS AND ARISTOTLE

Calippus, who had been taught the theories of Eudoxus probably by Polemarchus, conceived the idea of reforming them, and with this in mind he went to Athens, where Aristotle was teaching. Although we know very little of the final system outlined by Calippus, we do find, however, that he added another sphere to those of Eudoxus. He was trying to eliminate the serious flaws in the theories of Eudoxus, caused particularly by Mars, but also by Mercury and Venus. Calippus had two spheres for the sun, to represent the anomaly of its motion in longitude, which had been discovered a hundred years before by Meton and Euctemon. This anomaly became evident with the inequality of the four intervals into which the two equinoxes and the two solstices divided the total length of the year. The duration of the four seasons, given by Calippus with errors not larger than half a day, shows what progress the Greeks had made in observations of the sun between the years 430 and 330 B.C. The accuracy obtained by Calippus, by adding two spheres, is almost equal to the accuracy obtained much later with the eccentric and the epicycle. The first of these two spheres had its poles on the third sphere of Eudoxus and described the solar circle with uniform motion in the interval of one year. The second sphere had its poles on the first and its axis somewhat inclined to the latter's axis, and carried the sun with equal and opposite motion, in order to represent the longitudinal motion of the sun.

Calippus' modification represented the motion of the moon more exactly than Meton's theory. The "Calippic period" of 27,759 days comprised 940 moons, so that the duration of one lunation exceeded the real duration by only 10 seconds.

Aristotle took over the system of Eudoxus and Calippus with the intention of uniting the motions of the various spheres to form a single system, making the inferior spheres dependent upon the superior ones. He wanted to justify his cosmic dynamics, according to which the motive force of the universe should be located on the circumference and be propagated to the center. If all the spheres of Calippus were connected, the movements of the superior bodies would be communicated to the inferior bodies; to avoid this communication, Aristotle was compelled to insert a certain number of new spheres, which he called "counteracting," below the innermost sphere of each planet and above the outermost sphere of the planet immediately below. This complicated mechanism of Aristotle could not survive long and was soon to be superseded by all the new ideas that were arising. The variable brightness of the planets, especially Mars and Venus, had to depend upon their variable distance from the earth; and the variation in the apparent diameter of the sun and moon was absolutely irreconcilable with the concentricity of all spheres about the center of the earth.

NEW CONCEPTS BY HERACLIDES PONTICUS

Heraclides, called Ponticus from his birthplace Heraclea in Pontus, went to Athens as a youth and became one of Plato's most illustrious disciples. He wrote books on astronomy and geometry, from which only a few dry excerpts have survived. He considered the heavenly bodies to be worlds suspended in the infinite ether, each one a solid round body, an "earth" surrounded by an atmosphere. He thought that the moon was surrounded by fogs visible as spots on its surface, and that the comets were very high clouds illuminated by the upper fire, the fire of the Pythagorean Olympus. It is generally believed that Heraclides Ponticus explained the apparent diurnal motion of the sky by the diurnal motion of the earth. He did not think, as Philolaus did, that it was a circular motion around a central fire, but a rotary motion from west to east about its own axis, which completed its cycle in almost a day. In this manner the rotation of the earth was for the first time clearly defined.

Another important step made by Heraclides toward the Copernican doctrine was that he set the sun at the center of the motions of Venus and Mercury, a contribution erroneously credited to the Egyptians. The earth he set at the center of the motion of the superior planets. The study of the motions of Venus and Mercury to the right and left of the sun, and of the pronounced variations of their apparent magnitude would intuitively lead to the supposition that the earth was not the center of their revolutions. But this idea was in conflict with the fundamental belief that no motion could be admitted except around the center of the earth. Heraclides, for the first time, introduced the new concept of one body revolving around another, which itself revolved around the center of the universe; and he thus opened the way for the heliocentric system.

5 : the school of Alexandria

ARISTARCHUS AND ERATOSTHENES

ARISTARCHUS OF SAMOS, WHO LIVED IN THE
first half of the third century B.C., is famous as an astornomer, as a
mathematician, and especially as a geometer, as a result of his book
"On the Magnitudes and Distances of the Sun and of the Moon." He
also made astronomical observations, for instance, those of the summer solstice in 280 B.C. Along with Heraclides Ponticus he is credited
with being among the first to assert the diurnal motion of the earth
about the axis of the equator. Not only that, but he proposed a new
system in which the sun remains immobile in the center of the world,
while the earth revolves around it along the oblique circle of the
zodiac, and he explained that the seasons were produced by the inclination of the rotational axis to this circle. It seems that Aristarchus
had some idea of the infinitely great distance of the stars and that the
sun was one of them. As later befell Galileo, Aristarchus was accused
of impiety, by Cleanthes, a Stoic philosopher, "for having disturbed
the peace of Hestia," that is, the earth, which was believed by most
people to be the heart and central fire of the world.

Aristarchus understood that the sun must be much bigger than the
earth and estimated it to be about 7 times larger in diameter and
about 300 times larger in volume. He was thus led to think that the
earth, which was so much smaller than the sun, had to revolve around
the "lantern of the world." Aristarchus must have been the head of a
school from which Seleucus came, a man of Chaldean origin born in

Seleucia on the Tigris, who expounded a new and unusual theory on the ocean tides. The diurnal rotation of the earth, and the revolution of the moon in contrast to this, agitated in conflicting directions the air between the two bodies, so that the waters of the ocean were shifted back and forth according to the fluctuations of the moon. This hypothesis of Seleucus agreed with his observations of the ebb and flow of the Eritrean Sea, where he had discovered periodic inequalities. The tides seemed connected not only with the phases of the moon, but also with their distance from the equator. According to Plutarch, Seleucus admitted even a translatory motion for the earth. This must have been the annual motion of the earth around the sun, since his hypothesis was derived from that of Aristarchus. Seleucus was the last person in the West to maintain the hypothesis of the motion of the earth.

Aristarchus belonged to the school of Alexandria, to which the center of studies after the Aristotelian era had been moved from Greece under Alexander the Great about 322 B.C. Along with the famous library, an observatory was founded where many astronomers worked, among them Aristyllus and Timocaris. They were the first to determine new positions of the principal stars, which they collected in a catalogue with precise numerical data. At that time Euclid had developed the "doctrine of the spheres," that is, the system of spherical co-ordinates, which are used to determine the position of the axes and fundamental planes to which the co-ordinates of the celestial bodies are referred. An application of this doctrine may be found in the construction of solar clocks, which were perhaps imported from Babylonia to Greece and then perfected. They were widely used by the Greeks and during the Middle Ages.

Another Alexandrian astronomer was Eratosthenes, who lived about 230 B.C. and was among the first to calculate the size of the earth. During the summer solstice he measured the zenith distance of the sun at noon in Alexandria, and he knew that at the same instant the sun was in the zenith at Syene in Upper Egypt. Assuming that Syene had the same longitude as Alexandria and knowing the distance between the two places, he concluded that the circumference of the earth was about 250,000 *stadia*. It is difficult to evaluate the accuracy of this figure, since we do not know the exact measure of a *stadium* in our units.

THE EPICYCLE AND DEFERENT SYSTEM
OF APOLLONIUS

By now the time was ripe for a geometric pattern that could better represent the planetary motions and still keep the earth at the center of the universe. In particular the motions of Mercury and Venus, which are always close to the sun, must have given rise to the idea of the "epicycle" moving on a concentric "deferent." The deferent was the orbit of the sun around the earth; the epicycle was the secondary orbit of the planet around the sun. Even ignoring the sun, with a system of epicycles and deferents one could find an explanation for the direct and retrograde motions and stations of the planets. This was true not only for the inferior planets, but for the superior ones, which could travel along an epicycle around an ideal center which, like the sun, had a primary revolution around the earth. Thus the theory of epicycles with their arbitrary radii and velocities was generalized with the construction of a mechanism useful in geometrically representing the anomalies of the planetary motions, but it always assumed the earth to be the center of the world. It might have seemed strange that the revolution of a celestial body should take place around an imaginary point with no corresponding fixture in the sky. Yet this theory found favor among the mathematicians, for it seems to have been proposed and illustrated by Apollonius of Perga, an Alexandrian mathematician who lived in the latter half of the third century B.C. It was adopted by Hipparchus, and then generally accepted in place of the theory of homocentric spheres, which was insufficient to explain the observed phenomena. Since the order and magnitude of the spheres remained entirely arbitrary, the possibility arose of giving a new form to the hypothesis, that of a solid sphere, whose "epicycle" was represented by a little sphere attached to the thick wall of a larger hollow sphere, concentric to the center of the world and representing the deferent.

In the motions of the planets two facts were difficult for the ancients to explain. The first is their variable velocity, which has as its period the sidereal revolution; the second is the apparent stopping of their movement, which changes from direct to retrograde and vice versa. The first difficulty was explained for the sun and the moon by means of eccentrics, but the second required the principle of epicyclic motion. The planet moves with uniform velocity along a circle, which is the epicycle, whose center in turn moves along the circumference of the eccentric circle (the deferent) around the earth. Apollonius of Perga in 225 B.C. explained how it is possible to determine the ratio of the two radii, and how the path along the epicycle corresponds to the synodic period and the path along the deferent to the sidereal period. From this fundamental concept Ptolemy, after Hipparchus, was able to develop the theory of the planets, which completed the astronomy of the Greeks of the Alexandrian School.

CONTRIBUTIONS OF HIPPARCHUS

Hipparchus, certainly the greatest of the ancient astronomers, was born about 180 B.C. in Nicaea in Bithynia and lived in Rhodes, where he founded an observatory, and in Alexandria, where he made many astronomical observations, about the middle of the second century B.C. The works of Hipparchus have not come down to us directly but have been recorded by Ptolemy, his great admirer who lived three centuries later. Among his noteworthy contributions to astronomy are his systematic and critical comparisons of ancient observations with his own observations, in order to discover variations of small magnitude which might appear over long periods of time. He also developed the theory of eccentrics and epicycles to represent the motions of the sun and moon. After having recognized the motion of the sun along the ecliptic, Hipparchus developed the idea of Apollonius and imagined a convenient combination of uniform circular motions, using an eccentric for the sun. On the basis of the observations the necessary eccentricity could be deduced to represent the annual course of the sun along the ecliptic. No suitable instrument existed to establish the co-ordinates of the sun, especially in longitude. In fact the very computation of time was uncertain, being based on primitive water or sand timekeepers. Hipparchus determined from his observations the length of the seasons, that is, the intervals between the solstices and equinoxes, and he obtained the "equation of center," in other words, the excess of the actual longitude of the sun over the longitude which it would have if it moved uniformly. Thus Hipparchus was able to construct a table which gave the position of the sun for every day of the year.

The motion of the moon, being more complicated than that of the sun, required a more elaborate construction. First Hipparchus understood the importance of determining the period in which the moon returns to the same position with respect to (*a*) the sun (synodic month), (*b*) the stars (sidereal month), (*c*) the nodes (draconitic month), and (*d*) the apogee and perigee (anomalistic month), and he obtained considerable accuracy by using the Chaldean period and some ancient observations of eclipses. It was not easy to represent this complicated set of motions. For the sun he devised an eccentric whose center described a circle around the earth in approximately nine years, corresponding to the shift of the line of apsides. The plane of the eccentric was inclined to the ecliptic at an angle of 5°, which is actually the inclination of the orbit of the moon to the ecliptic. The eccentric regressed in such a way that the nodes moved from east to west along the ecliptic and completed an entire revolution in about nineteen years. Nevertheless some discrepancies remained, noted by Hipparchus himself, between calculated and observed positions, for it was impossible to represent the complicated motion of the moon by only one eccentric.

For the planets Hipparchus made new observations to determine their period of revolution more exactly, but he did not construct any system of epicycles and eccentrics to explain their movements in the sky. Following the method of eclipses, devised by Aristarchus, he determined the size and distance of the moon. He observed the angular diameter of the shadow of the earth on the moon, during eclipse, and compared it with the known angular diameters of the sun and moon. He thus obtained a relation for the two distances, by which either one could be found if the other were known. He concluded that the distance of the moon was almost 59 times the radius of the earth. Combining the values of Hipparchus and Aristarchus he indicated that the distance of the sun was 1200 times the radius of the earth, or about 19 times smaller than the true value. This highly erroneous value, which corresponds to a parallax of about 3′, was confirmed by Ptolemy and retained until the first half of the seventeenth century, both because of the authority behind it and because of the difficulty of a more exact determination.

It is said that the appearance of a "new star" in the constellation Scorpio in 134 B.C. led Hipparchus to compile a catalog of more than a thousand stars in which he gave their co-ordinates and divided them into the six magnitudes visible to the naked eye. By comparing the positions of these stars with the positions given by Timocaris and Aristyllus about one hundred and fifty years before, Hipparchus discovered that their distances from the equinoctial points had changed. This change consisted of a general increase in the longitude of the

stars, measured from west to east, which Hipparchus understood not
as a movement of the individual stars but rather as a shift of the
equinoctial points, which are the origins of the longitudes. These
points are the intersections of the equator and the ecliptic; therefore
one of these circles must have changed position. Since the obliquity
of the ecliptic and the latitudes of the stars revealed no variation in
the course of time, Hipparchus concluded that the equator must have
been slowly shifting from east to west, keeping constant its inclination
to the ecliptic. He thus discovered the phenomenon known today as
the "precession" of the equinoxes, which led him to define two different kinds of years. One was the "tropical year," the period required
by the sun to return to the same position with respect to the equinoctial points, and the other was the "sidereal year," the period required
by the sun to return to the same position with respect to the stars.
Hipparchus computed the length of these years with considerable
accuracy and discussed the possible errors of his observations.

His improved theories of the motions of the sun and moon enabled Hipparchus to predict more exactly than his predecessors the
ecipses of the sun and moon. Knowing the duration of the synodic
and draconitic months, he was able to calculate the period after
which the eclipses repeat themselves. The *Saros*, for example, contained very nearly 223 synodic months or 242 draconitic months. The
prediction of solar eclipses was more difficult, for the position of
the observer on the earth had to be considered, that is, the parallax of
the moon had to be calculated. Lunar eclipses could be predicted
within one or two hours, but solar eclipses were far less accurately predicted, especially in respect to determining the limited regions on the
earth where they were visible as total or partial.

In the years which followed the death of Hipparchus there is no
record of any noteworthy progress in astronomy. People began to
realize that the stars were not necessarily placed all on one sphere
but at various distances from the earth. Pliny (23–79 A.D.), to prove
the spherical form of the earth, emphasized the well known phenomenon of a ship which sinks gradually beneath the horizon as it moves
away from the observer. A few not very accurate observations and
some practically worthless treatises are the sole proofs that astronomy
was still cultivated in an age so rich in poets and orators. The Roman
calendar was reformed by Julius Caesar and by the Egyptian astronomer Sesigenes (46 B.C.), and new measurements of the circumference

of the earth, no better than those of Eratosthenes, were made by
Posidonius, Stoic philosopher.

PTOLEMY AND THE "ALMAGEST"

We must come as far as Claudius Ptolemy, who lived between 100 and 200 A.D., to find a rebirth of astronomical study. Nothing is known of his life except that he wrote the *Almagest,* the famous
astronomical treatise which remained the fundamental text throughout the Middle Ages and the source of all our knowledge of Greek
astronomy. The original work has the Greek title of "great composition," which, on account of the Greek word *megiste* ("the greatest"),
was called by the Arabs *Al Magisti,* from which *Almagest* is derived.

The mathematical and geometrical methods employed by Ptolemy
in this work made it preferable to similar works of the same time
and rapidly gave it wide circulation. The *Almagest* was translated into
Latin by Boethius, but his translation has not survived. Then it was
translated into Arabic in Bagdad by order of the caliph Al-Mamun
about the year 827 A.D. The emperor Frederick II in Naples had it
translated from Arabic to Latin about 1230. A summary appeared in
print in 1496 in Venice, and the first complete Latin translation was
published by P. Liechtenstein (Venice, 1515). The Greek text, with
the French translation of Halma, was published in Paris in 1813.

Delambre discusses the *Almagest* fully in his "History of Ancient
Astronomy," and writes: "The astronomy of the Greeks is all included
in the mathematical synthesis of Ptolemy." The *Almagest* is divided
into thirteen books. In the preface Ptolemy explains the great importance of astronomy, which reveals the greatness and order of creation. He points out that it is not only an abstract science but it has
considerable influence on human life. The first two books contain
definitions and general elementary theorems. He proves that the earth
is round and that gravity is directed everywhere toward the center of
the earth; he describes the position of the ecliptic and the location
of the inhabited regions of the earth. Ptolemy states that the phenomena of the celestial bodies will be studied on the sound basis of
observations and geometrical methods, taking as the starting point
what is evident, real, and certain. He gives two methods for determining the obliquity of the ecliptic, with appropriate instruments; he
finds the altitude of the pole and the length of the day for various

places, and calculates tables of angles and arcs formed by the intersection of the ecliptic with the meridian and the horizon.

In the third book he considers the motion of the sun and the length of the year. On the basis of Hipparchus' and of his own observations on the position of the vernal and autumnal equinoxes, he discusses the irregularities of the course of the sun, which he explains by the hypothesis of eccentric motion. This chapter closes with a clear exposition of the circumstances on which the "equation of center" depends.

In the fourth book Ptolemy expounds the theory of the motion of the moon and his important discovery of lunar "evection." Hipparchus had discovered the first "lunar inequality" or "equation of center," which corrected the average motion at the syzygies, and had noted that another correction was necessary at the quadratures. Ptolemy completed the work of Hipparchus, discovering that the eccentricity of the moon's orbit was itself subject to an annual variation dependent upon the motion of the line of apsides. The variation of the position of the apsides produces an inequality of the lunar motion at the quadratures which is the so-called evection. To explain this new inequality, Ptolemy advanced the hypothesis of the "epicycle," a circle described by the moon around an imaginary point which glides along the "deferent." The latter, also called "eccentric," is a circle which sustains the motion of the epicycle; and the earth, according to Ptolemy, is close to its center. To explain other discrepancies between theory and observation of lunar motion, Ptolemy introduced a small oscillation of the epicycle to which he gave the name *prosneusis*, or "nutation." His final theory agreed so well with observation that the error of his tables, in which it was possible to calculate the position of the moon for any epoch, was seldom greater than one degree.

The fifth book begins with a description of the "astrolabe," an instrument made up of a combination of graduated circles, which had already been used by Hipparchus to determine the co-ordinates of the stars. The book continues with a detailed discussion of the moon's parallax and the distances of the sun and moon. He obtains the distance of the latter by the parallax method, as is still done today. This subject is continued in the sixth book, where is also found the method for calculating eclipses, essentially according to the work of Hipparchus. The seventh and eighth books contain a catalog of 1022 stars, which seems identical with the catalog of Hipparchus. It is highly probable that it is substantially the catalog of the latter, corrected for precession. In the eighth book there is also a description of the Milky Way, and a method for constructing celestial globes.

The remainder of the work deals with the theory of the planets, which is Ptolemy's most noteworthy original contribution to astronomy. He states that the planets are much closer to the earth than are the fixed stars, and farther away than the moon. He attempts to explain their apparent motion in the sky by a better theory than that proposed by Eudoxus, using his own observations and those of Hipparchus. Just as for the moon, he used an eccentric circle as deferent for the planets, but instead of having the center of the epicycle move uniformly along the deferent he introduced a new point, called "equant," located at the same distance as the earth from the center of the deferent, but on the opposite side. The motion of the center of the epicycle was such that the apparent motion, as seen from the equant, should be uniform. By means of this system, which had been elaborated with much labor and great care, Ptolemy was able to represent accurately the motions of the planets. Having no way to determine their distances, he could only place Mars, Jupiter, and Saturn at increasing distances from the sun, and Venus and Mercury, since they accompanied the sun, between the sun and the moon, with Mercury the closer to the earth.

The great merit of Ptolemy was that he transmitted by means of the *Almagest,* the astronomical doctrines of his predecessors, especially preserving and developing those of Hipparchus, and in addition he brought new and noteworthy contributions to the knowledge of his times. With Ptolemy ends the history of Greek astronomy, which was rich, if not in matters of observation, in the development of mathematical methods, especially geometric, which gave sufficient explanation and agreement between the theories and the phenomena observed.

6 : medieval astronomy (476–1500)

THE ROMANS CONTRIBUTED NOTHING, OR AL-
most nothing, to astronomy after the Greeks. During the fourteen
centuries from the publication of the *Almagest* to the Copernican era,
a period almost twice as long as the period from Thales to Ptolemy
and almost four times as long as the period from the death of Copernicus to the present age, there was no astronomical discovery of great
importance. This comparison certainly shows the general neglect of
astronomy. Seneca, in his "Natural Questions," mentions some astronomical problems, and also, without discussing them, expounds
some ingenious ideas on the size of the universe and the motion of
the celestial bodies. Pliny devotes the second book of his "Natural
History" to astronomy, from which it is clear that he was neither an
astronomer nor a geometer.

Leaving antiquity and approaching the Middle Ages, we find only
Latin compilers with no original works. Martianus Capella, who lived
in the fifth century discusses the seven arts, which in the Middle
Ages constituted the scholastic teaching and among which astronomy
was included. He states that the earth is not the center of all the
planets, but that Venus and Mercury revolve around the sun. Copernicus cites this author's passage as deserving of consideration. Bede,
the venerable English Benedictine monk, occupied himself with astronomy and proposed a reform of the calendar, very similar to the
Gregorian. He introduced the custom of counting the years from
Christ's birth, that is, the "Christian Era."

SEVENTH CENTURY ORIENTAL ASTRONOMY

One remarkable revival of astronomical study occurred in the Orient during the seventh century. The Arabs, after their territorial conquests, felt the influence of western civilization; and Bagdad, the capital of the caliphs, rapidly became a cultural center of some importance. It seems that in 772 an astronomical treatise was brought there from India, and it was translated into Arabic and was used for half a century. Translations of Greek texts were also begun, among them the *Almagest,* as we mentioned before.

At Damascus and Bagdad two observatories were founded, with instruments similar to those of the Greeks, but larger and much improved. Regular and continued observations were organized of the principal celestial bodies as well as of eclipses. The importance attached to the latter was so great that they were registered in signed writs, under oath, by a commission of astronomers and lawyers.

The best known among the Arabian astronomers was the famous Al-Battani, born about the middle of the ninth century in the neighborhood of Harran in western Mesopotamia. It seems that he was born in a town called Battan, from which his name was latinized into Albatenius by western writers. His father was renowned as a celebrated mechanic and builder of astronomical instruments. This background perhaps contributed to the excellence of his observations, which were begun about the year 877 and continued until 918 A.D., mostly in the city of Rakkah on the Euphrates river where he lived, and some in Antioch. Like other astronomers of his times, Albatenius was interested in astrology. But unlike many of his contemporaries, he dealt with astronomy scientifically, so that his biographers affirmed that "no one among the Moslems has equaled Albatenius in his precise observations of the celestial bodies and in his accurate investigation of their movements."

His major work has come down to us in an Arabic codex of the eleventh-twelfth century, which is now preserved in the Escorial. The orientalist C. A. Nallino translated it into Latin, and we find in it many new and unfamiliar elements of Arab astronomy, and especially the progress made by Albatenius. The reason which induced him to write his *Opus Astronomicum,* he explains in the introduction:

> For many years I have occupied myself with astronomy and spent much time in its study. I have observed many differences

in the books which deal with the celestial motions, and I have even seen that some authors have been wrong in their establishment of the fundamentals. Therefore after much reflection I have thought to correct and better establish all these things, using the methods of Ptolemy in his *Almagest*, tracing his footsteps, and following his precepts. In fact Ptolemy has carefully examined all the elements and demonstrated the cause of all phenomena with proofs which leave no room for doubt. He even exhorted others to observe and investigate after him, saying that it was not impossible that someone might add something to his observations, as he had done to the studies of Hipparchus and others. So great, in fact, is the majesty of this grand and heavenly science that no one alone can embrace it entirely and precisely. Therefore I have composed this book, in which my explanations of the difficult things and abstruce principles of this science will make the way easy for those who will want to study and follow it. I have corrected the position and the movements of the celestial bodies on the ecliptic which I have found from observations, from calculations of eclipses, and from other operations; and I have added other necessary things. To find the position of the celestial bodies I have added tables, reduced to the meridian of Rakkah, where all the required observations were made. And so may it be, God willing, because only with God may we find assistance.

The original title of the work has been lost. Unlike the *Almagest*, the theoretical and explanatory parts are reduced to a minimum, while full development is given to the calculations and to the tables which are used for the calculations. The first part is preceded by a preface by Nallino, in which he reviews the life of Albatenius and gives information on the various editions of the book and on the studies of it made by Regiomontanus, Halley, and Delambre. The book is divided into fifty-seven chapters which open with the invocation: *In nomine Dei clementis et misericordis.* In these chapters are discussed many problems of spherical astronomy, which Albatenius solves by means of orthographic projections, using new formulas. In these formulas he employs trigonometric functions, and he solves for the first time a spherical triangle, given two sides and the included angle. Since he had used larger and more accurate instruments than those used by the Greeks, he obtained more accurate results. It seems that he found meridian altitudes by using the *alhidada longa* or "parallactic triquetrum," as Ptolemy had done before, equivalent to a circle of sizable diameter and a wall quadrant. Time was determined by the altitude of known stars, and by sundials during the day. Albatenius was thus able to determine the obliquity of the ecliptic with an error of less than one minute of arc, as compared with the value known today. In addition he succeeded in establishing the equinoxes within one or two hours. He established the length of the year, which was afterward used in the reform of the Julian calendar. The intervals between the equinoxes and solstices, which he had determined, led to the discovery of the apparent solar orbit, which was much closer to the truth than the Greek conception. He corrected the error which the Greek astronomers had made, that the solar perigee was immobile with respect to the equinoxes and was not affected by the motion of precession.

In the last chapters Albatenius treats the parallax of the moon and its distance from the earth, the eclipses of the moon and of the sun for any region, and the positions of the five major planets on the ecliptic at the various epochs. He explains the construction of sundials, celestial globes, wall quadrants, and the triquetrum. In the second part of the book there are astronomical tables—the result of the observations and calculations of Albatenius—which contain data for the computation of the calendar and for the motion of the sun and moon. The co-ordinates of the constellations, the parallax of the moon in longitude and latitude, the motions of the five major planets, a catalog of the fixed stars, and finally even an "astrological rose" concludes the book. As is pointed out by Schiaparelli, who actively collaborated in Nallino's edition, Nallino not only preserved everything possible of Albatenius' astronomical work, but he also brought to light its indisputable merits and the remarkable results which he achieved. A comparison of this work of Albatenius and that of Ptolemy, which have so many points in common, is particularly interesting, especially for understanding the astronomical development of the Orient.

The last of the astronomers of Bagdad was Abul Wafa, who wrote a voluminous treatise on astronomy, known also as the *Almagest*, which contains new researches on the motion of the moon. Astronomy made some progress about the year 970 in the Mohammedan dominions of Spain and North Africa. The most important work is the "Toledan Tables," so called because they were computed in Toledo.

But after the Arabs had been routed from Cordoba and Seville, astronomy dropped out of the picture.

Another important astronomical school of the east arose in Bagdad, before the end of the reign of the caliphs, with the astronomer Nassir Eddin (born 1201). He founded a large observatory in Meragah in the northwestern part of modern Persia, with instruments remarkable for their precision and dimensions, surpassed only by those of Tycho Brahe. Nassir Eddin left a manual of astronomy and began a large work of astronomical tables for calculating the movements of the planets, which contained also a catalog of stars based on new observations. From these observations he established a more accurate value of the annual precession.

About two hundred years later astronomical studies flourished at Samarkand in Turkestan under Ulugh Begh, grandson of the oriental conqueror Tamerlane. He built an important observatory about 1420 and published new tables of the planets and a catalog of stars, comprising those of Ptolemy, with new observations. For the first time the stellar co-ordinates, celestial latitude and longitude, were given not only in degrees but also in minutes.

Although no important discoveries were made in the East, the accumulation of observations was sizable and important, as was the development of mathematical methods and the invention of our present system of counting, which greatly simplified arithmetic. From the times of the Arabs some astronomical terms borrowed from their language have remained in common use until today. Examples are zenith, nadir, almucantar, almanac, and the names of the most brilliant stars, like Aldebaran (α Tauri), which signifies "the following" because it follows the Pleiades, Betelgeuse (α Orionis) "shoulder of the giant," Altair (α Aquilae), "flying eagle," and so forth.

Among the instruments which were most frequently used by the astronomers of those times is the "astrolabe," made of a metallic disk of appreciable thickness, which was held vertically suspended by means of a ring. On the face of an external circle is represented the equator divided into 360°; inside the disk are hinged various thinner disks on which are represented, for different degrees of latitude, the co-ordinate systems of the equator and the horizon in polar stereographic projection. To these disks is also hinged a perforated plate with the representation of the zodiac and with various indices which correspond to the principal stars. By rotating this plate on the underlying fixed disks, it is possible to determine the position of the stars with respect to the equator and to the horizon for any given time and place. On the back of the astrolabe is engraved another division into 360°, besides a perpetual calendar and an apparatus like a gnomon which permits the determination of time from the shadow made by the sun. A pointer provided with two sights, which rotates on the axis of the astrolabe, serves to measure the altitude of the stars when the instrument is suspended vertically from its ring.

Another instrument employed in those times was the "wall quadrant." To a wall in the plane of the meridian a quarter of a circle of wood was attached, to which was affixed a copper strip divided into degrees. A wooden pointer which revolved around an axis in the center of the circle could be moved by means of ropes and pulleys. By means of a sighting contrivance, it was possible to point to the various celestial bodies as they crossed the meridian.

A third type of instrument consisted of "armillary spheres," more or less complicated, which were used for the direct determination of the equatorial and ecliptic co-ordinates of the celestial bodies. Sundials and water clocks were employed to supplement these instruments.

After the fall of the western Roman Empire astronomy was hardly studied any more, and progress is found only under Charles the Great, who in 782 called to his court, to direct a sort of academy, the Englishman Alcuin to discuss and lecture on astronomy, arithmetic, and rhetoric.

LIMITED PROGRESS OF TENTH TO FIFTEENTH CENTURIES

In the tenth century Arabic science began to spread out from Spain; and about 1000, Gerbert, who had become pope under the name of Sylvester II, became famous in the mathematical and astronomical sciences and also constructed astrolabes and other instruments. Two centuries later Gerard of Cremona was a very active translator of scientific treatises, among them the *Almagest* and the "Toledan Tables." Various centers of study began then to be organized, as for example the important University of Naples founded in 1224 by the emperor Frederick II, where the Aristotelian doctrines were held in high esteem. Another center of study was established about the same time in Toledo by Alfonso X of León and Castile,

who assembled there notable Jewish and Christian scientists to compute the "Alfonsine Tables." These tables were more accurate than
similar previous ones and had a wide circulation throughout Europe.
The publication of *Libros del Saber* resulted from Alfonso's interest
in astronomy. This book is a voluminous astronomical encyclopedia,
in which for the first time the orbit of Mercury is drawn as an ellipse
with the earth at the center.

In the thirteenth century Albertus Magnus, Roger Bacon, and
Cecco d'Ascoli should be mentioned, since they, although not astronomers, occupied themselves more or less with astronomical problems. At the same time John Holywood of Yorkshire, better known
under his latinized name of Johannes de Sacrobosco, professor of
mathematics, in Paris, where he died about 1256, wrote his *Sphaera
Mundi*. This is an elementary treatise on spherical astronomy which
was extremely popular until the end of the seventeenth century and
had a large number of translations and editions.

PURBACH AND HIS FOLLOWERS

In the fifteenth century an important center of astronomical
studies arose in Germany and Austria under George Purbach, professor of astronomy and mathematics in the University of Vienna about
1450. Essentially a supplement to the treatise of Sacrobosco, he compiled a "manual of astronomy" based on the *Almagest*, of which,
however, he had had poor Latin translations. Johann Müller, better
known as Regiomontanus, who became his pupil in Vienna, collaborated with him in regard both to the manual and to a revision of
the "Alfonsine Tables." Both men were invited to Rome to study the
Almagest and unify the translations. After the death of Purbach,
Regiomontanus remained seven years in Italy; and after having
learned Greek there, he was able to carry out his assignment and to
complete the "manual" of Purbach. Regiomontanus studied other
manuscripts and astronomical works of the Greeks, and he later settled down in Nuremberg, where the art of printing was being born.

The public benefactor Bernard Walther not only became Regiomontanus' pupil but helped him to construct an observatory and build a
workshop. There he could make the astronomical instruments with
which he observed, especially, the famous comet of 1472. Regimon-
tanus founded also a printing shop, where he published the "Planetary Theory" of Purbach, which had wide circulation. In this work

the difference is well marked between the Aristotelian and Ptolemaic doctrines.

It is known that Aristotle considered the sun, the moon, the five planets, and the fixed stars to be attached respectively to eight spheres. The first sphere being constituted by the earth, the outermost sphere of the fixed stars by its daily rotation caused the apparent motion of all the celestial bodies. This was the ninth sphere, called the "firmament" or *primum mobile*, which moved all the other spheres. The deferents and epicycles of Ptolemy were geometric abstractions which represented the planetary motions with sufficient accuracy, while the stars moved freely in space. Under the direction of Regiomontanus, almanacs and true astronomical ephemerides were published in Nuremberg. These contained even the method of "lunar distances," discovered by Regiomontanus to determine the "fix" at sea—that is, the co-ordinates of the ship—at any time when the moon was visible. The ephemerides and this method were considerably superior to those already in existence; it seems that they were even known to Christopher Columbus and certainly were employed by A. Vespucci on his voyages to America.

In 1475 Regiomontanus was recalled to Rome to attend to the reform of the calendar, but he died there the following year at forty years of age. Walter continued the observations and completed some works of his master, and he made the first attempt to explain the phenomenon of astronomical refraction.

Meanwhile in Italy regular and comprehensive instruction was developed, including mathematics and astronomy, especially at the University of Padua.

TOSCANELLI: FROM MEDICINE TO ASTRONOMY

Paolo dal Pozzo Toscanelli, born in Florence in 1397, was induced to study medicine in Padua, where he became a great friend of Nicholas of Cusa. It is interesting to note that Master Paolo, like Galileo, studied medicine, but he continued to practice it, whereas Galileo soon abandoned it. Besides being a physician, Paolo, like Galileo, was a humanist, astronomer, mathematician, and geographer. It is not surprising that medicine led them both to thoughts of astronomy, for many of the artifices of medicine were derived from astrology. Minds like those of Toscanelli and Galileo could not accept all the fabrications of astrology which had been made or were being made from a confused mixture of observations and real and well-established facts, together with fantasies formulated without scientific basis by more or less ignorant scholars. In those times and for many years afterward, only the greatest minds could distinguish the true from the false in such a confusion. The false doctrine was often developed because of temporary necessity, in order to satisfy those powerful persons who wanted to know from the stars their good or bad fortune, or in order to answer the frequent and common questions of the many people who believed in the influences on their daily life of the various celestial configurations and of the appearance of new stars. Toscanelli, who was studying medicine in the University of Padua and had special inclination and ability for the exact sciences, could not remain immune to the astrological disease; but he was able to control it and repress it. In order to find the truth, he freed himself from the fantastic fabrication by making celestial observations and deriving results from them.

In the fifteenth century the so-called "judicial astrology" had assumed in Florence great importance in the affairs of state. It is certain that Toscanelli, who was considered by the Florentine *Signorìa* as the most celebrated and trustworthy astronomer of the times, was often consulted on state affairs and under special and important circumstances. But he must have had the same thoughts and opinions of astrology as Galileo and Kepler did many years later. In fact, his contemporaries tell us that largely as a result of the experiences he had had and of the fabrications he was required to make, he believed the judicial art to be uncertain and false. He brought forth several proofs, among them his advanced age which, according to the constellations and celestial combinations dominant at his birth, was not favored.

Paolo Toscanelli, student of medicine, and Nicholas of Cusa, student of law, imbibed the teachings of the University of Padua, the former in the experimental and mathematical field, the latter in the philosophical field. Nicholas of Cusa was later to become the reviver of Pythagoreanism and the forerunner of Giordano Bruno, and he acquired so much mathematical knowledge that he even discussed the problem of squaring the circle and foresaw the Copernican theory. Although only excerpts remain of the writings and works of Toscanelli, which cannot therefore be evaluated, there is no doubt that his contemporaries, especially Cusa and Regiomontanus, believed him to be the most learned living mathematician, not just in mathematics but in other sciences. It would be interesting to know what Master Paolo thought of Cusa's anticipation of Copernicus, but no documents are available on this matter.

The great height of the cathedral dome of Santa Maria del Fiore in Florence inspired Toscanelli with the idea of attaching a gnomon there, which is actually the highest one built before or since. He thus made an astronomical instrument of great value which earned well-deserved fame. Little is known of this accomplishment, but the records of Father Ignazio Danti, the well-known cosmographer of the Grand Duke of Tuscany, are sufficient proof, although written a century later. Danti states that Master Paolo made a hole at the base of the lantern at the top of the dome of Santa Maria del Fiore. Through this hole the rays of the sun passed, and the day of the solstice could be thus accurately determined. The hole is nearly 300 feet above the ground level, and the rays of the sun at high noon, on the day of the summer solstice, fall on the floor of the Chapel of the Cross. Here various stones have been inserted at different times, of which the oldest one, according to Ximenes (who in 1755 studied and reconstructed this sundial), is actually the one set by Toscanelli in 1468.

With such a simple contrivance, which is the first type of astronomical instrument employed by man, one can obtain quite accurately the time of meridian transit of the sun, and therefore the local time. Also various important problems can be solved, not only in astronomy, but in the regulation of certain ecclesiastical dates. Master Paolo understood that, by determining the moment when the sun reached its highest altitude in Florence at the summer solstice, he could find the moment when the sun entered Aries, and consequently the moment of the vernal equinox. For this problem he needed good tables which would well represent the apparent positions of the sun throughout the various seasons. At the time of Toscanelli there were only the "Alfonsine Tables," which were still very imperfect. With a better knowledge of the sun's motion—that is, the earth's motion in its orbit —which he obtained from observations of his sundial in Santa Maria del Fiore, he was able to correct and improve these tables. By extending his observations to the stars, he determined a value for the precession of the equinoxes which was more accurate than any value used before. Regiomontanus, writing to Giovanni Bianchini, the celebrated professor of astronomy at Ferrara, confirms the precise observations of

Master Paolo on the motion of the sun and the obliquity of the ecliptic. Thanks to the height and stability of the gnomon of Santa Maria del Fiore, these observations surpassed in accuracy all other observations of that time.

OBSERVATIONS ON THE COMETS

The astronomical contributions of Toscanelli were not limited to these observations. He made many interesting ones of six comets which appeared in those years, and which he followed with great care, probably because of the astrological beliefs of his times. In April, 1864, the Florentine astronomer G. B. Donati communicated to the German periodical *Astronomische Nachrichten* some of his observations of comets made in Florence with the refractor of Amici, to which he added:

> I have the pleasure to announce that here in Florence there have been discovered very interesting old observations of some comets, of which only vague information has been available until now. Professor Puliti found them in an old manuscript in our National Library. The observations refer to the comets which appeared in the years 1433, 1449, 1456, 1457, 1472. They were made by Paolo Toscanelli, celebrated for his letter to Christopher Columbus and for the great gnomon which he built in our Cathedral. I propose to make a detailed investigation of these observations and as soon as possible I shall inform you of the results.

Donati, who was then busy founding the Observatory of Arcetri and who died prematurely a few years after the discovery, was not able to carry out his project. Giovanni Celoria, Schiaparelli's successor at the Observatory of Brera (Milan), undertook the study of the Toscanelli codex. These observations are of fundamental importance in positional astronomy before the telescope. They preceded by a century the observations of Tycho Brahe, which were made at the observatory of Uraniburg with much better equipment than Toscanelli had at his disposal. The codex furnishes proof that, if Toscanelli had extended his observational methods to the planets, he, before Tycho, would have given Kepler the elements which led him to the formation of his famous laws. The author himself wrote on the back of one of the sheets of the codex that these observations had cost him long sleepless nights and much labor: *immensi labores et graves vigilie magistri Pauli de Puteo Toscanello super mensura comete.*

We have information that the comet of 1433 was observed in Poland and China. From the few indeterminate existing observations, the comet's orbit around the sun has been approximately calculated. Toscanelli's much more accurate observations are given by a drawing on which are marked the relative positions of the comet and the principal stars which it approached each day. It was easy to identify these stars and to discover that this was not an approximate sketch, but a drawing with real measurements, just as Toscanelli states. Having determined the positions of the stars and from these the position of the comet, Celoria was able to calculate the parabolic orbit, verifying Toscanelli's path by the European chronicles and the Chinese annals. The tail attained its maximum length of 6° a few days before the comet reached perihelion.

Of the second comet observed by Master Paolo in the winter of 1449–1450, the European chronicles give insufficient and uncertain information, but the Chinese annals give more reliable data. For this comet also, Toscanelli's observations furnish true measurements and therefore the possibility of a calculation of the orbit. In one of the tables of the codex we see how Toscanelli tried to establish the position of the comet by means of straight lines passing through certain stars, at the intersections of which the comet was located on successive days. The hour of observation is given for two of these intersections. In two other tables he returned to the system of drawing the relative positions, giving the dates and often the hour of observation. To facilitate the identification of the stars, he traced contours of the constellations, showing the figures of Ophiuchus, Serpens, and Boötes. Since the observational data are numerous and extend through several months, Celoria was able to compute with considerable accuracy the parabolic orbit of this comet, which was not a very bright one and had a tail of rather limited dimensions. This fact explains the rarity of observations other than those of Toscanelli.

The comet of 1456 is the periodic comet known to us as Halley's comet, in one of its many apparitions. Since its elliptic motion around the sun is well known, it can confirm the accuracy of Master Paolo's observations. Among the apparitions of this comet, which can be traced back to epochs before Christ, the apparition in 1456 must have been of considerable importance, according to the chronicles of the times. One chronicle tells us that the comet was large, terrible, and of extraordinary magnitude, with a very long tail extending through 60°, therefore covering a third of the sky. Its head was round, the size of an ox's eye, from which came forth the fan-shaped tail, like that of a peacock, variable in length from one day to another. Other records give the position of the comet, as usual without any accuracy.

A celestial phenomenon of such importance could not fail to arouse public interest, especially in view of the astrological beliefs of those times. It is not surprising then that we find among the codices of Toscanelli a copy, made by Master Paolo himself, of a letter by Pietro Bono Avogario, mathematician at the University of Ferrara and en-thusiastic follower of judicial astrology, wherein he predicts all kinds of disasters due to the comet. Toscanelli is not free from the craze, for on other sheets of his manuscript he gives information about his observations for the purpose of investigating the eventual effects of the comet upon the earth, according to current ideas and prejudices. Toscanelli prudently refers to these without comment, but he adds a list of the comet's positions in the sky during June and July of that year, giving the longitudes and latitudes. In the manuscript of Tos-canelli, if we except the astrological considerations, we have a set of genuine observations of prime importance, as much for the history of Halley's comet as for positional astronomy, and in no way inferior to those made years later by Regiomontanus. The co-ordinates of the comet were deduced by Master Paolo from drawings similar to those used for other comets. Since, however, in this case the celestial region is around the ecliptic, he added a rectangular graph, ruled in squares, marking on the horizontal sides the longitudes and on the vertical sides the north and south latitudes. He adopted this same system later for his famous nautical chart.

As Celoria proves, the positions of the stars adopted by Toscanelli are taken largely from Ptolemy's *Almagest*, corrected for precession in order to refer them to the right epoch. Although almost sixteen centuries had passed since Hipparchus, the effect of this motion was very imperfectly known. In general, Hipparchus and Ptolemy admit-ted that there was a uniform motion of the eighth sphere, so that all the stars shifted annually by a very small amount of longitude. At the time of Toscanelli there were many values for this shift, none of which was adopted. He recognized their inadequacy and wanted to calculate his own, which in fact came closer than any other to the exact value known today.

The phenomenon of precession, still a mystery at that time, had aroused Toscanelli's interest; and as Giovanni Pico relates and Celoria clearly proves, he was able, by means of stellar observations, to improve the value of Albatenius. From Toscanelli's final positions of Halley's comet, Celoria calculated, after long and patient labor, the elliptic orbit which the comet completes after seventy-six years, so that after six periods we were able to see it again in its last passage close to the sun in 1910. The calculations of Celoria confirmed the precision and the importance of Master Paolo's observations and the entirely new and original form in which they were made and recorded. The greatest uncertainty at his time was undoubtedly the determination of the instant of the relative position of the comet to the stars. We may recall that in those times there existed only sundials and some crude combinations of wheels kept in motion by a weight without any regulator, such as the pendulum or the balance. The very fact that Toscanelli in most cases gives only the date of his observations, sometimes the hour, and very rarely the minute, shows that it was not easy for him to determine time with any precision. Since he was a master in the art of sundials, we can surmise that these gave him the time during the day, and perhaps he measured it at night with some imperfect clock or by ascertaining the altitude of known stars with some rudimentary form of sextant. Only many years later could time be measured to the minute. Since Master Paolo did give the time in a few cases, it seems that he was able to determine it within a certain degree of accuracy, even under the existing difficulties. Since he was so far ahead of his times, he succeeded in opening up new roads rich in returns for the field of astronomical observations.

The year after the passage of Halley's comet, Toscanelli observed the comet 1457 I, about which the existing data are scarce and inaccurate, except for the few but important notes which are found in his manuscripts. The positions of this comet, with a tail approximately half a degree in length, are marked among the stars of the constellation Cetus, together with a scale of longitudes and latitudes. Despite the few observations made in a short interval of time, Celoria was able to plot an orbit of this periodic comet, confirmed later by its reappearances in 1818 and 1873.

In the summer of the same year (1457) there appeared in the constellation Gemini another comet (1457 II), of which some reports are found in the chronicles of the times and in the Chinese annals. It was thin, straight, similar to a spear, with a tail 15° long, and it was visible for about three months. Of all the observations made of that appearance, only those of Toscanelli, found among his papers, are precise enough for its orbit around the sun to be calculated. The drawings, on which the positions of the comet and the stars are marked, contain in this case also a rectangle, ruled in squares, on which the longitudes and latitudes are given, degree by degree. The graduating lines are not drawn in ink or pencil but are engraved right in the paper and seem to have been drawn by a comb especially made for that purpose. Of the seventy-six stars to which the comet is referred in its successive positions, five are not in the *Almagest,* and Toscanelli must have determined their co-ordinates on the basis of his own observations. When we compare these co-ordinates with those known today, it is again possible to see how accurate his observations and measuring methods were. Because of the high precision and large number of observations, the orbit of this comet is very well represented and has a greater accuracy than that of the other comets.

At seventy-five years of age Master Paolo observed his last comet, the one of 1472. Perhaps because of his advanced age or because the comet appeared in the dead of winter, he did not leave, or at least we have no record of, drawings like those for the previous comets. We have only a short manuscript in which he describes, with his customary gravity and profusion of numbers, the motion of the comet among the stars. Celoria was able to obtain two fairly accurate positions from these observations, but he could draw no conclusion at all from the Chinese annals and other chronicles. Regiomontanus also observed this comet and diligently described its course among the stars. However, it is impossible to deduce any useful position, since he recorded no times of observations nor even dates for the successive positions of the comet in the sky. Only one complete observation was found after his death, and it was mistakenly believed to be the first of its kind until the manuscripts of Toscanelli were discovered. Moreover, we have seen that Master Paolo in 1433 had modestly begun similar methods which were far more precise. Halley, from only incomplete indications of Regiomontanus, and Laugier, combining these with some Chinese indications, calculated the orbit of this comet without being able to guarantee its reliability in any way. Celoria was able, by combining the two positions of Toscanelli and other data from his manuscript with the positions of Regiomontanus, to calculate an orbit which well represented the course of the comet during January of that year. It must be noted also, that since the comet passed very close to the earth and thus possessed a very rapid motion, the computation of the orbit was somewhat difficult, but in any case Celoria's orbit was more precise than the one computed from Regiomontanus' observations alone.

In the history of astronomy the analysis of Toscanelli's observations stands as proof that Toscanelli preceded Regiomontanus in time, in the use of measuring instruments and methods, in the continuity and precision of the observed phenomena, and in the recognition of the most difficult problems of sidereal astronomy. Besides his manuscripts, in themselves very eloquent, for the rest of his work we must unfortunately resort to conjectures, or to what his contemporaries say, and first of all to Regiomontanus himself, who held his illustrious competitor in high esteem.

DA VINCI, FRACASTORO, AND OTHERS

We cannot say that Leonardo da Vinci in his encyclopedic activity occupied himself particularly with astronomy. Yet the few observations he made show that he was ahead of his times also in this field. He was probably influenced by Nicholas of Cusa. Leonardo must have had an idea of the great distances of the stars and the dimensions of the sun, for he says in reference to the latter: "I can never cease blaming those ancient people, especially Epicurus, who said that the sun had no other size than that which it shows to us . . ." Leonardo also imagined the high temperature of the sun: "They say that the sun is not hot because it is not the color of fire, but it is whiter and clearer. And to these people one can reply that when melted bronze is very hot it is more like the color of the sun, and when the bronze is less hot it is more like the color of fire." Leonardo recognizes that all earthly life is due to the sun, and that when the sun fails, shadow and cold will reign. The sun illuminates the other planets just as it illuminates the earth and the moon. Leonardo drew the spots of the moon in which he found great variety, and he concluded that the brightest regions were seas and the darker regions "islands and solid ground." He explains correctly the reasons for the phenomenon which he calls "moon luster" but which we call "earthshine." Even at the time of Galileo, this phenomenon was the object of much discussion and erroneous interpretation. Concerning the earth's position in the universe, Leonardo certainly was aware of the daily rotation, since he speaks of it in the problem of falling bodies and explains the "deflection of the vertical."

Following the footsteps of Leonardo and Toscanelli, Girolamo Fracastoro and Francesco Maurolico in Italy were interested in astronomy and made some new contributions. Fracastoro, born in Verona in 1483, tried to improve, but without success, the homocentric spheres of Eudoxus and Calippus. He increased their number in order to make the theory agree better with the observations. In his work entitled *Homocentricorum seu de Stellis Liber Unus* he mentions some experiments which he made, superimposing two lenses in order to magnify the object seen, perhaps the first suggestion of the telescope. He attempted to explain the different magnitudes of the planets which were moving on the spheres, by attributing different density to the celestial ether in the different parts of their orbits. During his lifetime, or more precisely on February 11, 1524, the so-called "great conjunction" of all the planets in the constellation Pisces took place, which prompted all the astrologers to prophesy a new universal deluge or even the end of the world.

Fracastoro and Peter Bienewitz, better known as Apianus, both had noted that the tails of comets were always pointed away from the sun, a fact which has been confirmed and studied in modern times. The principal work of Apianus is the *Astronomicum Caesareum*, containing important observations on the comets which appeared between 1531 and 1539. The comet of 1531 is Halley's comet.

Maurolico, born in Messina in 1494, was a philosopher and mathematician. In his work *De Lineis Horariis* he proves how the extremity of a gnomonic shadow describes an arc of a conic section every day. In his "Cosmography" he expounds the Ptolemaic system and discusses the theory and use of various astronomical instruments and the computation of time. To him we owe the use of letters in the place of numbers in arithmetical calculations, and the first rules of algebraic notation.

The rebirth of science, and particularly of astronomy, was in process. The theories which had been devised to represent the motions of the celestial bodies in the solar system became always more insufficient and incomplete when confronted with the more precise and continued observations which were being gathered together. These observations made necessary a fundamental reformation, which was soon accomplished by the work of great intellects, the first of whom is Nicholas Copernicus.

II : REFORMATION OF ASTRONOMY

7 : Copernicus and his system

NICHOLAS COPERNICUS, OR COPPERNICUS, WAS born February 19, 1473, in Torun on the Vistula River, and studied at the Polish University of Cracow with the intention of becoming a priest, though he had a decided inclination toward astronomy and mathematics. When he was twenty-three he went to Italy, attracted by the famous University of Bologna, where celebrated masters and numerous Italian and foreign scholars were to be found. In the astronomical field we shall mention Giacomo di Pietramellara and Domenico Maria da Novara; in the mathematical field, Scipione del Ferro and Benedetto Pancarasi. It seems that Copernicus enrolled for law study, but it is certain that his thoughts and interests were turned far more to astronomy and to the study of Greek and Latin. He spent ten years in Italy, the best years of his adult life, from twenty-four to thirty-four. His stay may be divided into two periods, the first in Bologna, the second in Padua. In between, he managed a short visit to Rome and a trip to his homeland. Besides continuing his mathematical, astronomical, and philosophical studies, Copernicus occupied himself in Italy with two entirely different sciences. In Bologna he studied law, and in Padua he continued his theological studies, which he completed in Ferrara while continuing studies in medicine. In the *Annales Clarissimae Nacionis Germanorum*, as well as in the *Matricula Nobiliss. Germ. Collegii*, under the year 1495, the name of Copernicus is written as follows: Nicolaus Kopperlingk de Thorn, as a student of law. We have even the list of lectures (*rotuli*) which he attended, as well as the names of his professors.

INFLUENCE OF DA NOVARA

The principal representative of astronomy in Bologna at that time was Domenico Maria da Novara, born in Ferrara and pupil of Giovanni Bianchini. Although few of his writings remain, we know from Cavalieri and other mathematicians of the time that he was held in great esteem as a man of great intellect and a teacher of Copernicus, who even in his old age remembered him with gratitude. Yet we know very little of his teachings or in particular of the scholastic life of Copernicus. Copernicus in fact always avoided speaking of himself, and in his work *De Revolutionibus* he mentions only in passing some astronomical observations which he made in Bologna and in Rome. In reference to these he recounts how, when he was studying in Bologna, at the fifth hour of the night of March 9 he had occasion to observe with his master "the occultation of the brightest star of the Hyades [Aldebaran] behind the dark portion of the moon." In other words, master and pupil observed an important occultation which later gave Copernicus grounds to prove the validity of his theory about the parallax of the moon.

We have additional information on the friendship between master and pupil from George Joachim, an able Tyrolian astronomer, known by the Latin name of Rheticus from the region Rhaetia where he was born. After having been professor at the University of Wittenberg, Rheticus went to Frauenburg to learn about the new system of the world from Copernicus in person. In his writings on the works of Copernicus we have proof of the influence which da Novara had on his young disciple and how the ideas of both master and pupil came very soon to full agreement. They both believed that astronomy was one of the principal and most important sciences and that a complete renewal of ideas was necessary to explain the position of the world. In the preface of his "Ephemerides" Rheticus states that "Copernicus lived with Domenico Maria in Bologna and came to know fully the methods which he followed." We can conclude from this that, according to the customs of the times in the Italian universities and as was later done by Galileo, the teacher boarded his pupils in his house, among them Copernicus.

Besides da Novara, Copernicus had as teachers in Bologna Scipione del Ferro, who in those years was lecturing on mathematics and geometry, and in the humanities, Antonio Codro Urceo, who was lecturing on Latin and Greek literature. From the former, as Copernicus himself writes in the *De Revolutionibus*, he learned those doctrines which, together with the doctrines of Purbach and Regiomontanus, he employed in his treatment of the new system of the world. From the latter he acquired that familiarity with the Greek language which was for him of particular importance. In fact, since the Ptolemaic system was becoming steadily less capable of representing the celestial bodies of the solar system, Copernicus found it necessary to know, directly from the sources, the cosmological ideas of the Greek astronomers and philosophers, before and after Hipparchus. The numerous acquaintances of Urceo, among whom were Aldo Manuzio, Angelo Poliziano, and Pico della Mirandola, his active teaching which had surrounded him with many devoted pupils, the elegance of his Latin prose and verse must have influenced the thoughts of Copernicus. However, we do not know exactly what Greek works he studied with his master in Bologna, and the *rotuli* do not specify which authors were read.

LAW STUDIES

During his last two years in Bologna Copernicus had with him his brother, also enrolled in the study of law. In spite of the fact that both of them benefited from contributions toward their education from the church of Frauenburg, the expenses of their studies and university life must have been rather high, for we know that they often lacked money. At the beginning of 1499 it seems that Copernicus made a short visit to Frauenburg, to return afterward to Bologna where we know he made other celestial observations with Domenico Maria. Soon afterward he left the University of Bologna, followed by his brother, to go to Rome, where he arrived in Holy Week of the year of Jubilee, which Alexander VI was preparing to celebrate with great solemnity. We know little or nothing of the stay of Copernicus, which lasted almost a year, in the eternal city. The two brothers must have gone there more for the studies than for the exceptional religious celebration with its great gathering of people. At any rate, Copernicus left some traces there, as Rheticus tells us, since he taught, or more probably gave lectures or conferences, which many scholars and illustrious personages attended. In his simple and lucid style he probably discussed the new cosmological ideas. Much later, in his quieter days at home, he recalled with satisfaction and pleasure his Roman visit, when he had occasion to observe another lunar eclipse. He writes in the *De Revolutionibus: alteram quoque, magna diligentia observavimus Romae anno Christi millesimo quingentesimo post nonas novembris duabus horis a media nocte.*

Copernicus' desire to continue his studies in Italy must have been very strong because we find that the two brothers, when they had returned home, asked the cathedral Chapter of Frauenburg for another leave of two years. It was instantly granted, provided that Copernicus studied medicine. It is not quite clear why the Chapter wished to support such an encyclopedic man who could handle theology, law, and medicine. Besides, it was already evident that his major interest was in astronomy. It is necessary to put oneself in the spirit of the times and to consider that in the canonical position which awaited him in the Cathedral of Frauenburg his executive duties must have been of several kinds.

On his return to Italy Copernicus chose the University of Padua, the only one which could equal the University of Bologna. In this stay also, which lasted until 1504, we know nothing about him, so that it is even doubtful that he ever attended the university. But an important document, found not many years ago in Ferrara, states clearly that the University of Padua claimed Copernicus among its students, and that he finished his law studies there and took up those in medicine. In fact, his doctor's diploma, dated 1503, says textually among other things: *Venerabilis ac doctissimus vir dominus Nicolaus Copernich de Prusia Canonicus Varmensis et Scholasticus ecclesie S. Crucis Vratislaviensis: qui studuit Bononie et Padue, fuit approbatus in Jure Canonico nemine penitus discrepante et doctoratus.* The University of Padua was then, at the beginning of the sixteenth century, in one of its periods of greatest splendor, especially in the fields of medicine and law, with many celebrated teachers. The first among these was Girolamo Fracastoro, who then held a professorship of law and at the same time was *Consiliarius Anatomicus.*

It is therefore probable that the two young people, Copernicus and Fracastoro, were friends and studied together, directing their activities toward that *novus ordo* to which they both afterward made a great contribution. We cannot figure out why Copernicus, at the end of his stay in Italy, chose to receive his degree in canon law from the lesser University of Ferrara. It is not very probable, as some people think, that the reason was financial. Whatever it was, in the spring of 1503 we find Copernicus in Ferrara, ready first to take the *privata examinatio*, then to write his thesis, and finally to be *licentiatus* with the *publica examinatio*, or *conventus*, for which the title of Doctor of Canon Law was conferred on him in the palace of the archbishop, with the document quoted in part above. This important document was found in the notary's archives of Ferrara and was published in 1877 by Prince Baldassarre Boncompagni in the Acts of the Pontifical Academy of the "Nuovi Lincei."

MEDICAL STUDIES

We recall that the period in which Copernicus was in Ferrara was that of the luxurious court of Lucrezia Borgia, who was the wife of the heir Prince Alfonso. Personalities were not lacking, among whom was Celio Calcagnini, one of the precursors of the heliocentric theory. Presumably Copernicus spent a rather long time in Ferrara in order to obtain his acadamic title. In Padua he continued his studies in medicine, which were the principal reason for his return to Italy. There were then professorships of theoretical and practical medicine, but as yet none in anatomy. Even though some laboratory work was done on corpses, anatomy did not appear on the *rotuli* of the University of Padua until 1540. We cannot tell whether Copernicus obtained his medical degree in Padua, since the *Acta Collegii Medicorum* from 1503 to 1507 are missing. In the official documents of Frauenburg he is called Doctor Nicholas, but this title naturally can refer to the one he obtained in Ferrara. It is not known precisely when he ended his medical studies and how he distributed them during his stay in Padua. We do not even know the date of his return home, but certainly the leave of absence which he obtained for two years must have been at least doubled, so that we can count on his having spent an entire decade in Italy. At the latest, early in 1506, or perhaps already in the preceding year, he returned home for good and ended his student days. The same year he retired to the castle of Heilsberg to serve his bishop as medical adviser. There, full of the teachings he had received first in Cracow, then in Italy, he began, as he himself tells us, to think of his new cosmological system, setting the foundation of his immortal work, which did not make its appearance in the world until thirty-seven years later, shortly before his death.

DEVELOPMENT OF THE NEW THEORY

Seventeen centuries had had to pass by before the idea of removing the earth from what was then thought to be the center of the universe, and locating the sun there, would flourish again in the world through the work of the astronomer from Torun. But there is no doubt that it was in Italy that Copernicus found the heritage of Greece and that interest and development in astronomical research which were to bring about their complete renewal. Copernicus felt the real necessity of substituting for the complicated Ptolemaic system some other hypothesis that would agree better with the observations, steadily growing more numerous and more precise. But even more he felt that the sun, the generous giver of life and heat, must rule over the much smaller planets. Copernicus writes in the *De Revolutionibus:* "in the center of everything the sun must reside; in the most beautiful temple created by God, there is the place which awaits him where he can give light to all the planets."

His immortal work, pondered much and elaborated, written with the feeling of a scientist and a man of faith, should have persuaded anyone. But the work was too difficult for the average reader, and the time was not yet ripe for its acceptance and publication. Conceived in Italy, this new doctrine was to find there its most valuable supporters and also the most violent opposition, with various and tragic outcomes to which are bound forever the names of Giordano Bruno and Galileo. In Germany only Kepler appreciated its great importance, and he dedicated himself entirely to elaborating the observations of Tycho Brahe, which were to lead him more and more to confirm the theory of Copernicus. With increasing controversial and lively spirit its supporters plunged into the fight for its triumph. Bruno, who was well acquainted with the metaphysical-mathematical works of Cardinal Nicholas of Cusa, intuitively felt the truth propounded by Copernicus and enthusiastically became a passionate champion of the new ingenious system:

> Who will be able fully to praise the great spirit of this German who, unmindful of the stupid multitude, has been so steadfast against the torrent of opposition? And, although almost disarmed of living reasons, he has taken hold of these poor and rusty fragments from antiquity, he has cleaned them up, joined them together, warmed them up so much with his discourse

more mathematical than natural, that he has rendered the cause, once ridiculous, abject and despised, honored, esteemed, more like than contrary, and most certainly convenient and efficient for theory and practice of computation.

Though Bruno was not an astronomer, he discusses with wide knowledge the six books of the "Revolutions" and tries to counteract the many objections set forth by Italian and foreign Peripatetics. He violently attacks Osiander, who was the author of a preface to the work of Copernicus in which he attempted to excuse the daring of the new ideas, presenting them in the form of a modest hypothesis, so as not to encounter the opposition of the ecclesiastical authorities.

Giordano Bruno enlarged the ideas of Copernicus and was among the first to conceive of a construction of the universe similar to what we can imagine, from inside the solar system, with the powerful methods of observation and research at our disposal today. But fifty-seven years after the death of Copernicus, he was burned at the stake for defending his concepts, which were too advanced for his times.

Meanwhile a young professor of mathematics, Galileo Galilei, who was lecturing at the University of Padua on Ptolemy's planetary theory, in a letter to Johannes Kepler in Graz confessed that he had been for many years a convinced Copernican and that thus he had discovered the causes of many natural phenomena which otherwise could not have been explained. He did not dare, however, to publish his ideas, knowing what had happened to Copernicus and fearing ridicule. Kepler answered him at once expressing a twofold pleasure: for the friendship he had made with the Italian scientist and for the agreement of their opinions regarding the Copernican cosmography. Their true masters, he writes, are Plato and Pythagoras, and since the teaching of Copernicus, the fact that the earth moves is no longer new. Yet the Italians are not the only ones who will not believe that they are in motion, even a motion which cannot be felt, because in Germany also this opinion has found no favor. The letter of Galileo is meanwhile very precious to him as a means of helping him to convince the skeptical, and he exhorts Galileo to continue his studies and to communicate privately to him whatever he may discover in proof of the new theory. Thus this theory, conceived in Italy by the great mind of Copernicus, was to find in Italy one of its most powerful and ingenious champions, who brought it triumphant through all the vicissitudes that we shall have occasion to relate in the following pages.

After his return home Copernicus studied the problem of the constitution of the solar system with assiduous care, and, as he himself writes: "I reread all the philosophical books which I could find, trying to find out if anyone had ever thought that there were movements of the spheres different from those claimed by the teachers of mathematics in the schools. And I found, in Cicero first, that Nicetas believed that the earth was in motion; then in Plutarch, that some others were of the same opinion; among them Heraclides Ponticus and Ecphantus the Pythagorean."

The news that he was elaborating such a revolutionary hypothesis as that of the sun in the center of the world, with the earth condemned to be its satellite, was spreading throughout Germany. In fact Luther, speaking of it in his "Table Talks," openly called Copernicus a fool because he held opinions contrary to the Bible and therefore intolerable. Thus the work of Copernicus was maturing slowly and almost secretly, when, as though to give a sample of it, he published about 1530 an interesting paper entitled *Commentariolus,* a kind of short summary in which he presented his system without diagrams and computations. It seems that this pamphlet was presented in Rome to Pope Clement VII, who in 1533 attended an explanation of the Copernican system given by the chancellor Widmannstadt in the Vatican gardens. Some years later the archibishop of Capua, Cardinal von Schoenberg, strongly urged Copernicus to make his system public.

PUBLICATION OF "DE REVOLUTIONIBUS"

Shortly after Rheticus went to Frauenburg to visit Copernicus, as mentioned above, he was able to write and publish a paper entitled *Prima Narratio de Libris Revolutionum,* in which he clearly expounds the new doctrine. So great was his interest in the new theories that his stay with Copernicus lasted almost two years. Probably because of the urging of his disciple, Copernicus was finally persuaded to publish his work, to which he prefaced a dedication to Pope Paul III. Rheticus brought it to Nuremberg to have it printed. Because of the opposition of Luther, Melanchthon, and their followers, Rheticus fell into disgrace and moved to Leipzig where he was professor of mathematics. He entrusted the supervision of the printing to Johannes Schoner, professor of mathematics in Nuremberg, to whom Rheticus had addressed his *Narratio*, and to Andreas Osiander, pastor in the same city and fiery champion of Lutheranism. From Kepler we know that there was correspondence between Copernicus and Osiander, but only the latter's reply to Copernicus remains in an excerpt from a letter of 1541. Osiander says:

> I have always believed that hypotheses are not articles of faith but that they are the foundations of calculation. Thus it does not matter whether they are true or false, provided they reproduce exactly the phenomena of the motions. In fact, if we follow the hypothesis of Ptolemy, who can assure us that the irregularities in the motion of the sun are due to an epicycle or to an eccentric, since both are possible? It would therefore be desirable to say something about this matter in the preface. You would thus pacify the Peripatetics and the theologians, who you fear will contradict you.

Almost the same thing happened to Galileo when he was trying to persuade the ecclesiastical authorities to grant an *imprimature* for his "Dialogue on the Two Principal Systems of the World." We do not have the reply of Copernicus to Osiander, who evidently was afraid of the tempest which the new ideas might arouse. This fear was not shared by Copernicus, however, who in his dedication to Pope Paul III courageously fights against "those who are completely ignorant of mathematics and yet will dare to judge such questions, and who will blame and reject my work, relying on some badly interpreted passage of the Holy Scriptures."

In the meantime, while Copernicus was sick and near the end of his life, Osiander, probably on his own initiative, had printed at the beginning of Copernicus' work an "Address to the Reader," wherein he repeated the ideas which he had expressed the year before in his letter to the author. Right away and also afterward there was general indignation; Giordano Bruno defined the letter as "a superfluous letter attached by I do not know what ignorant and presumptuous ass to the book of Copernicus." And Galileo said: "It is certainly the work of an incapable person, who has committed such gross errors as Copernicus would never have made. Kepler revealed the identity of the author of this false "Address," writing to Peter Ramus, who had been shocked by reading in it that "the hypotheses need not be true nor even probable, even if they give results which agree with observation." Kepler declared:

> It is indeed a most absurd fiction to explain natural phenomena by false causes. But let it be known that this fiction is not due to Copernicus, who not only believes that his hypotheses are true but even proves them. Do you want to know the author of this fiction, who irritated you so much? It is Andreas Osiander, as is noted in my copy by the hand of Hieronimus Schreiber of Nuremberg. While this Andreas was superintending the edition of Copernicus, he inserted in the frontispiece his own preface which you call most absurd, but which he (as we can gather from his letter to Copernicus) thought most prudent, while Copernicus was already dead or certainly unaware of the fact.

An intimate friend of Copernicus, the Bishop Giese, confirms that Copernicus' illness was so serious in the last year of his life that he was unable to follow the progress of the printing of his work under Osiander's direction. Giese wrote to Rheticus, congratulating him on the beautiful biography of the master which he had written, and describing the last days of Copernicus: "Many days before his death he lost his memory and the use of his mind, and he saw the completed work on the very day of his death."

The original manuscript of the famous work *De Revolutionibus Orbium Caelestium* was rediscovered in 1854, in the possession of Count Nostitz of Prague, when a deluxe edition of the complete works of the great astronomer was being prepared. The first edition appeared in Nuremberg in 1543; it was printed again in 1566 with the *Prima Narratio* of Rheticus and in 1873 in Torun under the auspices of the *Societas Copernicana Thorunensis*. The *Almagest*, the *De Revolutionibus*, and the *Principia* of Newton are three books which represent three basic stages in the development of astronomy. In the second of these is exposed for the first time the complete theory in which the apparent motions of the celestial bodies are not generally real motions but are due to the motion of the earth on which the observer stands. Copernicus knew that the Greek astronomers before him had presented the same idea, but nobody as yet had proven it to be true. The Copernican system, much simpler and far superior to the others which preceded it, avoided basic difficulties but still was not free from all objections. Further study and investigation were necessary to bring it to final victory and make it acceptable to everybody.

In the treatise of Copernicus some rather involved mathematical postulates are given in order to represent the motions of the celestial bodies and bring calculation and observation into agreement. The first postulate attempts to prove, though not very conclusively, that the universe is spherical. More convincing proofs are given for the spherical form of the earth. A third postulate states that the motions of the celestial bodies are uniform circular motions or combinations thereof. One cannot admit any lack of uniformity in these motions, he says, because "the mind turns back with horror, for it is unworthy to hold such a view in regard to bodies which are constituted in the most perfect order." Copernicus then explains the principle of relative motion, according to which the appearance is the same, whether the sun or the earth is moving. He attributes to the earth a motion of rotation about its axis to explain the total motion of all the stars. He explains the apparent annual motion of the sun, according to which the sun seems to revolve around the earth in an almost circular orbit, by assuming instead that the sun is fixed and the earth follows the same orbit around the sun. Copernicus was forced to introduce a third motion to explain the phenomenon of precession. Thus in his new theory the earth revolved around the sun in the plane of the ecliptic, while it completed every day one rotation about its axis, whose poles were continually directed toward the poles of the celestial sphere. Ptolemy had previously advanced the objection that if the earth underwent a rapid rotation it would have been broken into small pieces, and that the air and the objects on its surface would have remained behind. Copernicus replies that if such a motion were dangerous for the earth, it would be much more dangerous for the celestial sphere which, being so much larger, would have to move more rapidly to complete its daily rotation.

The most difficult problem was that of explaining the apparent motion of the planets. It was already known that Mercury and Venus, which always remained relatively close to the sun, must have smaller orbits than the other three planets. Since the outer three planets could even move in a direction opposite to that of the sun, they must necessarily have orbits larger than that of the earth. The order of the planets, based on the duration of their revolutions around the sun, had thus been well determined, and Copernicus was able to sketch a diagram which represented, according to his theory, the solar system, with circular orbits and considerably erroneous relative distances.

CONTENT OF THE ''REVOLUTIONS''

The first of the six books of the *De Revolutionibus* contains as the main subjects the proof that the earth is spherical and has a threefold motion, the definition of the celestial sphere, and some theorems on the spherical triangle. The first book closes with a catalog of stars, the same as Ptolemy's, but revised and corrected for precession. In the second book he gives the value for the obliquity of the ecliptic and discusses its decrease. An acute discussion of the precession of the equinoxes, from which he deduces a very accurate value, is found in the third book. He explains that precession originates from a slow motion of the earth's axis such that it is inclined always at the same angle to the ecliptic and that it will return to its original position after approximately 26,000 years. Then follows a discussion of the apparent annual motion of the sun around the earth, which is explained by the real annual motion of the earth around the sun. Copernicus, following the Ptolemaic theory of the *Almagest*, employs an eccentric and finds a more accurate value of the eccentricity. By determination of the position of aphelion and perihelion he verifies Albatenius' discovery of the motion of the line of apsides.

The theory of the moon is discussed in the fourth book with the purpose of diminishing the existing disagreement between theory and observation. Copernicus does not adopt the equant of Ptolemy, both because he thinks an irregular motion is improper for the celestial bodies and because of the above-mentioned disagreement. He succeeds in representing the principal irregularities of the moon's motion by a special arrangement of the epicycles. He verifies Ptolemy's value for the distance between the earth and the moon, but he increases the distance of the sun to 1500 times the radius of the earth, thus improving somewhat the previously used traditional value. The movement of the planets is discussed in the fifth and sixth books. For Mercury and Venus it was easy to pass from the Ptolemaic theory to the Copernican, since the sun itself could become the center of the epicycle. The planet revolving around the sun with its own distance and velocity will present to us an apparent motion equal to the motion explained by the epicycle and deferent of Ptolemy, if the orbit of the planet around the sun is substituted for the former, and the apparent orbit of the sun around the earth is substituted for the latter. Copernicus determines the synodic and sidereal periods of these two planets, and also the relative sizes of their orbits compared to the earth's, and finds values very close to the true ones.

For the superior planets, Mars, Jupiter, and Saturn, the explanation of their motions becomes difficult, given the hypothesis that they revolve around the sun. In fact, the center of the epicycle is not always in the direction of the sun, but it can be anywhere on the ecliptic. However, it can be shown that the motion of a superior planet is exactly like that of an inferior planet, provided that the radius of its epicycle has a larger radius than its deferent. Thus without altering the position of the planet on a circle around the sun, while the sun moves around the earth or more simply the earth around the sun, the Copernican theory is substituted directly for the Ptolemaic. From observation of the oppositions of the superior planets, Copernicus obtained accurate values for their synodic and sidereal periods. In order to obtain their distances from the sun, he observed their position at the instant when, as seen from the planet, the earth would appear at the maximum distance from the sun. In this case the triangle formed by the sun, the earth, and the planet is known, and consequently the ratio of its sides.

The discussion of the stationary positions is very elaborate. Copernicus concludes that they have to exist, and he shows how their exact positions may be calculated. Here it is evident how much simpler the Copernican system is in comparison with the Ptolemaic. In fact, if we consider the motion of the earth around the sun and that of the outer planets with their respective velocities, it is easily seen that for a certain length of time an inversion of their motions must take place, with the stations intervening. Copernicus repudiated the equant of Ptolemy as "unworthy" of the celestial bodies. In its stead, for the irregularities of the movements caused by different inclinations of the planetary orbits, Copernicus adopted a complicated system of epicycles and supposed that the orbit of each planet was inclined to the ecliptic by a small angle, a different one for each planet. He employed 34 circles in all, four for the moon, three for the earth, seven for Mercury, whose motion is very irregular, and five for each of the other planets. This number is regularly less than the one used by the Ptolemaists; we may recall that Fracastoro admitted 79 spheres.

MERITS OF THE SYSTEM

The Copernican system does not really represent the heliocentric system as we know it today, especially in relation to the discoveries of Kepler and Newton. It has the weakness of the epicycles, which could not explain the variable direction of the planet, due to its elliptic motion around the sun; and errors necessarily resulted in the computed positions of the planets. These disagreements, however, could not be detected from the rather inaccurate observations at the disposal of Copernicus. Only after the observations of Tycho Brahe could a new geometric representation, which was not epicyclic, be considered. Even though Copernicus retained his epicycles, it is still superfluous to note how great was his genius; he opened the way to Kepler and Galileo. He understood how the motion of the earth around the sun would have been noticeable in the stars, if they had been sufficiently close to the earth. To Copernicus all the stars must have been equally distant, and he must have supposed them so far away that any motion of the earth remained too small to be noticed. We shall see later that only many years afterward was it possible to measure these small deviations, the "annual parallaxes" of the fixed stars which were to disclose their distances.

Copernicus grasped and profoundly sensed, in the spirit of the Pythagorean philosophy, the geometric foundation of the universe, of which one can comprehend the divine structure by steadily widening the boundaries of investigation. He was tne first person capable of posing the "new foundation" of the world (as his faithful disciple George Joachim Rheticus said), which can be reduced to the foundation of the "absolute order," or of a law of inherent harmony of the universe. Astronomy, therefore, he defines as a divine rather than a human science, since the very motion and courses of the stars, their distances, and their magnitudes are governed by God. Copernicus refers several times to the opinion of those philosophers and poets who consider the heavens a "visible God." At the commencement of his work his first thought is to turn his spirit and regard to the grandeur and beauty of the sky, than which there is no greater mystery. Admiring the order and harmony of the heavens, he raises his thoughts to the supreme creator of the universe. Nicholas Copernicus profoundly sensed the importance of the study of the sky, and through his work, at first so much debated and then so much admired, he became one of the great pioneers who made it understandable to mankind.

8 : Tycho Brahe

THE COPERNICAN THEORY, WHICH WAS IN AP-
pearance opposed to dogma and too difficult to be generally understood, made no rapid progress directly after the publication of the
De Revolutionibus. After the enthusiastic support of Rheticus, only
one German astronomer, Erasmus Reinhold, professor of mathematics and astronomy at the University of Wittenberg, adopted the
theory (about 1550); he calculated from it the *Tabulae Prutenicae*
(Prussian Tables), published at the expense of Duke Albert of Prussia. From these tables the position of the principal celestial bodies
for any epoch could easily be determined. More precise than the
"Alfonsine Tables," they were superseded only by the "Rudolphine
Tables" of Kepler, three quarters of a century later. The Copernican
system spread abroad gradually, especially in England; but before
it could be accepted without restriction, the principles of dynamics
had to be stated, as was done by Galileo and Newton. In the meantime astronomical calculations were made much easier by the rapid
progress of mathematics, especially by the introduction of the system
of Arabic numerals, decimal fractions, and logarithms.

After the death of Regiomontanus an important series of observations was begun by Landgrave William IV of Hesse. He was much
interested in astronomy and had built an observatory in Cassel, the
first one with a rotating dome. Among his able collaborators was
Justus Bürgi, mathematician and watchmaker, who was able to construct a real and original clock, which could determine the time of

the observations more accurately than had ever been done before. It seems that he applied a pendulum to his clock as a regulator, the device thought of later by Galileo and Huygens. At Cassel, therefore, a stellar catalog was begun by comparing the positions of the stars with those of the sun, Venus, and Jupiter, in order to determine their positions with respect to the equator and the first point of Aries. The catalog, which was to contain a thousand stars, was not completed, perhaps because at the same time Tycho Brahe had begun his vast astronomical work with superior means.

Tycho Brahe was born in 1546 of a noble family of Swedish origin, which had settled in Denmark, in Knudstorp in the county of Schonen. From his youth he showed great interest in astronomy, and even in astrology. He observed in 1563 a conjunction of Jupiter and Saturn and he noticed that the *Tabulae Prutenicae* were in error by several days. After having lived in various cities of Germany, Tycho returned to Denmark with a large "quadrant" which he had designed and constructed for celestial observations and a celestial globe on which he was marking the position of the stars. In November, 1572, there appeared in the constellation Cassiopeia, a new, very luminous star, which equaled Venus at her greatest brightness. Tycho observed it accurately in its various phases of luminosity, and noted that it must have been much farther away than the moon, since it showed no visible parallax and therefore must be among the fixed stars. After having given a few lessons in astronomy at the University of Copenhagen, he returned to Germany, where he met and became friendly with Landgrave William, and had occasion to become acquainted with the *Commentariolus* of Copernicus. During this trip he went as far as Venice and thought of settling down with his family in Basel. King Frederick II, who did not want Tycho to abandon Denmark, granted him the little island of Hveen in The Sound and gave him ample means to found an observatory there, the truly magnificent construction of which Tycho began in 1576.

THE HVEEN OBSERVATORY

The main building was called Uraniburg (castle of the sky) and was situated in the center of a large square garden surrounded by high walls like a fort, with the corners directed to the cardinal points. It was provided with terraces and large working spaces and living quarters, and it was furnished with a rich supply of sextants, equatorial *armillae*, parallactic instruments—part wood, part metal, all naturally without any optical parts—and clocks of various types. Another building, constructed later by Tycho as the number of his collaborators and pupils increased, was called Stellaeburg (castle of the stars). It had the special property of being in great part underground, probably because instruments could be more stably located there than above ground. The instruments were mounted beneath stationary domes and had to be used by observing through slots in the walls or in the roof of the dome. Here also there were a large sextant, a steel quadrant, and armillary spheres with two graduated circles, one representing the equator and oriented to it, the other representing a great circle perpendicular to it, so that it was possible to read off directly the equatorial co-ordinates of the stars observed. The many visitors to the island included James VI of Scotland (later James I of England), who on this occasion made several gifts to Tycho and wrote some verses in his honor.

The astronomical work accomplished in Hveen was very distinguished. In the course of twenty-one years a rich and complete series of observations was assembled, more exact than all the others prior to that time. In 1577 Tycho observed the brilliant comet which appeared in that year, and he established the fact that it could not belong, as was generally believed, to our atmosphere, but that it revolved around the sun at a greater distance than Venus. These observations and results, and those concerning the new star which had given him occasion to publish the pamphlet *De Nova Stella*, induced Tycho to write a complete treatise on astronomy. It was to consist of three preliminary volumes devoted respectively to the new star, to the comet of 1577, and to later comets, then to continue with other volumes which would have contained theories of the sun, moon, and planets. He was able to carry out only a small portion of this great project. The first introductory volume is entitled *Astronomiae Instauratae Progymnasmata*, begun in 1588. It was never completed in Tycho's lifetime, but only in 1602 by Kepler. Although the complicated celestial motions did not permit Tycho to treat the new star satisfactorily, they did induce him first to discuss the position of the fixed stars, precession, and the annual motion of the sun. The second volume, *De Mundi Aetherei Recentioribus Phaenomenis Liber Secundus*, was finished earlier and sent off to his friends and correspondents. Another book, *Astronomiae Instauratae Mechanica*, contains a detailed description of the instruments which were conceived and constructed by him, together with a short autobiography and a report of his principal discoveries.

TYCHONIAN SYSTEM

Tycho did not accept the Copernican system, perhaps for religious reasons, perhaps because the arguments of Copernicus were still imperfect. Tycho proposed a hypothesis which explained the observed phenomena, leaving the earth at the center of the world as in the Ptolemaic system. The sun and moon revolved around the earth, while Mercury, Venus, Mars, Jupiter, and Saturn revolved around the sun. This "Tychonic" system leads to practically the same complications as the Ptolemaic, but nevertheless it represents considerable progress in satisfying the observed phenomena. This system would have had more followers if it had been devised before the Copernican, to which it owed its better parts. If one admitted on faith, as Tycho did, that the earth was immobile, then his system was the only permissible one; but actually it was only a mixture of three older systems, the Egyptian, Ptolemaic, and Copernican. It was superior to the first two, but it did not possess the wonderful simplicity of the third. The most plausible objections which Tycho made to the Copernican system referred mainly to the lack of knowledge of the laws of motion, which were discovered by Kepler and Newton.

Tycho was the first to introduce in astronomical computations the effect of refraction, due to the earth's atmosphere, on the position of the celestial bodies. This effect had only been suspected by his predecessors. By means of a great number of observations he showed that comets are not just ordinary meteors, but have a regular motion, with the sun at the center. Concerning the new star he notes that, after having changed color successively from white to reddish-yellow, it apparently disappeared in March, 1574. This famous phenomenon gave him occasion to correct Ptolemy's value of the precession of the equinoxes and to refute Copernicus on the pretended motion of the fixed stars. On the large celestial globe already mentioned Tycho had marked, according to his observations, the position of all the stars known up to that time. The introduction to his work includes a catalog of 777 stars, besides observations of the sun and moon.

The great expenditures which Tycho made for the maintenance

of his observatory, the continued quarrels which his stormy character brought about, and finally the death of his benefactor, which was followed by the suspension of the contributions granted him, compelled him to leave, not only the island but also Denmark. He was received in Bohemia by the emperor Rudolph II, a great patron of the sciences, and he was able to settle there with his family toward the end of 1599 in the castle of Benatek (about twenty miles from Prague), where he was able to set up some of his smaller instruments. He was joined there by the young Kepler, who was to make so fruitful the observations performed by his master. But difficulties soon arose between the two, made more serious by the fact that Tycho was rapidly approaching his death, which occurred in November, 1601. Thus little use was made of his instruments in the new location, and they were soon afterward scattered about, during the Bohemian civil war.

RELATIONS WITH GALILEO

In these last years Tycho, perhaps in his search for new living quarters, tried to enter into relations with Galileo through one of his disciples, the Bohemian nobleman Franz Tengnagel, who had married one of his daughters. Tengnagel met Galileo in Padua, both to find out what Galileo thought of the system devised by his father-in-law (knowing that Galileo was decidedly Copernican) and also to obtain his assistance in some projects which Tycho had in mind and had already discussed with Giovanni Antonio Magini, professor of mathematics at the University of Bologna. For the great number of projects with which he intended to revive astronomy, Tycho Brahe had need of large means, such as he had received during his stay on the island of Hveen. Lacking these, he anxiously sought new benefactors, and thus he addressed, besides the emperor Rudolph, the Venetian Republic and the Grand Duke of Tuscany. He desired to institute astronomical observations in more southern latitudes, as in Italy, but even more in Egypt, in order to find out if there was any noticeable variation in the obliquity of the ecliptic from the time of Ptolemy. He thought of sending one of his many sons and tried to secure funds for the expedition, but the Tuscan Court, which probably had asked Galileo's advice, showed itself in no way disposed to fulfil his desires. After discontinuing the relations with Galileo begun by Tengnagel, Tycho in the spring of 1600 addressed himself directly to Galileo and expressed again his great desire to correspond with him. If Galileo answered, we do not have the reply, but Tycho's death soon afterward cut short any relation between the two scientists. Although Galileo held Tycho and his work in high esteem, it is clear that he could not share his opinions, on account of his fundamental hypotheses about the solar system, and also on account of others which were too Aristotelian. Thus Galileo, in many of his writings, as in the "Dialogue on the Two Principal Systems of the World," groups Tycho with Aristotle and Ptolemy, although he approves of Tycho's observational work. He even quotes it frequently, to show the fallacy of Tycho's arguments. Galileo admires the instruments used by Tycho, but he comments that they could have been built more simply, more accurately, and less expensively.

OBSERVATIONS AND DISCOVERIES

The main characteristics of Tycho's work are the great accuracy of his observations, never attained by his predecessors, and their regular continuity. It can be said that his observational errors were not greater 1' or 2'. This accuracy was due to the stability and dimensions of his instruments, and also probably to the use of greatly improved clocks. His table of refractions, based on special observations, although imperfect, enabled him to take into account this considerable source of error in the determination of the position of stars. He repeated his observations under very different conditions, in order to decrease the effect of accidental errors. As regards the continuity of the observations, he determined, for example, the position of the sun every day for several years, as well as of other celestial bodies. He thus made available to Kepler and his successors valuable material for the establishment of a theory of the motion of the earth, the moon, and the planets.

In connection with the theory of the moon Tycho made important discoveries, for example, a new irregularity in its motion called the "variation" and an "annual equation," which is a small inequality dependent upon the position of the earth in its orbit around the sun. Furthermore, he found that the inclination of the moon's orbit to the ecliptic was not fixed but that it oscillated regularly, and that the motion of the nodes was also variable. His catalog of stars furnishes a very exact value of precession, and from his planetary observations he made the discovery that the planetary motions deviated considerably from the motions calculated in the already existing tables. The progress which the Copernican theory was making in the minds of the most learned people and the observations of Tycho Brahe made the time ripe for another great step forward in the science of astronomy which was soon to be accomplished by Galileo and Kepler.

9 : Galileo

THE LIFE AND WORKS OF GALILEO ARE TOO WELL known to be mentioned in detail here, and we shall limit ourselves to his contributions to the progress of astronomy. His contributions are very important in the history of astronomy, since they mark a new era, rich in returns, especially because of the introduction of a new method of observation of the celestial bodies which extended the study of the universe in an extraordinary manner. If we consider the progress from the day in which Galileo turned his telescope to the sky, we must agree that it has been remarkable in the fields of both practical and theoretical astronomy, nor is there any indication that it will cease in its rapid, fascinating development.

Galileo was born in Pisa in 1564, and we know that his father wished him to study medicine. Instead, attracted to the physical sciences by natural inclination, he devoted himself to these. He was called to teach at the universities of Pisa and Padua, where he lectured, as was then customary, on the "theory of the planets" of Ptolemy, adhering to it more or less faithfully. The unwieldly system which hardly satisfied the observed facts did not convince Galileo, who was attracted more and more to the Copernican system. He considered it more plausible than the theories of Aristotle and Ptolemy, as he declared first to Jacopo Mazzoni, his teacher and friend, in 1597. As has already been mentioned, he had also written to Kepler in Graz, stating that he had been converted to the Copernican system many years before. These are the first steps of Galileo in the astronomical field, which in a few years were to lead him ever more deeply into this science. But his real triumph began on the occasion of the apparition of a new star in 1604.

The New Star of 1604

This was not the first time such a phenomenon had occurred. At that time remembrances were still vivid of the new star of 1572, so carefully observed by Tycho Brahe. Today, in the light of modern observations, we can classify this famous star among the so-called "supernovae," since we are dealing with a star intrinsically much brighter than the, let us say, ordinary "nova," as must have been the star studied with such interest by Galileo in 1604. Today we know that these stars of relatively weak luminosity, which suddenly in a matter of a few hours, following an explosion of the whole gaseous sphere of which they are constituted, become very, very bright and then return gradually to their original brightness. Since this phenomenon was naturally connected with human events, not only by the populace, we can understand the lively interest in and general curiosity about the new star, and that numerous and endless discussions must have arisen concerning its substance and its position among the other stars.

Galileo was soon drawn into the current, and perhaps we can date his first astronomical observation from the appearance of this new star. His rude instrument consisted of "a little handle of a penknife," fixed on the window of his house close to the church of St. Anthony in Padua, and of the point of the roof of a neighbor's house. This was somewhat simpler than the observatory of Tycho Brahe on the island of Hveen in Galileo's times, or the great telescopes of today! Sighting the star by means of the "little ball," which was probably at the end of the little handle, and the point of the roof, he was able to determine its position and to discover whether or not from one evening to the next the star was moving with respect to the neighboring stars.

Galileo becomes a little upset by the reproofs addressed to the "public mathematician at the University of Padua" for not having discovered the new star himself. Galileo replies that he does not think this oversight is unbecoming to his office, nor can he pretend it is his duty to be on the lookout every night for the detection of some new star! In a short time Galileo gathered his observations and hypotheses together for three public lectures, of which unfortunately only the introduction and a few rare passages have survived. A great crowd of students rallied to these lectures, anxious to learn from the master himself, by now well known and loved at the University of Padua, the true nature of this new celestial body. Some believed it an evil omen, but most people considered it an extraordinary phenomenon about which they desired to know the substance, the position, the motion, and the reason of the apparition. The fame of these lectures and the active exchange of letters with his friends and correspondents, prove how highly the opinions of Galileo were esteemed. Among his correspondents were the Jesuit Father Clavius, the friar Altobelli, the physicians Tedeschi and Brenzoni of Verona (in those days, in order to study medicine, it was necessary to study mathematics too), who all made haste to communicate their observations and conjectures to Galileo. Not everybody, however, held the same opinions, and from that time began the controversies and disputes which were never to leave him in peace. In the problem of the new star his principal antagonist was the plagiarist Baldassarre Capra, who, motivated either by a desire to show off or by envy or perhaps by some mistaken or naïve points which were not uncommon in Galileo's reasoning, attacked him in his *Consideratione Astronomica*.

Galileo, in fact, ventured the hypothesis that the new star was produced by very rarefied emanations from the earth, which at a very great distance reflected the rays of the sun. The new star was diminishing in brightness because it was moving farther and farther away from the earth. Though Galileo was completely on the wrong track here, he rightly estimated that the "nova" was not inside our atmosphere, but was even outside the moon's orbit in the region of the fixed stars. Viewed from different regions of the earth, the "nova" showed no parallax, that is, apparent displacement with respect to the other stars. Galileo had proved this fact clearly in his lectures and also in strong controversial replies, as in the "Dialogue of Cecco di Ronchitti of Bruzene" (in Paduan dialect between two persons, a scientist and a literary man) and in his famous "Defense Against the Slander and Imposture of Capra."

GALILEO'S TELESCOPE

Galileo became ever more interested and occupied in astronomical problems. The summer of 1609 brought to Padua and

Venice from beyond the Alps a sample of an eyepiece or marvelous "cannon" which made distant objects appear very close. Within a few days Galileo, with the help "of the most hidden speculations of perspective," as he writes to the Doge of Venice, constructs an even more perfect one than those used in Flanders, and after having determined its power, or magnification, he turned it at once toward the sky.

This is how Galileo himself relates his invention to his brother-in-law, Benedetto Landucci, in a letter dated from Venice August 29, 1609:

> You should know that about two months ago the news was spread around here that a telescope had been presented to Count Maurice in Flanders. This telescope was built in such a way that it made objects far away appear very close, so that a man at a distance of two miles could be seen distinctly. This seemed to me such a marvelous effect that I started to think about it. Since I thought its fundamentals should be in the science of perspective, I started to think about its construction. I finally discovered it and so perfectly that my telescope even exceeds in fame the one of Flanders. And the news having reached Venice that I had built a telescope, six days ago I was called by the most serene Signory to show it to them and to the entire Senate, and everyone was completely astonished. There were a great many gentlemen and senators who, although old, climbed the stairs of the highest belfries of Venice several times to look for sails on the sea, and ships so far away that even under full sail two hours and more went by before they could be seen without my eyepiece. In conclusion, the effect of this instrument is to represent an object which is, for example, 50 miles away as large and as close as if it were 5 miles away. Now having recognized how useful it would be on land and at sea, and perceiving that our most serene Prince desired it, I resolved on the twenty-fifth day of this month to appear in the Collegio and make a free gift to his Serenity.

Aside from this rapid re-invention of the telescope, the merit of Galileo was that he understood its great usefulness in the study of the starry sky. This instrument, conceived and employed for practical purposes, as in war and navigation, becomes in his hands a powerful

means for the study of the heavens. With it Galileo began the series
of discoveries and observations which in three and a half centuries
have raised to such a high degree our knowledge of the universe in
which we wander. Galileo became enthusiastic over what he was able
to see with his "cannon," and his first thought was to sing a hymn
of thanks to God, who had made him the first observer of such
marvelous things, which has been hidden from so many people for
so many centuries. His emotion, in this first examination of the sky
with such a modest and imperfect telescope, that yet revealed so
many marvels, is evidenced in his notes and in his letters. These letters
were assembled with more scientific calm in the *Sidereus Nuncius,*
written in Latin so that everyone on both sides of the Alps could
know about them.

"SIDEREUS NUNCIUS"

This "Sidereal Message" or "Astronomical Announcement,"
as he more modestly calls it, was published in Venice at the press of
Baglioni in March, 1610, a few months after the commencement of
his observations and is dedicated to Cosimo II de' Medici. Among
all Galileo's works it is certainly the one which made the greatest
sensation and excited the greatest curiosity in the entire scientific
world of that time. The full title is almost a summary of the contents:

> "A Sidereal Message revealing many great wondrous spectacles,
> suggesting to everybody, particularly to philosophers and astron-
> omers, things to observe which have been seen by Galileo,
> Florentine patrician and public mathematician at the Univer-
> sity of Padua, with the aid of the telescope recently invented
> by him, in the surface of the moon, in the innumerable fixed
> stars, in the Milky Way, and in the *nebulae,* but above all in the
> four planets which revolve around Jupiter with wondrous speed
> and with different intervals and periods, which planets, hitherto
> known to nobody, have been recently discovered for the first
> time by the author, who decided to call them the "Medicean
> Planets."

The *Sidereus Nuncius* opens with the history of the invention of the
telescope, which is followed by observations of the physical surface
of the moon, the first body that Galileo studied. He describes the
very high mountain chains, which appear dark on the side not facing

the sun, and bright on the other side, and he presents explanations and fine detailed sketches. He discusses the possibility of the existence of an atmosphere on the moon. He also notes that the summits of the highest mountains are illuminated at a considerable distance from the edge of the lunar crescent, and with simple geometrical reasoning, taking the diameter of the earth for comparison, he proves that the lunar mountains are at least four times higher than the earth's mountains. After having discussed how the sun's light is reflected to us from the surface of the moon, and how the same thing must happen conversely to the light of the earth, he affirms that this is a most valid proof against those who maintain that the earth must be excluded from the family of planets on the grounds that it lacks motion and light. Instead he confirms, always by means of these demonstrations and natural observations, that the earth moves and surpasses the moon in brightness, and is not, as some people would have it, a "common cesspool of earthly loathsome filth."

From the moon Galileo passes to the study of the constellation Orion, where he finds and marks with precision many stars, never before beheld with the naked eye, in the belt and in the sword of the hunter. The same is true for the Pleiades, where he added numerous other stars to the ones already well known to the naked eye. The Milky Way reveals itself as a collection of many, many stars, which before the invention of the telescope appeared as luminous clouds in the sky. Thus the nebulae, which because of their great distance were believed to be denser portions of the sky reflecting the light of the sun and stars, revealed themselves as star clusters, wherein only the limited power of the telescope could not succeed in distinguishing the separate stars.

SATELLITES OF JUPITER

But the greatest marvel of all is the discovery of the satellites of Jupiter, on January 7, 1610, when Galileo was examining the surface of the planet and studying its motion. In the manuscripts of Galileo, preserved in the national library of Florence, are found some well-known pages which must be considered, if not actually the notes made by Galileo during the observations, at least a first draft of the *Sidereus Nuncius*. The first page of the manuscript begins in Italian, and then continues in Latin. The manuscript shows the excitement and astonishment of Galileo as he observed, not the movement of the planet as he expected, but the leaping, rapid motion, the appearance and the disappearance first of three, then of four, satellites around Jupiter. On the first night of the discovery Jupiter appeared to him accompanied by three neighbors which he thought were fixed stars. The stars were small but very bright, much brighter than other similar stars, and were arranged in a straight line parallel to the ecliptic. The next day, January 8, he saw them again but differently arranged with respect to Jupiter, and by the night of the tenth he had to conclude that their apparent change of position was due not to Jupiter but to the stars themselves. The next night he saw again two stars located on the same side of Jupiter, but at different distances and one brighter than the other, whereas the preceding evening they had had the same magnitude. Galileo writes: "From this it appears that around Jupiter there are three other wandering stars, invisible to everyone before now." On the thirteenth four stars suddenly appeared, three to the west and one to the east. On the fourteenth he was not able to observe, but on the fifteenth, in the third hour of the night, again he saw the four stars, but all to the west. The suspicion which he had already begun to form on the basis of the second observation had by now become a complete certainty: the stars were not fixed but were "wandering," like the planets.

In the calmer and more studied version of the *Nuncius* he states that there are "wandering" stars around Jupiter, like Venus and Mercury around the sun. He writes that he was unable to determine their periods for lack of time and for want of a better telescope than the one he used in those first days. But the great discovery had been made: four tiny planets move around the larger planet in circular orbits of different amplitude, in planes little different from the plane of the ecliptic, and with a velocity the greater, the smaller the distance of the satellite from Jupiter. The fact that it was hard to distinguish one satellite from another made the determination of their periods very difficult. Thus in the series of observations from January 7 to March 2, of which Galileo gives us a detailed report, only to the fourth satellite, which is more detached from the others, is he able to assign a period, one of approximately fifteen days.

Galileo immediately realized that such a discovery would provide a formidable argument with which to remove the doubts of those who were opposed to the Copernican system. Such persons did not want to believe in the possibility of the planets moving around the sun, and they were especially disturbed by the conclusion that, if the moon revolved around the earth, then both bodies would have to revolve around the sun. They would rather conclude that the arrangement of the solar system proposed by Copernicus could not exist. But Galileo's discoveries evidenced the existence of bodies rotating around other larger bodies and thus together following a wider course around the sun. In fact, he determines that Jupiter with its family of four satellites (which by now have become eleven) completes in an interval of twelve years its great revolution around the central body, just like the earth in its interval of one year. With this bold statement, which was to cause so much uproar and so many consequences, and with the name of the "Medici" assigned to the newly discovered planets the "Sidereal Message" ends.

TELESCOPE TECHNIQUE

There is reason to believe that Galileo, while making these memorable observations, lived in Padua in a large tenement house in Borgo dei Vignali, close to the basilica of St. Anthony. This house had a flower garden and a vegetable garden which Galileo enjoyed cultivating, with the aid of his students. But we cannot discover what technique he used for his observations, whether he rested his telescope on the window or observed from the garden, using an easel of some kind. As far as I know, there has never been found either a support or any drawing of a support, which could tell us how he made his telescope stable enough to follow the diurnal motion of the stars which he was observing. This seems even more strange, since he insists several times in his writings on the necessity of "fixing the telescope tube in some stable place to avoid the trembling of the hand which comes from the throbbing of the arteries and from breathing." Anyone who has ever used a 10-power field-glass knows from experience how difficult it is to observe an object without resting the hands or the arms. It would be much more difficult with Galileo's telescopes which, with a magnifying power of 20, were rather long and had a very small field. No wonder then that some of his friends and correspondents, who did not know how to use the new instrument at all, were not able to verify the discoveries of Galileo right away, and that his enemies denied them absolutely.

Some years ago at the Observatory of Arcetri observations were made with the first telescopes of Galileo (with more ease and comfort than Galileo could have had). The telescopes were attached to a larger companion telescope equipped with an equatorial mount and a clockwork mechanism, so that they followed automatically the diurnal motion of the celestial sphere. The first object lens of Galileo and his two famous telescopes—one (unfinished) made of wood lined with paper, the other of wood lined with leather—were mounted on the equatorial of Amici, whose objective is ten times greater in diameter than the lens of Galileo. Through these telescopes we were able to see the same bodies observed by him; the sun, the moon, Jupiter, and Saturn. We were able to determine the accuracy of his observations and the optical imperfections which these instruments necessarily possessed, as well as to admire the sharpness of his eyesight and his intuition. His first object lens, which is larger than the others, seemed to us the best of all. Although it is now broken in several pieces, it shows better optical characteristics and a resolving power of about 10″, which therefore enabled Galileo to separate the disk of Jupiter from its satellites up to this angular distance.

RECEPTION OF THE "SIDEREAL MESSAGE"

In the meantime the first copy of the *Sidereus Nuncius* had been sent by Galileo "unbound and still wet" to Belisario Vinta, counsellor and secretary of state to the Grand Duke of Tuscany. Other copies were sent soon afterward to his Florentine friends, who under the *Loggia* of the New Market crowded around the courier who brought them from Padua. His work was avidly read, discussed, and appreciated by his friends. Other people, who for various reasons or only on account of ignorance and jealousy were soon to oppose openly the new ideas which Galileo was developing, received the *Sidereus Nuncius* with diffidence and incredulity. But enthusiasm for Galileo was overwhelmingly predominant. In honor of Galileo hymns and odes in Latin, Italian, and the dialects were chanted to celebrate the great discoveries. Thomas Campanella from his prison in the Castel dell'Ovo in Naples wrote: "After your 'Message,' O Galileo, all knowledge must be changed." Kepler in Prague is enthusiastic about the new discoveries and although he doubts the existence of Jupiter's satellites, he is anxious to be able to observe them. Shortly afterward a telescope sent by Galileo to the prince elector of Cologne was available to Kepler, and in his *Narratio* he confirms the discoveries of Galileo. He concludes with the epigrams of the Scotsman Thomas

Seggett, in which are the words uttered by Kepler himself: *Vicisti Galileae!*

MEDICEAN PLANETS

Of all the celestial bodies which Galileo observed one after the other, his attention was persistently drawn to following the Medicean planets, for the main purpose of determining their periods of revolution. This new system in its richness and variation seemed to reproduce in miniature the solar system. Moreover, Galileo may have had another reason to study it, which was soon to occur more forcefully to his mind. By April, 1611, a little more than a year after his discovery, he was able to distinguish one satellite from another, and he had approximately determined their periods. He had noticed, however, that the problem was very difficult, as had also been noted by Father Clavius and his pupils, whom Galileo had visited in Rome during the course of that year. Kepler thought it a most difficult business and even almost impossible. The reason for Kepler's statement can be understood if we recall that a few years before he had discovered the elliptic motion of the planets and the law of areas, and that only a few years later he was able to compute the orbit of Mars, which had been the object of long and laborious research. One may ask why Galileo, who corresponded so frequently with Kepler and who certainly knew his works, never made particular mention of these discoveries, which were to bring such great significance to the imperfect Copernican system. But we must remember two things: first, the discoveries of Kepler, which were later to pass the test of time and the further development of astronomy, were mixed up in his writings with many digressions, even of an astrological character; second, Galileo was always accustomed to think with his own mind, and his intuition could not bear to be guided by others, so that sometimes he even fell into error. Thus he could write to Belisario Vinta, from Rome where he had gone to show his astronomical discoveries to the cardinals, the Jesuit fathers, and the members of the Academy of the Lincei that despite the opinion of the "mathematician of the Emperor" (Kepler), he still had complete faith in God. Just as God had let him discover many marvels created by His hand, so He would let him discover the laws of motion of the new planets, so that he could determine their positions for any past or future epoch, even with the great labor of nightly observation.

DETERMINATION OF LONGITUDE

Galileo soon noticed that if he succeeded in calculating these tables with sufficient accuracy, he would have at hand a new method for determining the longitude of various places on the earth, a very important problem for navigators but very difficult to solve. For a long while this problem kept the scientists of Columbus' time busy and anxious, for Columbus, who thought he had arrived in Cathay, discovered America instead. The States-General of Holland offered a reward of 25,000 florins to the person who found the required solution.

Clocks had not yet been invented by which the time could be carried from one place to another, much less the radio, which now permits us to send time signals to all parts of the world. Therefore, for the determination of longitude, it was necessary to resort to some celestial phenomenon, like eclipses, which once predicted could be observed from wherever the traveler might be, on land or at sea. The travelers, by knowing on the one hand the moment at which a phenomenon was to take place in the time of a standard meridian, and by determining on the other hand the local time of the phenomenon from the position of the celestial bodies visible in their location, could arrive at a determination of their longitude. However, this determination was very uncertain because of the very nature of the phenomena and the imperfect knowledge of the motions of the celestial bodies. Furthermore, the phenomena which could be used for this purpose before Galileo's discovery were limited to solar and lunar eclipses and to a few occultations of the brightest stars. They were therefore too rare to be of any practical use. But the rapid motion of the Medicean planets around Jupiter, their frequent eclipses and transits behind and in front of the planet and in its cone of shadow, multiplied the observable celestial phenomena. If these events could have been predicted with sufficient accuracy, they would have enabled the navigators to obtain their position in longitude at all times when Jupiter was visible by mere observation of the aforementioned phenomena.

The determination of latitude was much simpler. In the first observations reported in the *Sidereus Nuncius* Galileo had not yet established a scale of distances. The distances which he indicates must have been estimated on the hypothesis that the diameter of Jupiter was approximately equal to one minute of arc. However, in subsequent observations the distances are estimated in terms of radii of Jupiter, and for each satellite the distances are measured, first from the circumference and then from the center. Today, when we can have exact measurements of time and also micrometers which yield accurate angular measurements in the telescopic field, we remain astonnished at the simple means by which Galileo estimated the maximum and minimum distances, comparing them to the size of the disk of Jupiter by an estimate of the eye. He thus succeeded in following the four Medicean plants in their motion, their interrelation, and their eclipses and transists.

A year or so after his discovery Galileo is able to tell the Grand Duke Cosimo II, in the "Discourse concerning things which stay on top of the water," the times of revolution of each of the four satellites, which vary from a little less than two days for the innermost to almost seventeen days for the outermost. Using these periods of revolution Galileo composed the first table of mean motion, which he hoped could be used for the prediction, at any future instant, of the position of the satellites and of the times of their eclipses. By noting the difference between the times actually observed and the times previously computed, he was able gradually to modify and improve the first values and also the first table. But for a good determination of the mean synodic motion of the Medicean planets, that is, the mean value of the time interval between two successive conjunctions of the satellites, it is better to compare two very remote conjunctions, observed in the same point of the orbit of Jupiter around the sun, which Jupiter completes in about twelve years.

The celestial observations of Galileo lasted from the day of his discovery until the end of 1619, first at the Villa delle Selve near Florence, then in Rome, and lastly at Villa Segni in Bellosguardo, from where he finally moved to Arcetri. After 1619 the vicissitudes of his life and the uncertain conditions of his health did not allow him, to his great sorrow, to observe the sky any more. Therefore in regard to the problem of the Medicean planets, his investigations lasted less than the period of Jupiter, so that he was compelled to entrust their completion to his disciples. While he was working on this problem in the years after 1611, he always continued to think up better methods of correcting his observations. He built a real micrometer, made of a scale outside the telescope tube, which was observed with the left eye while the right eye looked through the telescope at the distance to be measured. Furthermore, some "Jovilabes," drawn on pieces of

cardboard and conveniently attached with strings, enabled him, with
the addition of the method of calculation called "prosthaphaeresis,"
that is, applying the correction for the relative motion of the earth
and Jupiter around the sun, to reduce the observed geocentric positions to heliocentric positions. He was thus able to determine rapidly
the various elements of the motions of the satellites and their relation to Jupiter.

Since Galileo was unable to continue his observations and to find
the solution of the problem which bothered him, he asked for the
help of his disciple Father Renieri, an Olivetan monk, professor at
the University of Pisa, whom he had known in Siena in 1633. He
entrusted to him his observations and calculations of the Medicean
planets, so that he might improve the tables of mean motions. He
also thought of sending him to Holland to show the States-General
the practicability of his proposal for the determination of longitude
at sea. Father Renieri was actually able to complete the ephemerides
but not to publish them, because of his death five years after Galileo's
death.

Both master and pupil found extraordinarily accurate values of the
synodic revolutions of the four satellites. In fact their values, especially of the second satellite, are only slightly different from the values
of today and are more accurate than the values of rivals, among whom
was Simon Marius. But in those times they could go no further, in
view of the imperfect methods and instruments at their disposal, of
the difficulty of determining time, of the lack of timepieces sufficiently
accurate, and of the lack of good astronomical tables. Furthermore,
there was no good theory of planetary motion or any realization of
the "motive virtue" of the sun. From the beginnings made by Galileo, such theories were to emerge later with the development of
celestial mechanics following the discoveries of Kepler and Newton.
This does not in any way diminish the value of the results obtained
by master and pupil; on the contrary we admire them even more, for
half a century later they enabled Gian Domenico Cassini to compute
the first table that was sufficiently accurate to predict the configurations of the Medicean planets. This table, published in the *Ephem-
merides Bononienses Mediceorum Siderum* in 1668, led the Danish
astronomer Olaus Roemer three years later to discover the velocity
of light.

The "Atlantic business" of longitude again occupied the last years
of Galileo's life, when he wrote a letter from Arcetri on the problem

of longitudes to the "States-General of the United Provinces of the Low Countries." Objections were again raised to Galileo's proposal, similar to those raised in the Spanish Court. They were based principally on the difficulty of carrying out observations of the phenomena of the satellites, and of determining the times during navigation. Galileo replies to the Dutch admiral L. Reael, entering into greater detail concerning his invention, and he describes for the first time his time-regulator based on the use of a pendulum. Neither the death of Martin Hortensius, professor of mathematics and navigation at the University of Amsterdam, who was about to come to Italy on behalf of the States-General for the purpose of conferring with Galileo on the longitude problem, nor the death of three commissioners who were delegated to examine Galileo's proposal, nor Galileo's complete blindness, nor the very bad impression which his dealings with heretical powers had created in Rome could stop him from such occupations until the last days of his life; he even refused the present of a necklace offered to him by the States-General as a gift for his work.

As Galileo clearly shows, there were four difficulties to overcome in order to solve the problem: (1) to know precisely the laws governing the Medicean planets, in order to be able to compute the ephemerides and predict the phenomena which could be observed from one region or another of the earth; (2) to build telescopes so perfect that the satellites could be clearly seen and observed; (3) while using the telescope on a ship, to overcome the difficulties arising from the instability of the ship caused by the ocean waves; (4) finally, to invent an accurate timepiece which would enable one to determine at all times the hour and its subdivisions, so as to establish accurately the instant of the observations. With respect to the theory of the orbits of the satellites and the determination of the ephemerides, Galileo certainly had hoped and believed that they would be simpler than they are. With respect to the telescope and its use he had thought of special devices. The observer would be located in the center of the ship in a small compartment which would always hold its horizontal position, and the telescope would be attached to the observer's head. For the determination of time Galileo had in mind to use a pendulum as a regulator and counter, but it seems that it never occurred to him that it was impossible to employ a pendulum clock on shipboard. We can excuse him in his own words—he was not a seaman, nor fitted for navigation.

In the problem of the sunspots, Galileo's glory does not lie in their actual discovery, for it was known that they had already been seen with the naked eye. Instead his glory lies in his rapid and precise intuition of the phenomenon and its various particulars, which none of his contemporaries nor competitors knew how to interpret. In the summer of that historic year, famous for astronomy, Galileo observed the image of the sun, projected on a white screen placed at a convenient distance from the eyepiece. On this image he noted day by day the sunspots which were present. Today the well known frequency period of eleven years and the observations of our predecessors enable us to state quite accurately that in the autumn of 1610 there must have been a minimum of solar activity, with few or no spots. But Galileo found them nonetheless.

Afterward the sun was approaching its maximum, and in the summer of 1612 Galileo, while a guest of his friend Salviati at the Villa delle Selve at Signa near Florence, was able to make a continuous series of observations on numerous and important groups of spots. He sketched them and followed them accurately in their apparent motion across the solar disk. We do not know why Galileo, who in the *Sidereus Nuncius* had so speedily communicated to the scientific and lay world his other celestial discoveries, neglected to speak of this one, so that Father Scheiner preceded him. However, we can guess his reason from his letters. Galileo recounts in the three letters which were published immediately by the Academy of the Lincei as a prompt and decisive reply to the three of Father Scheiner, how the sunspots had already been seen with the naked eye. But the erroneous Aristotelian concept that the celestial bodies were immutable had led people to think that Mercury or some other body or vapor was interposed between us and the sun. At the time of Charles the Great a black spot had been seen on the disk of the sun by the people of France for eight consecutive days, and they believed it to be Mercury. Galileo says that this was a very stupid error, because Mercury cannot stay in conjunction with the sun, even for seven hours. It is therefore probable that Galileo wanted to be sure of his ground before proclaiming a fact already known but not explained. His attentive observation of the appearance and motion of the sunspots led him rapidly to the conclusion which he summed up in a few lucid sentences. These sentences could not be written better even today, to explain accurately this grand and interesting phenomenon. They far surpass Galileo's imitators, who believed that the spots were produced by a multitude of tiny planets, flying around the sun in an orbit inside the orbit of Mercury, visible only when they passed in front of the sun's disk.

Galileo states right away that the spots must be bodies or matter belonging to the solar globe, which rotates about its axis in a period easily determined by the apparent motion of the sunspots which rotate with the sun. The spots cannot be stars, he further states, because they have no parallax, that is, no apparent displacement when they are observed from different parts of the earth, and because they do not vary their form and arrangement, which resemble clouds on the earth. He is able to make an exact photometric evaluation of their intensity, by observing that they are not so dark as the moon shadows but actually are as bright as the full moon. They appear dark only in contrast to the high luminosity of the sun's photosphere. Galileo notes also that the spots are confined to the equatorial zone of the sun between $\pm 30°$ of heliographic latitude. Now we know that the sunspots, together with their frequency cycle, present during the eleven years of this cycle a progressive displacement in latitude. When Galileo published his discoveries, he had observed the spots for only two years and had not been able to discover this fact. But, since his observations happened to fall between the minimum and maximum activity when the spots of the old cycle end near the equator and the spots of the new cycle begin in higher latitudes, he was able to sense the location of the zone preferred by the spots and their apparent wandering in latitude.

Later he noticed another strange phenomenon, of which he speaks in detail through the mouth of Salviati in the third day of his "Dialogue on the Two Principal Systems of the World." Salviati and he were together in the Villa delle Selve and they both happened to observe a spot with a nucleus so well defined and of such large dimensions that they could trace its apparent path across the face of the sun for several days afterward. Having noticed that its path was not along a straight line but along a curved line, they were anxious to continue their observations. One day, there came to the mind of our "Academician," that is, Galileo, the "great consequence" which could be deduced from this phenomenon. This consequence today is very accurately known, but then it was unthought of and totally unexpected, especially in the conception of the Ptolemaic system. It is that the equator of the sun does not lie in the plane of the ecliptic, but is inclined to it at a certain angle. By admitting this we can explain the apparent curvature of the path of the sunspots across the face of the sun. This curvature varies with different seasons and sometimes has a maximum toward the North Pole, sometimes toward the South Pole, and sometimes it even becomes a straight line. In very clear language and with extraordinary acuteness Salviati strives to explain the various aspects of the phenomenon to the two other persons of the "Dialogue." He proves geometrically that the apparent path of the sunspots may be explained very simply by having the sun rotate about itself at the center of the ecliptic, with its axis inclined at a certain angle to the plane of the ecliptic. The earth, while revolving around the sun along the ecliptic, rotates about its own axis, which is inclined at a different angle to the plane of the ecliptic.

For Sagredo this explanation is as yet a bit complicated, but he rightly observes that he will be able to understand it better by studying the phenomenon on a celestial globe where he can mark the ecliptic, the sun's equator, and the earth's equator. Simplicius confesses that he does not fully understand the arguments of the "Academician," as related by Salviati. He strenuously and cleverly maintains the position of Aristotle and Ptolemy and finds no necessity for adopting the Copernican system to explain this new phenomenon. In fact, he argues, it is always possible, because of the relativity of motion, to refer all observed phenomena to the sun moving along the ecliptic. "If you do not prove first to me," he says, "that one cannot explain such appearances by making the sun mobile and the earth immobile, I will not give up my opinion and my belief that the sun is moving and the earth is not." Simplicius was not entirely wrong, but Galileo writes to Federico Cesi from the Villa delle Selve about this discovery, triumphantly declaring that it means the "funeral or rather the extreme and last judgment of pseudophilosophy," and that several other proofs had previously been given by the celestial bodies. Still Galileo had not found the fundamental basic proof, and he was never to find it, not even at the end of his labors.

SATURN'S RINGS

In the bizarre shape of Saturn, Galileo made another discovery, however, when he was still in Padua, which seemed to outdo all the other proofs—which were for him and other enlightened per-

sons of his time already more than sufficient, if not decisive—to confirm the theory whose triumph he so much desired. From Padua, on
July 30, 1610, he announced his discovery to Vinta in Florence, with
the following words:

> I began on the twenty-sixth of this month to observe Jupiter
> again, in the early morning in the East, with its group of Med-
> icean planets. Moreover, I have discovered a most extraordi-
> nary marvel, which I want to make known to Their Highnesses
> and to Your Lordship, but I want it kept secret until it is pub-
> lished in the work which I am going to have printed. But I
> wanted to announce it to Their Most Serene Highnesses so that,
> if someone else should discover it, they would know that no one
> observed it before I did. Yet I believe that no one will see it
> before I inform him. The fact is that the planet Saturn is not
> one alone, but is composed of three, which almost touch one
> another and never move nor change with respect to one another.
> They are arranged in a line parallel to the zodiac, and the mid-
> dle one is about three times the size of the lateral ones. They
> are arranged in the form °O°, as I will soon show Their High-
> nesses this autumn, when it will be very easy to observe the
> celestial object with all the planets above the horizon.

At the same time Galileo communicated his discovery to his friends
in Italy and Germany with the famous anagram which was unraveled
as *Altissimum planetam tergeminum observavi.*

Saturn therefore appeared to Galileo as a disk surrounded by
two lesser disks. Since he could not realize, with the magnification
which he possessed, the true form of the rings, it was natural that
he would think the planet was surrounded, like Jupiter, by two
very close satellites, revolving around the central planet with a rapid
motion. He writes to Giuliano de' Medici in Prague: "So! we have
found the court of Jupiter, and two servants for this old man, who
help him to walk and never leave his side." In fact, to his great
astonishment and perhaps regret, they did not move from one day
to the other; although, continuing his observations, he noted some
changes, and two years later from the Villa delle Selve he saw Saturn
"solitary." Astonished by this extraordinary phenomenon, which he
was not able to explain, he discusses it in his third letter on sunspots, where he makes various conjectures. He jokes that Saturn has
eaten up his children, and he thinks that all he has observed up to

that time may have been fantasy—thus yielding to all his tenacious opponents. As we now know, every fifteen years, when the plane of the rings passes through the earth, the rings of Saturn are so thin that they almost completely disappear from sight. Near the time of disappearance the rings appear like a thin needle of light projecting from each side of the planet, which could not be seen with Galileo's telescope. Having verified the disappearance, although very confused by the fact, Galileo does not give up: he returns to his concept of the presence of "two lesser Saturnian stars." He even ventures some predictions which, although incorrect in their details, are really exceptional for the picture as a whole if we compare them to the phenomenon which is now well known and exactly predictable. Galileo, in fact, believed that the two supposed satellites, at first so close to Saturn that they seemed attached to it, were going to appear for a short time around the summer solstice of the coming year, that is 1613, and were going to appear again around the winter solstice of 1614. This phenomenon would repeat itself again and again until the satellites would appear very distinct and brighter and larger than ever. He even predicted that they would remain visible for many years without interruption. Thus Galileo did not doubt their return, but it is not clear how he arrived at such certainty. Perhaps his acute sense of observation, the way in which the supposed stars, that is, the rings, had disappeared, and his intuition gave him some indication of what was going to happen. In fact the rings were opening up little by little as the earth was leaving their plane, and Galilelo, observing Saturn again in 1616, sketched it so accurately that he would probably have understood its real form if he had seen it thus in his first observations.

PHASES OF VENUS

The phenomenon of the phases of Venus which Galileo had discussed with one of his most beloved disciples, Father Benedetto Castelli, completes his astronomical discoveries and in some ways should have compensated him for the trick which Saturn played upon him. Galileo announced this discovery also to Giuliano de' Medici in Prague, with an anagram. This anagram was solved as soon as Galileo was sure of his observations and it signified: *Cynthiae figuras aemulatur mater amorum* (Venus imitates the aspects of the moon). Galileo adds:

From this marvelous experience we have a sensible and sure proof of two great suppositions which have been doubted until now by the greatest minds of the world. One is that all planets are dark by nature (the same for Mercury as for Venus). The other is that Venus must necessarily revolve around the sun, just like Mercury and all the other planets, a fact believed by the Pythagoreans, Copernicus, Kepler, and me, but not actually proved. Thus Kepler and the other Copernicans will have something to boast about for having believed and reasoned well, although we are considered and will yet be considered ignorant and little less than stupid by all the philosophers *in libris*.

From the beginning of his observations Galileo had been attracted by Venus with her aspects similar to those of the moon. He no longer doubted the motion of Venus around the sun, which formed the center of the revolutions of all the other planets. He observed and sketched the planet which, at the time when it is seen with horns, presents a disk forty times larger than when it is round, because of its distance from the earth and because of its position with respect to the sun. On the basis of his discoveries and reasonings, Galileo by now supported openly the Copernican doctrine with all the well known troubles which were to follow.

THE "DIALOGUE" AND TIDES

To these beliefs we can perhaps add the fact that in his famous work, which he considered decisive and persuasive, he believed he set forth as the main argument and basic proof, which he had tried so hard to find for so many years, an interpretation, although incorrect, of the ocean tides. The work which he had thought about for many years had been announced to Vinta in 1610 as being "on the system and constitution of the universe, an immense conception, full of philosophy, astronomy, and geometry." This work was realized as the "Dialogue on the Two Principal Systems of the World."

For a moment he thought of calling it, perhaps because he had to be cautious and wanted to obtain the permission of the ecclesiastical authorities, by the more modest designation "Dialogue on the Tides," so much did he believe that the argument would be decisive and give him an uncontested victory. As is well known, this did not happen, and his argument, based on correct premises but incorrectly developed, gave some vantage points to his opponents and enemies, even if they did not know how, and were unable, to refute it effectively.

Galileo, a profound observer of natural phenomena, had noted several times that the water in the barges full of drinking water for city use, which were going through the Venetian Lagoon from Fusina to Venice, flowed forward to the bow or backward to the stern, when for some reason or other the barges retarded or accelerated their uniform motion. "The tides," says Salviati, in the fourth day of the "Dialogue," "are an analogous phenomenon." What the barge does with respect to the water contained in it is "exactly what the Mediterranean vessel does with respect to the water contained in it." We know today that the complicated phenomenon of tides is caused by the attraction of the moon and sun on the masses of water on the earth. This fact really was known to the ancients, and in Galileo's time, Kepler was one of the staunchest supporters of the right interpretation. Kepler was limited to the observation that the tides repeated themselves following the position of the moon, for he advanced no reasonable hypothesis to explain the effect of the moon. Actually, the effect of the moon is stronger because it is closer than the sun to the earth. There flashed before Kepler's mind, however, the idea that the phenomenon was due to the mutual forces of the masses, even though he did not know the "virtue of the motive force."

Starting from a well-established physical fact, Galileo goes wrong in applying to it the motions which the masses of water on the earth would have to assume as a result of the combination of its two motions, the revolution around the sun and the rotation about its axis. Having begun incorrectly, he tries to explain to his interlocutors the phenomena of the tides with their daily, monthly, and yearly periods. He is astonished that Kepler, with such an acute mind, relies on actions at a distance, to the domination of the moon over the water and to similar "childishnesses." Galileo was not entirely unjustified, in view of the astrological digressions in which the astronomer of the Bohemian Court quite often indulged. It appears, however, from the statements of Sagredo and Simplicius that Galileo was not entirely persuaded by the arguments which he put in the mouth of Salviati. Sagredo finds them so hard to understand that his mind is confused. Simplicius confesses that they are more ingenious than many others in those times, yet he does not believe them to be true and conclusive.

Salviati then concludes that besides the proof of the mobility of the earth expounded on the first day of the "Dialogue," one should hope for highly accurate future observations of astronomers, which would reveal those very small displacements, the "parallaxes" of the fixed stars. Copernicus believed that they could not be observed, but yet they must exist and might be measured for the closer stars with respect to the more distant stars. This, in fact, would have been the most tangible proof which Galileo so vainly sought, and which, only two centuries later, was revealed by the precision of instruments and observations. Despite the error which Galileo made in the fourth day of the "Dialogue," it must be kept in mind that he considered the problem of tides essentially a dynamic one, and not static. He discussed the predictable aspect of the more open or closed seas and of the different depths, and was far ahead of the hypotheses advanced by his opponents.

LAST DAYS

After the storm raised by the "Dialogue," Galileo dwelt in the confinement and peace of Arcetri, abosolutely forbidden to occupy himself with the universe, the sun, and the earth. As is well known, he returned to the studies which he had begun forty years before in Pisa, writing his immortal pages on the "strength of materials," and on the "science of motion," now called dynamics or more precisely kinematics. Galileo calls the latter the "science of local motion." This science is important also from the astronomical point of view, for it announces for the first time the important concept of uniformly accelerated motion or uniform acceleration, this is, the motion in which a moving body receives an equal increment of velocity in equal intervals of time. He gives laws for the motion of heavy bodies and presents the concept of inertia, that is, the principles of modern mechanics. In spite of the prohibition, the science of the sky attracts him so much that in the last days of his life he returns eargerly to it and leaves other unforgettable traces with which he ends his earthly life. With the telescope he observed the mountains and seas of the moon and noticed certain oscillations with respect to the line of sight so that objects close to the edge were seen more or less far from it, or more or less close to the center of the disk. This phenomenon is known today under the name of "optical libration." Galileo supposed that this effect was due solely to the parallax, and that it would not be seen at the center of the earth because it resulted from the different locations of the observer with respect to the straight line connecting the center of the earth to the center of the moon in the course of the lunar day and month. Galileo could not have discovered, for lack of sufficient observations, that the greater part of the phenomenon is due instead to the variable motion in longitude of the moon and to the inclination of its axis, which causes the "libration in longitude and latitude." Galileo calls this phenomenon observed by him the "apparent titubation of the moon" and describes it in one of his letters dated from his "prison of Arcetri," to Alfonso Antonini, soldier and scientist of Udine. Two years later Prince Leopold de' Medici, founder of the Accademia del Cimento, asked Galileo's opinion about the objections raised against the true cause of the earthshine (visible on the moon at the beginning and end of the lunations), which had appeared in a work by Liceti on the luminous or phosphorescent stone of Bologna. Galileo was then already blind and he dictated to his eighteen-year-old disciple, Vincenzo Viviani, a long paper, one of his most beautiful, both for scientific vigor and purity of language. He proves once again, indisputably, that the sun's light is reflected, first by the earth to the dark part still in the shadow of the moon, and then by the moon to us, so that we observe it as if the moon were phosphorescent.

In his last years Galileo dictated the "Astronomical Operations," wherein he predicted how they will develop in the future. Everything which had been done by the ancients and by his predecessors, before the invention of the telescope, had to be done over. He foresees that only the telescope will reveal to men the extraordinary marvels of the universe. Together with the micrometer and other auxiliary instruments it will bring positional astronomy to great accuracy and physical astronomy to its beginning and development. The telescope is not enough, the sand clock or a free wheel clockwork is not enough, but a system of wheels is necessary, strictly controlled by the pendulum. He maintains that thus we shall be able to observe the variations in the diameters of the sun, moon, and planets, and thus know when these bodies come close or go away from us. We shall observe also the meridian stars with perfect and powerful telescopes even in full daylight. We shall mark their positions on the celestial sphere, thus making stellar catalogs, even if this task is "really herculean, thanks to the too numerous herd of fixed stars."

10 : Kepler

JOHANNES KEPLER, BORN IN WEILDERSTADT (Württemberg) in 1571, showed very early his exceptional intellectual gifts, so that he was sent to study theology at the University of Tübingen. There, under the guidance of the astronomer and mathematician Father Michael Mästlin, he learned of the Copernican theory. When he was twenty-two years old he abandoned theology, after the professorship of science at the same university had been offered to him. But the religious influence remained fixed in his mind, so that he came to discover in the harmony of creation some laws which he thought ought certainly to exist in relation to earthly things and events. Thus thinking that he had reached his goal he published in 1596 his *Mysterium Cosmographicum*, which he made haste to send to Tycho Brahe in Germany and to Galileo in Padua. Galileo replied immediately, having read only the introduction, to express his great pleasure in being able to correspond with a colleague and friend, who, just as he did, wanted to investigate and discover the truth, leaving behind the mistaken ideas of ancient philosophy. The content of this letter, and of Kepler's reply has already been noted, in part. Foreseeing the difficulties which Galileo might meet in his own country, Kepler thought it would be easier for him to make his work known in Germany. Since Kepler had no instruments for astronomical observations, he asked Galileo to determine on certain dates, six months apart, the altitude of the North Star and a star in the Great Bear, in order to prove the existence of the parallax of the fixed stars. We shall see that this problem could be solved only two and a half centuries later with instrumental means much more perfect than those which were possible at the time of Galileo and Kepler.

AS COURT MATHEMATICIAN

Several years later, because of the edict against the Protestants, Kepler was compelled to abandon Graz and he sought refuge in Prague as an assistant to Tycho. He soon became his successor, for after Tycho's death he was called "court mathematcian" by the emperor Rudolph II. Thus he had at his disposal all the precious observations of Tycho, and these, together with his own famous discoveries, enabled him to form a better, and actually the real, theory of the solar system. This was the principal occupation of his life as an astronomer.

Because of the requirements of his position, in fulfillment of the emperor's wishes, and because of his own tendencies toward mystical speculation, which were just as deepseated as his intuition in a true positive science, Kepler became involved in astrology. He even published a treatise in which he tried to separate the horoscopes and predictions of persons and human events from what was predictable on the basis of the astronomical observations and theories, however imperfect, of his times. Beginning with the emperor, Kepler had continual requests for predictions and horoscopes. Kepler excuses this well-paid activity of his by saying that just as Nature offers a means of subsistence to all human beings, so she has made astrology to assist astronomy, which would not have been able to survive by itself.

STUDIES IN OPTICS

It is interesting that Kepler occupied himself with optics a few years before the discovery of the telescope, which, however, he did not foresee. He published his *Astronomiae Pars Optica*, which contains his fundamental concepts on the theory of vision, such as the definition of the light ray, later generally adopted in geometric optics, the explanation of the phenomenon of the reflection of light, an approximate law of refraction, and a most important investigation of the mechanics of vision.

FIRST TWO LAWS

Following this, in the same year in which Galileo introduced the telescope, Kepler reduced and discussed the observations of Tycho. He completed then his "great martian work," having succeeded, as he says, in bringing the planet Mars as "a prisoner to the feet of the imperial throne." In view of the accuracy of Tycho Brahe's observations, Kepler understood that they could in no way satisfy a circular orbit, but only an elliptic one. In his *Astronomia Nova, seu Physica Coelestis Tradita Commentariis de Motibus Stellae Martis ex Observationibus G. V. Tychonis Brahe,* published in Prague in 1609, he expounds two fundamental principles of modern astronomy, the law of elliptic orbits and the law of equal areas. He was able to separate, in the combination of the motions of the earth and Mars around the sun, those irregularities which pertained to the former from those of the latter, in their supposed circular motions. He found that with combinations of eccentrics, epicycles, and equants there remained residual errors of 8', with respect to Tycho's observations. This, states Kepler, cannot be, "since the Divine Goodness has given to us in Tycho Brahe a very accurate observer." Consequently, in a further study of the problem, Kepler first came to the conclusion that the orbit of Mars must be some kind of oval, and he proved at once that the simplest of all the known oval curves, the ellipse, satisfied the observations in the best possible way, provided the sun was assumed to be at one of the foci. He noticed that the planet moved faster when it was closer to the sun and slower when it was farther way, so that the surface described by the straight line which connects the sun to Mars is always proportional to the time, and he thus formulated his second law. He was then easily able to establish that the orbit of the earth must be elliptic, and believing firmly in the harmony of nature, he was convinced that all the planets must move according to the same laws. These laws are mixed up in Kepler's works with many digressions, and there is even a hint of the law of universal gravitation. In fact, he explains that in the celestial sphere there must exist an unknown force similar to the attraction of the earth; for example, if the earth and the moon were not held in their respective orbits "by some vital force or other they would precipitate one against the other." Kepler tries to establish a relationship between terrestrial gravity and the force of attraction which the sun exerts on the planets, but then he deviates by supposing an analogy between universal and magnetic attraction. He states furthermore that the tides observed on the earth are due to the influence of lunar attraction on the liquid masses of the earth.

ON THE "SIDEREUS NUNCIUS"

Meanwhile Galileo, after having collected and presented his astronomical discoveries in the *Sidereus Nuncius*, sends a copy of it immediately to Kepler, the "Caesarian Mathematician," through Giuliano de' Medici, Tuscan ambassador to the emperor at Prague, expressing his keen desire to know Kepler's opinion. Kepler is not long in replying, for a few days later, even before he is able to observe the sky, he cannot keep from sending Galileo a long letter entitled *Dissertatio cum Nuncio Sidereo* in which he expresses his doubts, particularly of the actual existence of the satellites of Jupiter. A convinced Copernican, he states that, if it is true that "the sun is in the center of the world, its heart, the source of light and heat, the origin of life, then it is also true that after the sun there is no celestial body nobler than the earth. If Jupiter were really surrounded by no less than four moons, one cannot well understand why they should be there, since on the planet there is no one to admire such a spectacle."

One can understand, from the lively correspondence exchanged in the excitement produced by the great discoveries of Galileo, that the major difficulty in verifying them was having a good telescope and holding it steady during the observation. Galileo took great pains to build telescopes and present them to his benefactors, to the greatest personalities of Europe, and to his friends. He confesses, writing to Belisario Vinta, counsellor and secretary to the Grand Duke of Tuscany, that he had built a hundred or more "eye glasses" at great expense and trouble, but that only ten were satisfactory for seeing and observing the new Medicean planets and the numerous fixed stars. One of these ten Galileo had sent to Ernest of Bavaria, prince elector of the Holy Roman Empire in Cologne, who passed it on to Kepler in order that he might verify Galileo's discoveries. In possession of this good telescope, and even confessing that he found great difficulty in aiming it and following Jupiter, Kepler is rapidly converted in the face of reality. A few months later he published another short paper: *Narratio de Observatis a se Quatuor Jovis*

Satellitibus Erronibus, in which he enthusiastically addresses the friendly reader, communicating his celestial observations of September, 1610, which fully confirm the marvelous discoveries of Galileo, and invites the reader to admire them, never ceasing to praise God for His work.

THEORY OF THE TELESCOPE

The telescope, which had made an obscure entrance into the pre-Galileian world, would probably have remained imperfect for a long time if Galileo had not re-invented it and raised it at once to the importance and dignity of a scientific instrument. The telescope gave much thought to Kepler who, already engaged in his work on "optical astronomy," was well prepared to study and develop its theory. This theory was ready and was published in the spring of 1611 in Augsburg, under the title *Dioptrice* or "demonstration of those things never before seen by anyone, which are visible with the telescope." This work really marks the beginning and the foundation of an optical science able to explain the function of lenses and their various combinations, like the lens used in Galileo's telescope, or the one used in Kepler's, also called "astronomical." In the introduction to the *Dioptrice,* Kepler at once stresses the importance of this science in widening the boundaries of philosophy. Since at that time the *Sidereus Nuncius,* like all the other writings of Galileo, was in the hands of the public, everyone could appreciate what kind of and how much progress had been attained with this new means of research. The wise optical tube is as precious as a scepter; he who observes with it becomes a king and can comprehend the works of God. For it are fitting the words: You subject the boundaries and paths of the celestial bodies to human intelligence! The letters directed by Galileo to Giuliano de' Medici in Prague, in which he explains his anagrams on three-bodied Saturn and horned Venus, are quoted in their entirety by Kepler in his introduction. He then continues with a fanciful discussion, no longer astronomical but entirely astrological, on the phases of Venus who revolves around the sun like a lover, with the same consequences to human beings on the earth as she endures during her course. The introduction ends with another letter of Galileo in which he discusses the difference between the fixed stars and the planets, leading to the conclusion that the former shine by their own light and the latter by light reflected from the sun. There is also a tribute to the great philosopher who was able to find such a powerful instrument to observe and comprehend the nature and the course of the planets of the solar system. From the *Dioptrice* and the correspondence between Galileo and Kepler we realize that the telescope, which had become an instrument serving the most noble of the sciences, was to transform optics radically and to open the way for its modern development.

THE THIRD LAW

While Galileo was working hard to find the laws of motion of the Medicean planets, Kepler, as already mentioned, thought that the "business was very difficult and almost impossible." Actually the determination of these periods within certain limits of accuracy was not really beyond the possibilities of the time. In fact Galileo, and later his disciple, Father Renieri, arrived, as we mentioned previously, at values of the synodic revolutions of the four satellites which were extraordinarily accurate. It was more difficult to determine the shape of the orbits of the Medicean planets, and Kepler was well aware of the fact. Having established his first two laws, it was only after a few years that he succeeded by long and laborious investigations in formulating his third law, which he announced in the *Harmonices Mundi Libri* V, thus obtaining all the data necessary to determine the orbits of the planets. This work of his has a musical title because Kepler believed that the ratio between the maximum and minimum velocities of the planets along their orbits should be harmonic in a musical sense. Thus, for instance, he found for Saturn the major third (4/5), for Jupiter a minor third (5/6), and so on. Only the sun could hear the celestial music. In fact, the study of the relationships among the various numerical quantities of the solar system led him to state his third law, which relates the magnitudes of the planetary orbits to their periods of revolution around the sun. Assuming as a unit of time the period of the earth's revolution around the sun, the times of revolution of the planets Mercury, Venus, the Earth, Mars, Jupiter, Saturn, are, respectively, 0.24; 0.615; 1; 1.88; 11.86; 29.457; and their respective distances from the sun are 0.387; 0.723; 1; 1.524; 5.203; 9.539. Squaring the first set of numbers and cubing the second set, we obtain two sets of equal numbers within the accuracy with which these data were then known, so that Kepler announced his law as

"exact" whereas, especially for the outer planets, there is some discrepancy, explained later by Newton. Thus Kepler obtained the proportions of the solar system without having to determine its true scale
in units of terrestrial measurements.

KEPLER'S HISTORY OF ASTRONOMY

About 1620 there appeared another important work by Kepler entitled *Epitome Astronomiae Copernicanae*, in which he told,
with almost no astrological deviations, the history of astronomy, explained from the Copernican point of view and including the discoveries of Galileo and Kepler. Kepler states that the fundamental
laws discovered for Mars are true also for the other planets, for the
moon which revolves around the earth, and for the Medicean planets around Jupiter. The theory of the moon is discussed in detail,
including evection and variation. He recognizes the necessity of correcting the distance from the earth to the sun, which had always been
believed, from the times of Hipparchus and Ptolemy, to be equal to
1200 times the radius of the earth, entailing a solar parallax of 3'.
Since Kepler was not able to discover any parallax for Mars, he concluded that the distances of Mars and of the sun must be greater than
had been supposed up to that time. With curious reasoning he concluded that the distance of the sun had to be about three times greater
than the supposed distance, which is still one-seventh of the true
distance. In the *Epitome* he also explained why the totally eclipsed
moon appears to be illuminated by a feeble light, generally reddish.
Kepler rightly supposes that the light of the sun, passing through the
earth's atmosphere, is deflected from its path so that it comes to be
reflected by the moon. He speaks also of the luminous ring which
appears around the globe of the sun when the sun is totally eclipsed
by the moon, and he recalls the description previously given by
Plutarch: "the moon at times obscures the sun entirely, but always
for a short time, and it is never big enough to prevent a certain luminosity appearing around the circumference of the sun which makes
the darkness never black and deep, nor completely obscure." These
are the first observations of the solar corona, of which Kepler tries to
give as rational an explanation as was possible at that time.

OBSERVATIONS ON COMETS

In the *Saggiatore* Galileo had argued with the Jesuit O. Grassi about the nature of comets and the form of their tails. He proves that he had not copied Kepler, as he had been accused of doing. Kepler had published in 1618, following the appearance of three comets, his observations in a treatise *De Cometis*. Galileo proves that he had formed different hypotheses about such phenomena. Kepler realized that the comets must be celestial and not terrestrial bodies, and he believed that they moved in a straight line, thus explaining their appearance and disappearance when they passed close to the earth. He confirmed the observations of Fracastoro and Apianus, that the tails of the comets were always turned in the direction away from the sun, and he supposed that the tails were formed by rays of the sun which penetrate the bodies of the comets. As one can see, this is not very far removed from what is thought today concerning the nature and formation of this phenomenon.

COMPLETION OF "RUDOLPHINE TABLES"

Kepler refused the professorship of mathematics which was offered to him by the University of Bologna, and because of religious persecution he was compelled to move from Linz to Ulm. There he compiled the results obtained from the observations of Tycho and his own theories, by computing and publishing in 1627 the "Rudolphine Tables," already begun by Tycho Brahe and so-called in honor of his protector, Rudolph II. The first of a series of ephemerides, calculated by Kepler on the basis of his three laws, was dedicated to John Napier of Merchiston, because in it he employed logarithms for the first time, which then spread rapidly throughout Germany. He was thus able to compute with great accuracy the orbits of Mars and of the other planets, thereby completing the above-mentioned tables. These are the first tables based on the new heliocentric hypothesis of elliptic motions, and for nearly a century they remained the classical astronomical tables.

OPINIONS ON SUNSPOTS

Concerning the nature of sunspots, we do not find that Kepler was in direct correspondence with Galileo, but at the end of

1612, when Galileo replied to the feigned Apelles, that is, Father
Christopher Scheiner, Father van Maelcote addressed himself to
Kepler to learn his opinion about sunspots, knowing that he had
observed them. The letter reached Kepler after a long delay and he
answered it in the summer of the following year. He wrote that
Galileo, after his astronomical discoveries, had begun to think that
the sunspots could constitute another proof of the Copernican system
and certainly of the sun's rotation about its axis. Kepler had attempted
to observe them with the good telescope which had been lent him
by the prince elector of Cologne, but he had not been able to see
them on account of the great brightness of the solar image. Later,
having read the pamphlet of the Dutch student Johannes Fabricius
and the letters of the feigned Apelles, he finally succeeded in seeing
them, and he also obtained the accurate discussion by Galileo of their
nature. He stated that he had already foreseen that the sun must
rotate about its axis in a period shorter than the period of revolution
of Mercury (88 days), and that in fact the spots proved that the period
of solar rotation is between 25 and 28 days. Concerning the physical
nature of the spots, he thought that, since they rotated with different
velocities and since they did not move parallel to the ecliptic, they
could not be attached to the globe of the sun, even though they
were not far from it. For these and other reasons, such as their irregular appearances and disappearances and the changes in their form,
the hypothesis could be made that they were something analogous to
clouds on the earth. God alone knew how such obscure formations
were formed in the flaming body of the sun, and the analogy with
terrestrial phenomena could go no farther.

Family misfortunes, financial troubles due to the insolvency of the
emperor, and religious persecution made the last years of Kepler difficult and painful. Yet his astronomical activity, including the publication of the "Rudolphine Tables" and the prediction of celestial
phenomena, had not diminished. He worked until he died in 1630
at the age of fifty-nine in Regensburg, after a disastrous winter trip
which he had to make to that city.

FORCE OF GRAVITY OF CELESTIAL BODIES

Among the many achievements which Kepler contributed to
the progress of astronomy, there is also that of having considered,
even if in a rather confused way, the possibility of actions at a dis-

tance which held the celestial bodies as if bound to one another. As opposed to the Copernican system in which no body was necessary as a center of motion for the epicycles and deferents, in Kepler's conception of elliptic motions, the sun, or the earth, or Jupiter, had to occupy one of the foci of the orbit traversed by the planets or the satellites. Thus there existed a point occupied by a central body, and it became important to ascertain the existence and the nature of the bond between the motion and the central body. Since the concepts of dynamics were still unthought of at the time of Kepler, he was compelled to resort to properties of a magnetic nature or to an "innate virtue" emitted by the sun in its radiations. Kepler writes in Book IV of the *Epitome:*

> It has never been said until now that the natural inertia of the planets exists against the motive power of the sun. This inertia causes the planets to try to remain fixed in their location, because of their matter. Therefore the motive force of the sun and the impotence of the planet, that is the inertia of its matter, fight against each other, and both have their part in the victory. The former moves the planet away from its position; the latter to some extent retrieves its body (the planet's) from those bonds with which the sun had captured it. So that from both sides arises this rotational force or circuit around the sun.

Beyond the bounds of scientific argument, Kepler thought that a "gravity" must exist, in the sense of the bonds of human nature, by which the various celestial bodies tended to unite and come together. Such, for instance, would be the action of the moon on the masses of water on the earth. As one can see, we enter here into the astrological field, which Kepler was compelled to treat as the final goal of his researches. However, astrology in his ingenious mind never overcame the solid foundations of astronomy, which owes so much to him.

11 : Huygens and Cassini

GALILEO HAD OPENED AND POINTED THE WAY for the memorable discoveries of Newton, but nearly half a century was to elapse after his death before the publication of the *Principia*. In this interval of time, however, interest and progress in astronomy did not cease, and among the foremost investigators were Huygens and Cassini.

Before discussing these, we must recall Johannes Hevel of Danzig who, by employing telescopes of increasingly greater power with long focal distances, made a very accurate study of the moon's surface and published his "Selenography." This is an atlas with figures, engraved by Hevel himself, which represent chains of mountains, craters, seas, to all of which he gave names. Part of his nomenclature still remains, but other names were changed by G. B. Riccioli in his "New *Almagest*." Hevel was very much interested in comets, and also compiled a catalog of 1500 stars and improved the tables of the sun.

CHRISTIAN HUYGENS

Christian Huygens was born in The Hague in 1629, and he was famous not only in astronomy but also in related sciences. He soon realized that an improvement of the optical parts of the telescope was a necessary condition for the progress of astronomy, and he began to study the problem of the manufacture of lenses. He discovered a new method to give them their required curvature with considerable precision. He thus was able to build telescopes vastly superior to those of Galileo and with greater magnifying power. He immediately obtained concrete results in the discovery of a satellite of Saturn, afterward called "Titan." He was able to comprehend the true form of the mysterious three-bodied planet, that is, of the ring which surrounds it. According to the custom of the times, as Galileo had done for his first discovery, Huygens announced his discovery in *De Saturni Luna Observatio Nova* in the disguise of anagrams, explained later in his publication *Systema Saturnium*. In the latter he explains clearly the various appearances of the planet as the phases of a ring inclined 20° to the ecliptic. For a comparison of his results he reproduces drawings of early observations, which evidently came close to discovering the ring without being able to comprehend it.

The necessity of recording accurately the times of his astronomical observations led Huygens to study the problem of the application of the pendulum to the regulation of timepieces, a problem which Galileo had left unsolved. In 1657 Huygens was able to present his first pendulum to the States-General, and he published immediately afterward his famous work *Horologium Oscillatorium,* which describes several original discoveries on the theory of the pendulum and on the problem concerning the motion of bodies along circles or other curves. This latter theory is important in connection with the planetary motions produced by gravitation. His formula for the duration of pendulum oscillations offered a very accurate means for the measure of the intensity of gravitational force on the earth.

After his return to his native country from France, where he had been called by Louis XIV, Huygens took up again the construction of lenses of long focal distance. These lenses were mounted on high poles without any tube connecting them with the eyepiece, and were rigged with ropes and pulleys. They constituted the so-called "aerial telescopes."

Subsequently Huygens left the astronomical field and devoted himself to his famous researches in optics. The use of a precise instrument, like the pendulum clock, in astronomical observations introduced the necessity of adding to the telescope some means of making angular measurements more acurately than had been done before. First the Tuscan mechanic Francesco Generini, then the English astronomer Gascoigne about 1640, and immediately afterward Geminiano Montanari of the University of Bologna introduced the use of the thread micrometer, thus facilitating the measurement of angular distances between neighboring stars and of the diameter of the planets. Later the Frenchmen, Auzout and Picard, connected the telescope to graduated circles in order to make the determination of stellar co-ordinates more accurate. Jean Picard was also the first to introduce the modern method of determining the right ascensions of the stars by observing their passage across the meridian.

Huygens went to Denmark to visit what was left of the observatory of Tycho Brahe, and he brought back with him a young astronomer, Olaus Roemer, who at the Paris Observatory had discovered the progressive motion of light and was able to determine its velocity. He had noticed that the intervals between successive eclipses of a satellite decreased regularly as the planet and the earth came closer together, and increased as they became farther apart. He deduced that this could depend on a finite velocity of light, and he made calculations from such differences; with the knowledge of the velocity of Jupiter and the earth in their orbits, Roemer obtained a first value of the velocity of light. He was also the first to invent the transit instrument, thus increasing the accuracy in the determination of time and right ascensions.

The times were now ripe for the foundation of observatories like the one of Uraniburg, but with instruments equipped with ever more powerful and improved optical means. Such observatories were started then, and they continue their work today, like the observatories of Paris and Greenwich. Picard in 1664 had already called to the attention of Louis XIV the fact that neither in Paris nor in his entire kingdom did there exist an instrument which would give an accurate determination of the altitude of the pole. Several years later the observatory which exists today was erected from the drawings of the architect Perrault, through the interest of the king and his minister Colbert. In the minds of its founders it was supposed to be a meeting place for the members of the Academy of France, a kind of museum and scientific laboratory where Frenchmen and foreigners alike would be able to perform their investigations. In all probability because of the direction and ability of the Italian astronomer Gian Domenico Cassini, the monumental building was used exclusively for astronomy.

GIAN DOMENICO CASSINI

Gian Domenico Cassini, the first of four generations of astronomers, was born in 1625 in Perinaldo (actually in the province of Imperia, Italy) a territory of the Marquis of Doria, who paid feudal homage to the Dukes of Savoy. At twenty-five years of age, he was called from Genoa, where he was already well known, to fill the professorship of astronomy at the University of Bologna as a successor of Father Bonaventura Cavalieri. Since at that time the mathematics professors had to teach Euclid, the theory of the planets, and the astronomy of Ptolemy, and since Cavalieri had been the first to explain in his public lectures the Copernican theory of the system of the world and the discoveries of Galileo, the task to which the young astronomer was called assumed great importance. During the nineteen years in which he remained in Bologna, Cassini gave considerable impulse to astronomical studies with the modest means at his disposal, and he was required to occupy himself with hydraulic and military problems. Meanwhile his fame had crossed the Alps, so that Louis XIV nominated him an "Academician" and invited him to Paris.

From the report of his great-grandson Cassini IV we have confirmation that Cassini, while examining the plans of Perrault, wanted to use the new building only for astronomical purposes.

> Gian Domenico Cassini arrived in Paris on April 4, 1669, and as soon as he presented himself to Louis XIV the king ordered that the plans and drawings of the observatory, which was then completed up to the second floor, be shown to him so that Cassini could give his opinion. Cassini quite rightly demonstrated that the project had no common sense. Then ensued a meeting with M. Perrault to discuss the matter before the king and M. Colbert. Perrault eloquently defended his plan and architectural style with beautiful sentences. My great-grandfather spoke French very poorly and in defending the cause of astronomy he shocked the ears of the king, Colbert, and Perrault to such a point that Perrault in the zeal of his defense said to the king: *Sire, ce baragouineur là ne sçait ce qu'il dit.* My great-grandfather kept silent and did well. The king agreed with Perrault and did badly. The result is that the observatory has no common sense.

Two years later Cassini was able to begin astronomical observations with instruments which he had obtained directly from those who had learned the art from Galileo and Torricelli. Campani and Divini had distinguished themselves among the best instrument-makers of those times, and they continuously furnished instruments to the Paris Observatory. From Rome Cassini had brought an object lens having a focal length of about 16 feet, given to him by Campani. With this lens he determined the period of rotation of Jupiter and Mars, and in France observed the sunspots and discovered a new satellite of Saturn. Cassini, Picard, Roemer, Huygens, Colbert, and Perrault often met at the Observatory to compare by actual tests the object lens of Campani and Divini, and the French ones. In Cassini's diary we often find notes of such meetings and the results of the tests, which gave the advantage sometimes to the Italians, sometimes to the French. Cassini himself explains in his notes how it was possible to sight and follow the celestial bodies with the "aerial telescopes," which were sometimes more than 150 feet long. Since the supporting poles were not long enough, a great wooden tower was erected in the garden of the Observatory. This tower was called "Marly" because it had been used in that locality to raise the waters of the Seine and send them to Versailles.

Cassini made many important contributions to and greatly stimulated the progress of specific astronomical studies and their geodetic applications. Father Ignazio Danti, mathematician and cosmographer of the Grand Duke of Tuscany, who had been a public lecturer of astronomy before Cavalieri and Cassini at the University of Bologna, had traced a horizontal dial in the Cathedral of San Petronio. After the enlargement of the Cathedral the dial could not be used any more, and Cassini thought of tracing a larger one in order to solve precisely some fundamental astronomical problems. After having observed in San Petronio the vernal equinox of the year 1656, Cassini was able to prepare tables of the sun's motion, and he soon noticed that in order to make them more accurate, atmospheric refraction had to be taken into account. He writes:

> When I afterward had the honor of being called by His Majesty the most Christian King to the Royal Academy of Sciences and to the Royal Observatory, the proposal was made to test whether these refractions of the sun, obtained from observations made in San Petronio, would be as I determined them, not only in our climate, but close to the equatorial regions where, on account of the great altitudes of the sun, the refractions are much less felt; also whether the astronomical elements which had been determined here, with the use of larger refractions, would be

the same as when these refractions are very small or vanish altogether. The job was therefore given to M. Richer of the Royal Academy of Sciences, who was sent to Cayenne, which is a French colony on a small island of America, at five degrees from the equator, so that he might make the greatest possible number of observations of the meridian altitude of the sun. These observations, corrected for refraction, gave positions of the sun in that locality, so that they were calculated for the ephemerides of Marquis Malvasia according to this hypothesis, and reduced to the meridian.

Cassini, when he was still in Bologna, observed the features on the surfaces of the larger planets, Mars, Venus, and Jupiter. He discovered their rotations about their axes and measured their durations. He saw the characteristic conformation of Mars and noted how it changed with the seasons. He was the first to give an accurate description of the bands and spots visible on the surface of Jupiter. He succeeded in computing in his *Ephemerides Bononienses Mediceorum Siderum* the configurations of the four satellites of Jupiter discovered by Galileo. Galileo had tried in vain to predict them but, as we have already mentioned, had not succeeded in solving the problem.

Cassini made considerable progress in this field and made it possible for Roemer to make his discovery. Studying Saturn and its ring, Cassini discovered a band on the surface of the planet and a division which separates the ring into two unequal parts. This division, which still bears Cassini's name, gave him an accurate idea of the constitution of the ring formed by a swarm of very tiny satellites which could not be seen separately and which revolved around the planet with different velocities. They are more dense in the inner part, less in the outer part, and form two concentric rings, separated one from the other. Soon after he had arrived in Paris, Cassini discovered the second satellite of Saturn, Iapetus, and attributed its variable brightness to the fact that it always presented the same face to the central planet, as the moon does to the earth. The next year he discovered the third satellite Rhea and twelve years later two more, Tethys and Dione. Just as Galileo had called the satellites of Jupiter the "Medicean planets" in honor of the Medici, Cassini called the satellites of Saturn "Ludovici" in honor of the *Roi Soleil.*

The distance of the planets which are closest to the earth and the "astronomical unit," that is, the distance from the earth to the sun, were very inaccurately known in Cassini's time. He tackled the problem fully, with new methods, splendid for that epoch. The same Richer, whom we have seen assigned by Cassini to determine the atmospheric refraction at Cayenne, had also the task of measuring the apparent distances of Mars from nearby stars at the same time that Cassini was measuring them in France. These simultaneous observations, executed by the two observers six thousand miles apart, enabled them to calculate the distance of that planet from the earth with an accuracy never before attained, and therefore also the dimensions of the planetary orbits and the earth's distance from the sun.

It is to Cassini's great glory that he was the first to remove the doubt and inaccuracies which had clung for so many centuries to these fundamental data.

The problem of determining the magnitude and form of the earth began to be of interest, and Picard had measured the length of a terrestrial arc at the latitude of Paris. Cassini proposed to the Academy to extend the measurement along a meridian through the entire kingdom. With the help of several collaborators he measured the so-called "meridian of France." He reported this determination in his fundamental work, published when he was seventy-five years old, "On the Magnitude and Form of the Earth." Cassini became blind in 1710, probably as a consequence of his long and laborious observational work, and he died two years later, bowed down with age and covered with glory.

12 : Isaac Newton and his times

AS OFTEN HAPPENS AFTER GREAT DISCOVERIES, the time came to formulate a law, with factors of mass and distance. It was later to become truly universal, for long after Newton's time his law was discovered to be valid for other systems of stars outside the solar system and for aggregates of very large numbers of stars, such as, for example, the Milky Way.

Isaac Newton was born in Woolsthorpe in Lincolnshire at the beginning of 1643, one year after the death of Galileo. He devoted himself very early to the study of the foundations of natural philosophy, and he brought about a complete revolution in the astronomical field with his discoveries on gravitation and the invention of the reflector telescope; in the physical field, with optics and the theory of colors; and in the mathematical field, with the method of fluxions. When he was very young, as he himself related many years later, he dedicated himself with much success to these three arguments. To quote Newton's own words, probably written when he was about seventy-three years old, in this golden period of his achievement:

> In the year 1666 I began to think of gravity extending to the orb of the moon and having found out how to estimate a force with which a globe revolving within a sphere presses the surface of the sphere, from Kepler's rule of periodical times of the planets being in a sesquialterate proportion of their distances from the centres of their orbs ["sesquialterate" means one and a half times, or, as we say, the squares of the years are as the

cubes of the orbits] I deduced that the forces which keep the planets in their orbs must be reciprocally as the squares of their distances from the centres about which they revolve: and thereby compared the force requisite to keep the moon in her orb with the force of gravity at the surface of the earth, and found the answer pretty nearly. All this was in the two plague years 1665 and 1666, for in those days I was in the prime of my age for invention, and minded mathematics and philosophy more than at any time since.

Galileo's discovery, that a body in motion will continue indefinitely in motion until an opposing force comes to alter it or causes it to cease, had developed new procedures in the problems of mechanics. In fact his disciple, Giovanni Alfonso Borelli, "Academician" of the "Cimento," was able to show that a body moving along a closed curve tended to move away from the center, and that for the planets one could surmise that they were held by an attraction toward the sun. This conception is one of the first to consider a force, acting at a distance, which holds the celestial bodies in their orbits. Huygens, though not actually referring to astronomical problems, made another step forward and found the numerical expression of centrifugal force. About the same time Newton, a student at Trinity College in Cambridge, had occasion to buy a book on astrology at a book fair, and seems then to have been persuaded to study astronomy. Even if this episode is not true, it is certain that his great physical-mathematical faculties would have led him, as happened to Galileo in regard to the Copernican system, to study the mysterious, fascinating problem of the motions of the planets. The experimental fact that every body raised to any height above the surface of the earth falls toward the center of earth if not held back led Newton to conjecture whether perchance the same unknown force held the moon in its monthly circuit around the earth.

APPLICATIONS OF KEPLER'S THIRD LAW

Kepler had already announced his laws, which prove the "moving power" of the sun. Newton, by using the third law, was able to show that the planetary motions which obey this third law could be explained by an action of the sun, supposing that the sun attracts the planets with a force inversely proportional to the square of the distance between them. It was then natural to wonder whether the earth exerted a similar force on the moon, and to investigate whether the unknown force, acting at the distance of the moon from the earth, was of the amount necessary to maintain the moon in its orbit. In this way Newton found that the moon during its motion around the earth, in order to remain in its orbit, had to move for every minute of time through a distance of 13 feet. But, knowing the distance covered by a heavy body at the surface of the earth in the unit of time and comparing it to the supposed distance of the moon, on the hypothesis that the force decreased as the inverse square of the distance, Newton found that a body at the distance of the moon would have to cover during one minute a distance of 15 feet. A less rigorous scientist would have been satisfied with the resulting proof, but Newton instead believed that the discrepancy between the two numbers was too large, and he abandoned the investigation for the time being. A few years later Newton entered into a discussion with his rival, the encyclopedic secretary of the Royal Society, Robert Hooke, on the curve described by a body falling from a certain height. On this occasion Newton again examined the problem of the moon. Since he then had a much more accurate value of the earth's radius than the one used in his first calculations—the measurement of a degree of latitude having been made at that time in France—he established the perfect equality of the two results, thus proving that his hypothesis was valid. According to Professor Andrade, the cause of the discrepancy found by Newton was something else when he put his work aside. To find the pull of the moon from that on bodies at the earth's surface, it is essential to show that the gravitational pull of a spherical earth is the same as it would be if the whole mass were concentrated at the center. This is true only for an inverse square law of attraction and for no other. It gave Newton some trouble to prove this point, which is the subject of a proposition in the *Principia*. This seems to be the reason why, having found that "it answered pretty nearly" Newton turned to other things. An essential link in the argument was missing, and this, it seems, was not produced by him until 1685.

LAW OF GRAVITATION AND THE "PRINCIPIA"

After several more years Christopher Wren, professor of astronomy at Oxford, but much better known as an architect, and Edmund Halley, who was later the Astronomer Royal at Greenwich, had occasion to examine and discuss with Hooke the law of gravitation, and they tried to construct the trajectory which a body would describe under a variable attraction according to the second law. Since he was unable to find a solution, Halley resolved to visit Newton to ask him what form the planetary orbits must assume on the hypothesis that the force of attraction decreases with the square of the distance. Newton immediately replied: "Ellipses," and on being questioned by Halley about the reason for his answer he replied: "Why, I have calculated it." He then sent Halley his proof and at the end of 1684 Halley announced to the Royal Society that he had visited Newton in Cambridge and seen his treatise *De Motu* which was the nucleus of his fundamental work, *Philosophiae Naturalis Principia Mathematica*. It was published in London three years later, although Hooke claimed the right of priority in the great discovery. Few of Newton's contemporaries were able to understand the work and Huygens himself maintained that the concept of gravitation was absurd. But Newton, in his immortal work, after expressing his opinion of scholastic vanities and subtleties, applies the mathematical calculus to the study of natural phenomena and treats rectilinear and curved motions along conic sections. He is able to give a single proof of the theorem of areas for all cases of variation of the central force, and in the first book of the *Principia* he reaches the celebrated conclusion that if every point attracts every other point, with an inverse square law, the attractive mass of a homogenous sphere may be considered as concentrated at the center.

In the third book, entitled *De Mundi Systemate*, Newton establishes the law of universal gravitation with its many consequences, and lays the foundation for the theory of the motions of comets. He thus resumes, completes, and extends the concepts expressed by Galileo, and places on solid mathematical foundations the principles of dynamics and the theory of universal gravitation, together with the general laws of motion. He introduces the concept of mass, and establishes with his law the motions of the planets around the sun. He finds again as a logical consequence the laws of Kepler, and in particular the laws discovered by Galileo, which are true for gravitational effects at the surface of the earth. He also finds, as a consequence of his discovery, the explanation of the mutual perturbations of the planets and proves that a material sphere, whose density is uniformly distributed with respect to the center, acts on external bodies as if all its mass were concentrated at the center. The modern theory of relativity, which has been incorrectly declared to take the place of Newton's law, leaves it practically unchanged, since it is true within the limits of the small velocities of the masses in question.

After Newton's discovery it was possible for the first time to determine the masses of certain celestial bodies, by comparing their attractions on other bodies with the earth's attraction on the moon. From the attraction exerted by Jupiter on its outermost satellite, Newton determined the mass of this planet in comparison with the mass of the earth, and the same for Saturn. Similarly a comparison of Venus' motion around the sun gave him a relation between the masses of the sun and the earth. This method could not be applied to Venus and Mercury, since it was necessary to observe some other body attracted by one of the planets whose mass is to be determined.

Newton proved also that in any system of bodies like the solar system there exists a certain point called the "center of gravity" or "center of mass," which can be considered at rest. The measurements of Cassini and Richer had proved that the earth is not a perfect sphere, and Newton proved this fact to be a consequence of the mutual gravitation of the particles which form the earth and a consequence of the earth's rotation. By imagining two streams of water, one of which traverses the earth from the pole to the center, the other from the center to a point on the equator, Newton calculated the conditions under which the two streams of water, both attracted toward the center of the earth, are in equilibrium. He thus obtained a sufficiently approximate value for the flattening of the earth's poles. He also computed the depression of Jupiter, which four years later was determined observationally by Cassini. The phenomenon of precession, so mysterious until that time, was explained by Newton by the attractive forces of the sun and moon on the sphere of the earth flattened at the poles. This attraction resulted in a motion of the earth's axis with the same general characteristics as precession. Newton's value of precession agrees well with the observed value, but this agreement is due to the accidental compensation of two errors, derived from the imperfect knowledge of the form of the earth and of the distance of the sun and the mass of the moon.

Newton also gave an explanation of the tides, already surmised but not proved by his predecessors, and he showed that the tides are caused by solar and lunar attractions on the liquid masses of the earth. He considered the lunar effect to be the larger, because the moon is closer to the earth. He concluded that the two fluxes take place, because of the rotation of the moon around the earth, with an average retardation of approximately 50 minutes a day, a result which agrees with observation. When the solar and lunar attractions are added together, the tides are the highest. Comparing the lifting forces of the tides, due to the sun and the moon, Newton thought to obtain the mass of the moon as a function of the mass of the sun, and consequently as a function of the mass of the earth. He obtained a value about twice as large as the one known today, for his theory of tides was based on certain premises which afterward had to be modified. This value, at that time, however, was certainly new and remarkable.

Although Tycho, Kepler, and Galileo recognized that comets were celestial bodies, they were unable to explain their appearances, their motions, and their disappearances. In the *Principia* Newton treats the comets as planets, and proves that they must describe conic sections around the sun, thus explaining their periodic returns. As the simplest example he employed the parabola and computed the orbit of the first comet of 1680, which well represented the observations. This discovery, that the comets are bodies of the solar system, was certainly one of the greatest of that epoch. The physical nature of comets interested Newton, and he came to the conclusion that the tail must be formed by a flow of minute particles, like smoke on the earth, which emanate from the head of the comet under the influence of the solar rays. This explanation agrees substantially with modern theories.

During the years when Newton was writing the *Principia*, he corresponded actively with John Flamsteed, Halley's predecessor as Astronomer Royal and Director of the Greenwich Observatory, about astronomical matters. In addition to those mentioned above, he discussed the motion of the satellites of Jupiter and Saturn, and the difference between the observed positions of Saturn and the ones computed from Kepler's tables at the time of Saturn's conjunction with Jupiter. Newton had foreseen the strong attractive force of Jupiter upon other smaller planets.

Halley, who had concerned himself so much in the printing of the first edition of the *Principia*, wrote to Newton in 1687: "I hope you will not repent you of the pains you have taken in so laudable a piece, so much to your own and the nation's credit, but rather, after you shall have a little diverted yourself with other studies, that you will resume those contemplations wherein you had so great success, and attempt the perfection of the lunar theory, which will be of

prodigious use in navigation, as well of profound and public speculation."

This in fact happened, because as soon as the first edition was
completed Newton began to prepare the second, for he was anxious
to improve the theory of the moon and planets.

DETERMINATION OF LONGITUDE AT SEA

The problem of determining longitude at sea, which had
troubled Galileo for so many years, was still unsolved in 1714, so
that in the House of Commons a petition was presented on the subject by captains of Her Majesty's fighting and cargo vessels and by
London merchants. Newton was sought, who recalled the possible
methods and criticized them all—clocks which could keep accurate
time, eclipses of Jupiter's satellites, lunar observations. It was therefore decided, as had already been done at the time of Galileo by the
States-General of Holland, to offer a reward, of an amount proportional to the degree of accuracy of the new method, to the person
who would discover and prove it. A method was developed several
years later with the invention of portable chronometers; meanwhile
Newton had also given attention to the reflecting sextant for the
observation of celestial bodies during navigation. He communicated
his idea to Halley without publishing it, and the description was
found among Newton's papers after his death.

REFLECTORS AND REFRACTORS

Astronomy owes much to Newton for his part in the invention of the mirror telescope, the "reflector," and for his studies of
the dispersion of light through prisms, the basis of spectrum analysis.
Although Newton did not apply these ideas to the celestial bodies,
he was among the first to open up this new field, so rich in results
in times much later than his. It is strange that, while he was experimenting with lenses and prisms, he did not see the absorption lines
of the solar spectrum discovered so many years later by Fraunhofer
and that he did not notice the different dispersing powers of the various qualities of glass. It was actually this last fact which led him to
deny the possibility of "achromatizing" the ordinary refractor objectives, that is, the telescopes of the Galileian type. He was thus induced to consider mirrors instead of lenses, and he invented the re-

flector which bears his name. By working on a metal surface which could be well polished and had a high reflecting power, he succeeded in making a parabolic mirror which gave excellent images of a star along the axis of the mirror, devoid of any coloration due to the instrument. Thus by 1672 the first reflecting telescopes had been built, and while Galileo's disciples were building objectives of larger aperture and with only one lens, which naturally caused a large chromatic aberration, mirrors of ever larger dimensions were being constructed. The fight between reflectors and refractors was under way, and in the following pages we shall see how it developed and where it stands today. Newton claimed that he saw and showed to his acquaintances the four Medicean planets and the phases of Venus with his first modest reflector, and that later he built a better one especially for objects observed in the daytime. He experimented on the nature and properties of light and color, but there is no evidence that he employed his telescope for systematic astronomical observations. He used instead the observations communicated to him from the Greenwich Observatory for his computations and theories.

Although the *Principia* was circulated widely and was of great interest to the scientists of the time, the concept that a powerful influence could exist between celestial bodies separated by an empty space seemed unacceptable to many of the scientists, who did not consider the importance of the perfect agreement with the observed facts. Especially on the Continent, nearly half a century elapsed before the great importance of Newton's works was known and appreciated. Their importance is really very great if we consider the results and the explanations given for a complex of celestial and terrestrial phenomena all dependent on one universal cause, even if we cannot know its innermost essence. As Newton himself wrote in a letter to R. Bentley a few years after the publication of the *Principia*: "You sometimes speak of gravity as essential and inherent to matter. Pray do not ascribe that notion to me; for the cause of gravity I do not pretend to know and therefore would take some time to consider it." This and other passages, both in the *Principia* and the *Optics*, make clear what Newton meant when he wrote: *Hypotheses non fingo*. He always made hypotheses in the modern sense, never willingly speculating beyond the limits where quantitative confirmation could be sought from nature.

FLAMSTEED, FIRST ASTRONOMER ROYAL

About seven years after the founding of the Paris Observatory, the Greenwich Observatory was built by Christopher Wren, by order of Charles II, for the principal purpose of finding a practical and precise method for the determination of longitude. John Flamsteed, who had previously discussed the methods which had been presented for examination to the English government, was called to the new office of Astronomer Royal. He understood that, in order to find a concrete solution of the complicated problem, it was necessary to have stellar catalogs and lunar tables, based on better observations than the existing ones. Thus in the new observatory, even with imperfect instruments which he assembled with the help of benefactors and also at his own expense, he started to work with enthusiasm and steadfastness. Over a period of thirty-three years he made an immense number of observations, whose results are collected in his *Historia Coelestis Britannica,* published in 1712 at the expense of Prince George of Denmark. Flamsteed devised several new methods of observation, among them a method for the determination of the co-ordinates of the first point of Aries. He was the first to use systematically a really accurate timepiece and optical means for the precise determination of stellar co-ordinates. He thus founded a new school of celestial observations, which were much more accurate than those of his predecessors. After making the observations it was necessary to find methods to reduce them and to obtain the best results, a task which Flamsteed set about with painstaking care. The length of time he required troubled Newton, who was impatient to prove his theories and was anxiously awaiting the results of the long series of observations made by the Astronomer Royal.

The "Celestial History" of Flamsteed contains his observations of fixed stars, planets, comets, sunspots, and Jupiter's satellites. A historical note follows, in which he gives a description of the instruments used by Tycho and by himself, as well as the catalogs of the fixed stars of Ptolemy, Ulugh Begh, Tycho, and Hevel, together with the "British Catalogue," which contains the co-ordinates of 2884 stars. Flamsteed excels in this work, for he was the first to introduce in common usage meridian observations of the right ascension of the sun and stars. He also explained the real principles of the equation of time, and he improved the lunar tables by introducing the annual equation. In order to have an idea of the great progress made in the determination of the positions of celestial bodies, it is enough to say that whereas Tycho could guarantee an accuracy within 1', the positions of Flamsteed contain errors of the order of only 10".

HALLEY, SECOND ASTRONOMER ROYAL

Edmund Halley succeeded the first Astronomer Royal. Born in 1656, he had already at twenty years of age gone to St. Helena to make observations of the stars in the Southern Hemisphere. The place was not a happy choice, on account of poor meteorological conditions. Nonetheless he succeeded in determining the co-ordinates of 360 southern stars, an accomplishment which awarded him the title of "austral Tycho." He was able to observe there a transit of Mercury across the sun, whose data suggested to him an important method of calculating the distance of the sun. Following his return to Europe he had occasion to observe with Cassini in Paris the great comet of 1680 after its passage at perihelion. Afterward he met Newton and collaborated with him on the *Principia*, especially on the part which treats of comets. Halley's researches on these celestial bodies, collected in his *Synopsis Astronomiae Cometicae*, represent his greatest contribution to astronomy, one of the most important since the time of Kepler. In this work he expounds original and profound ideas on the motions of comets. He proves that they must belong to the solar system and that they move around the sun in eccentric orbits, appearing visible when they are close to the sun. After calculating the orbits of several comets whose past observations he had collected, he noted the similarity of four orbits traversed by the comets of 1456, 1531, 1607, and 1682. He deduced that they must represent one periodic comet which travels along an extremely eccentric ellipse in the course of seventy-five years, and he predicted its return in future years. It is the very comet which bears Halley's name, but he did not live to see its return, predicted for 1758.

Succeeding Flamsteed at sixty-three years of age, Halley undertook lunar observations at the Greenwich Observatory to improve the theory of the moon, and he discovered the secular acceleration of its mean motion, whose cause was explained later by Laplace.

Halley understood that the transits of Venus across the sun would be more useful than those of Mercury in the determination of the distance of the sun. He emphasized the transit of Venus in 1761 and indicated the most advantageous methods and localities for its observation. The values of the sun's distance, as known at Halley's time, differed from one another by 20 to 30 per cent, whereas the new method, according to his predictions and provided the times of the transit of Venus were observed from different localities on the earth, would result in an error about one hundred times smaller, given the existing limits of accuracy. Until the time of Halley it was believed that the fixed stars never changed their relative positions. He discovered that at least three of the brightest stars in our hemisphere, Sirius, Procyon, and Arcturus, had shifted from the times of the Greeks by small angles which could not be caused by an ecliptic motion, such as precession. Halley foresaw that this phenomenon was general and more or less considerable, because of the effect of the different distances of the so-called "fixed" stars, and he discovered what were later called the "proper motions." We have also an interesting account of the total eclipse of the sun in 1715, in which he describes not only the mysterious "corona," but also the underlying solar envelope which radiates a dark red light, afterward called the "chromosphere."

The ever increasing precision which was attained in the determination of stellar positions with rapidly improving instruments and timepieces gave hope that it would be possible to determine the annual parallaxes of some of the stars closest to the solar system. In fact, at that time (1704) Olaus Roemer invented a type of meridian circle with a micrometer of illuminated threads, and later (1756) John Dollond constructed the first achromatic lenses. But attempts in this direction could not yet achieve any results because of the great distance of the stars and consequently the small parallax angles to be measured. However, other more remarkable changes, due to causes previously unknown, were discovered. Picard had already noticed an annual periodic motion of the Pole Star amounting to approximately 40″, which he was unable to explain. Flamsteed thought it was due to parallax, but Cassini proved that could not be the cause. James Bradley solved the mystery with his memorable discoveries, and was named third Astronomer Royal at Greenwich to succeed Halley.

BRADLEY, THIRD ASTRONOMER ROYAL

From his youth, though embarked on an ecclesiastical career, Bradley had a passion for astronomical observations, which were under the guidance of his uncle, the Reverend James Pound. In 1721, at the age of twenty-nine, he obtained the professorship of astronomy at Oxford. Always with the idea of finding a parallactic motion of the stars which would mirror the earth's motion around the sun, Bradley, in collaboration with his friend Samuel Molyneux, who had devoted himself to optics and astronomy in his private observatory in Kew near London, methodically observed with an almost vertical telescope the star γ Draconis. He was thus able to note small shifts, according to the seasons, of the star northward and southward, which resulted in a small ellipse, whose greater axis measured approximately 40″, as the star returned to the original position. He concluded at once that the effect could not be a parallactic motion, because the observed displacements were 90° out of phase from what they should have been according to the earth's position on the ecliptic. He resorted to another explanation and in 1728 he was able to announce to the Royal Society his discovery: "At last I conjectured that all the phenomena hitherto mentioned proceeded from the progressive motion of light and the earth's annual motion in its orbit. For I perceived that, if light propagated in time, the apparent place of a fixed object would not be the same when the eye is at rest as when it is moving in any other direction than that of the line passing through the eye and object; and that when the eye is moving in different directions, the apparent place of the object would be different. . . ." He then proceeds to explain geometrically the phenomenon of the "aberration of light" as it is still explained today, and he observes that it could not occur if the velocity of light were infinite.

Bradley established that the maximum value of aberration, that is, the "constant of aberration," must be between 20″ and 20.5″. The value adopted today is 20.47″. He found the time required by light to travel from the sun to the earth, and he confirmed the value obtained by Roemer with the observation of the eclipses of Jupiter's satellites. Continuing his observations for the verification of his theory, Bradley was forced to conclude that the correction introduced for aberration left some inexplicable residues, which he immediately suspected were dependent on another cause, for he had noted that the error increased for nine years and then decreased regularly for nine years. This period, equal to that required by the nodes of the moon to circle the ecliptic and return to their original position, was explained by Bradley in the following manner:

When I considered these circumstances, and the situation of the ascending node of the moon's orbit, at the time when I first began my observations, I suspected that the moon's action upon the equatorial parts of the earth might produce these effects: for if the precession of the equinox be, according to Sir Isaac Newton's principles, caused by the actions of the sun and moon upon those parts, the plane of the moon's orbit being at one time above ten degrees more inclined to the plane of the equator than another, it was reasonable to conclude that the part of the whole annual precession which arises from her action would in different years be varied in its quantity; whereas the plane of the ecliptic, wherein the sun appears, keeping always nearly the same inclination to the equator, that part of the precession which is owing to the sun's action may be the same every year: and from hence it would follow, that although the mean annual precession, proceeding from the joint action of the sun and moon, were 50″, yet the apparent annual precession might sometimes exceed, and sometimes fall short of that mean quantity, according to the various situations of the nodes of the moon's orbit. . . ."

Thus the second discovery of Bradley was announced as a small oscillation of the earth's axis caused by the moon's attraction on the bulging equator of the earth's spheroid. After having carefully observed this effect for twenty years, Bradley found that the phenomena were well represented by attributing to the pole a retrograde motion, completed in a period of eighteen years, about its mean position, along a small ellipse whose axes measured 18″ and 16″.

He observed for several years the eclipses of Jupiter's satellites, discovering new particulars which enabled him to improve the tables of Cassini. Although he realized that the mathematical treatment was not yet sufficient to represent their motion accurately, he was able to determine with remarkable precision, following the method of Galileo, the longitude of Lisbon and New York with respect to Greenwich. After 1749, when he was able to procure more accurate instruments, with the "mural quadrant" and the "transit instrument" he gathered a great mass of useful observations, which were published after his death. Later on Bessel emphasized their great importance in his *Fundamenta Astronomiae*, which contains a catalog of more than 3000 stars, based on Bradley's observations, of which he calculated the errors. On the average these errors were less than 4" in declination and 15" in right ascension.

FRENCH ASTRONOMERS

Meanwhile in France Gian Domenico Cassini had passed away, but his great personality lived on through his direct descendants. Though they did not equal his fame, they kept high the name of the family for many years. Giacomo Cassini, Sieur de Thury and assistant to his father, helped him in the great series of his works and continued them after his death, as "Academician" of astronomical and geodetical works. He set about to improve the meridian sundial of the Paris Observatory in order to give its gnomon ten times the length of Picard's pendulum, and thus he established an invariable and constant measure which was called the "toise of the Cassinis."

The times were now ready for a precise determination of the size and shape of the earth, which were then quite uncertain. Giacomo Cassini, assisted by Maraldi and de la Hire, in 1718 measured the arc between Dunkerque and Montdidier, thus completing the measurement of the meridian which had been begun by Picard and continued by Cassini's father. About twenty years later Giacomo's son, Cesare Francesco Cassini III, with Maraldi and Lacaille, verified the meridian of France by means of a triangulation, which was also employed for the tracing of a complete topographic map of the kingdom known under the name of "Cassini's map." This verification had become necessary because, contrary to the results obtained from the oscillations of the pendulum and the theoretical researches of Newton, the measurement of meridian arcs at different latitudes led to the conclusion that the earth was bulged at the poles and was flattened at the equator. This conclusion was especially maintained by Cassini's school.

Nicolas Louis de Lacaille, active and eager assistant at the Paris Observatory, corrected the anomalous result obtained by G. D. Cassini in 1684, and was appointed professor of mathematics at the Mazarin College, where he was able to continue his astronomical observations in a small observatory connected with the college. Convinced of the necessity of obtaining positions of the southern stars, he led an expedition, organized by the Academy of Science, to the Cape of Good Hope with the principal goal of determining the solar

1   Egyptian terra cotta piece, showing signs of the
    zodiac as used by Greek scholars in Alexandria.
    Courtesy of The American Museum of Natural
    History.

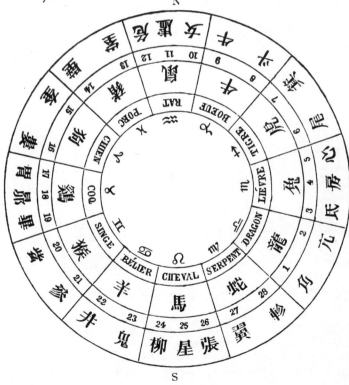

2   12 signs of the Chinese zodiac.

3   Woodcut of The Observatory at Pekin, China.

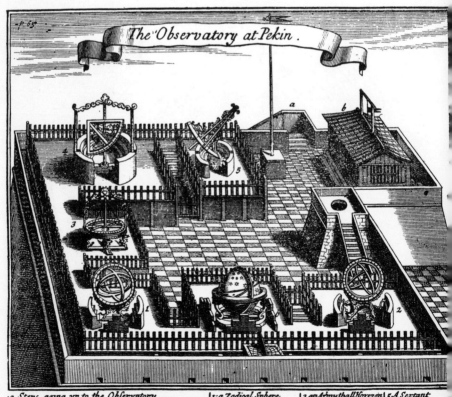

The Observatory at Pekin.

a. Steps going vp to the Observatory   1: a Zodical Sphere   3 an Azmuthall Horizon 5 A Sextant
b. A Retiring Room for those that make Observations 2 an Equinoctial Sphere   4. a Quadrant   6 a Celestiall Glob

4   *The Observatory at Jaipur, India, 1724 AD;
Planetarium diorama. Courtesy of The American Museum of Natural History.*

5 Above: *Copernicus. Courtesy of Yerkes Observatory.*

6 *Opposite above: The Copernican System.*

7 *Opposite below: The Ptolemaic System.*

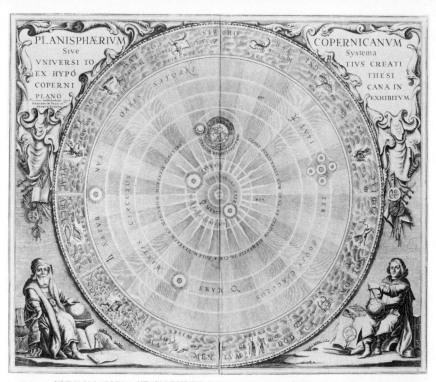

PLANISPHÆRIVM COPERNICANVM Sive Systema VNIVERSI TOTIVS CREATI EX HYPÓ THESI COPERNI CANA IN PLANO EXHIBITVM.

PLANISPHÆRIVM PTOLEMAICVM Sive Machina ORBIVM MVNDI EX HYPOTHESI PTOLEMAICA IN PLANO DISPOSITA.

8   Above: Silver Star Globe, attributed to Tycho Brahe.

9   Opposite: Detail of Silver Star Globe attributed to Tycho Brahe, Sweden, about 400 years old. Courtesty of The American Museum of Natural History.

Stellarum

Primæ
Secundæ
Tertiæ
Quartæ
Quintæ
Sextæ
Nebulosæ

Globus Cœlestis
In quo stellæ fixæ omnes quæ
à viro Tychone Brahæ suma in
dustria ac cura observatæ sunt,
accuratißime designantur: nec
non circa Polum Austr: quæ
à Peritiß. nauclero Petro
Theodori Mathescos studioso
annotatæ sunt.

CANCER

Castor aut Apollo

Pollux aliis Hercules

GEMINI

69

30   10   30

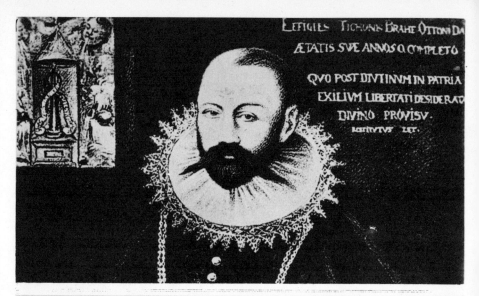

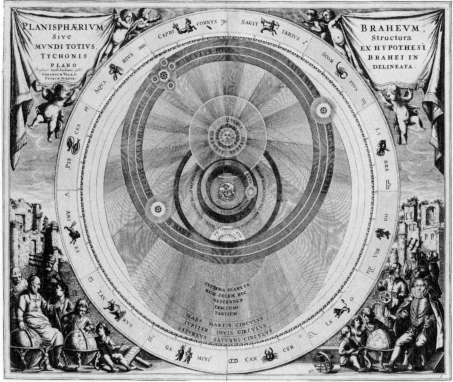

10   *Above: Tycho Brahe. Courtesy of Yerkes Ob-*
       servatory.

11   *Below: The "Tychonic System."*

12   *Armillary Sphere with wooden base, Tycho Brahe, ca. 1590. Photograph of a model made by Laurits C. Eichner. Courtesy Eichner Instruments.*

13   *Above: Some of the Saints in the Sky, as pictured by the Ancients.*

14   *Opposite above: Galileo. Courtesy of Yerkes Observatory.*

15   *Opposite below: Kepler. Courtesy of Yerkes Observatory.*

16   Above left: German Astrolabe, 1591. Made by
      Reinhold—antedates the Gregorian Calendar by
      one year, and gives the vernal equinox as March
      10th. Courtesy of The American Museum of
      Natural History.

17   Above center: French Universal Ring Dial made
      by Chapotot, Paris, about 1600. Courtesy of The
      American Museum of Natural History.

18   Above right: Quadrant, Tyrolean, date about
      1600. Courtesy of The American Museum of
      Natural History.

19   Below: Hevelius with a quadrant, one of his 17th
      century observing instruments.

20   *Hevelius and his wife measuring stellar altitudes.*

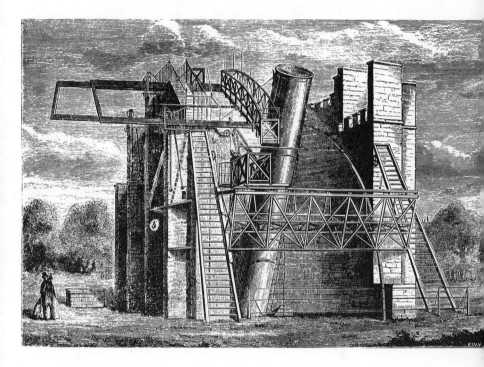

21   *Opposite above: Isaac Newton. Courtesy of Yerkes Observatory.*

22   *Opposite below: Eichner model of Newtonian telescope.*

23   *Above: Lord Rosse's Great Telescope.*

24   *Above: A view of The Inhabitants of The Moon as seen through the telescope of Sir John Herschel.*

25   *Opposite above: William Herschel. Courtesy of Yerkes Observatory.*

26   *Sir William Herschel's 40 ft. reflecting telescope*

27 *Giovanni Virginio Schiaparelli, famous Italian Astronomer.*

28   *Halley's Comet, 1910; May 12th and 15th. Courtesy of The Mount Wilson and Palomar Observatories*

29   *Albert Einstein. Photo by Lotti Jacobi.*

30   *A. S. Eddington. Courtesy of Yerkes Observatory.*

31   Above: A Giant Bolide or Meteor, Prague, Czechoslovakia.

32   Opposite: Spectograph attached to the 100″ telescope at Mount Wilson Observatory.

33   *Dome of the 72" reflection telescope, Dominion Observatory, Victoria, B.C.*

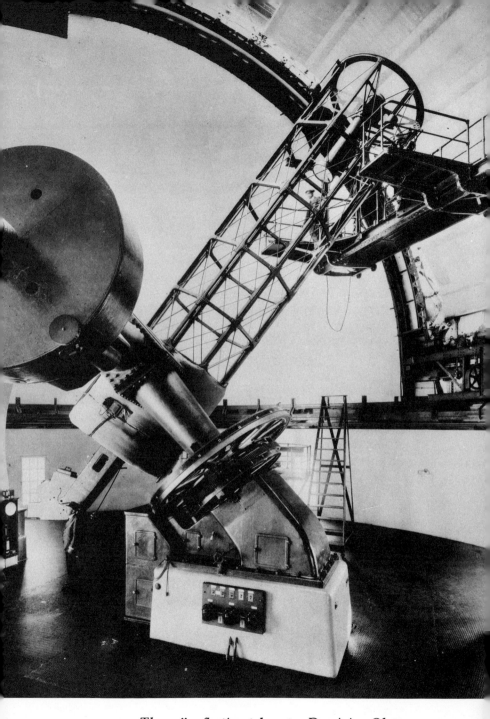

34   *The 72″ reflection telescope, Dominion Observatory, Victoria, B.C.*

35 *The Dome of the 26″ telescope of The Naval Observatory, Washington, D.C.*

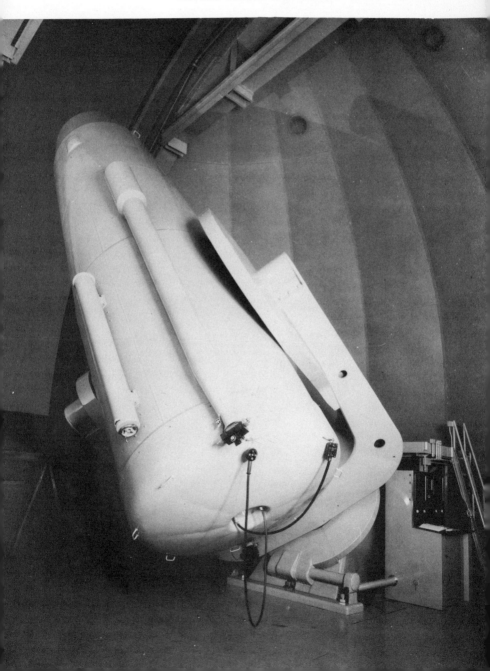

37   *The 60 ft. dome, and 150 ft. tower telescopes
from the balcony of the Hooker Telescope
Dome. Courtesy of The Mount Wilson and
Palomar Observatories.*

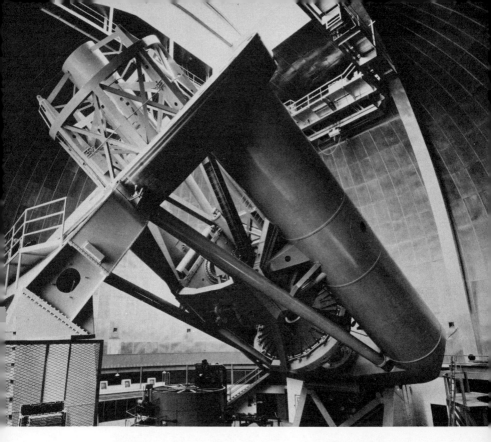

38   *The 200″ Hale telescope. Courtesy of The Mount Wilson and Palomar Observatories.*

39   *The 200″ Hale telescope pointing to zenith.
Courtesy of The Mount Wilson and Palomar
Observatories.*

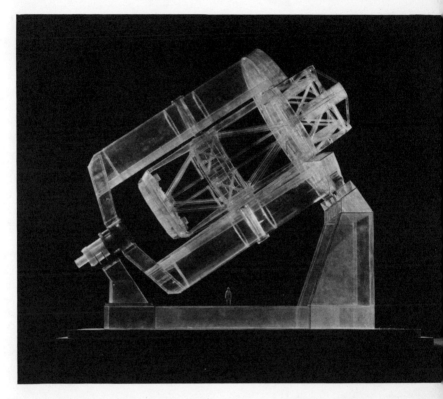

40 A Miniature model of the 200″ Hale telescope.
Courtesy of The American Museum of Natural
History.

41 *The Dome of the 200″ Hale reflector showing entrance. Courtesy of The Mount Wilson and Palomar Observatories.*

parallax by observations of the parallaxes of Mars and Venus while similar observations were being made in Europe, and of compiling a catalog of circumpolar southern stars. With his extraordinary activity, in only one year, without assistants, he observed 10,000 stars and published the co-ordinates of about 2000 of them in his *Coelum Australe Stelliferum* in 1763. He also found time for numerous experiments with the pendulum at the Cape and at Mauritius and for the measurements of a meridian arc which comprised a little more than one degree, all in order to determine the flattening of the earth. Furthermore, he made observations of the moon at the same time as Lalande in Berlin, in order to determine its parallax by direct observations made at the extremities of a meridian arc more than 85° apart. He made considerable progress in the theory of celestial refraction. In 1757 he published his *Astronomiae Fundamenta,* which comprised a catalog of 400 of the brightest stars, executed with considerable accuracy, greater than that of his predecessors and equal to that of Bradley.

The problem of the shape of the earth increasingly attracted the attention of eighteenth century astronomers. The French Academy of Sciences, wishing to find the solution, decided to measure the length of two arcs, one at the equator and one at the highest accessible latitude. In 1735 three French astronomers, Pierre Bouguer, Charles Marie de la Condamine, and Louis Godin, were commissioned by the French government to measure an arc of approximately 3°, close to the equator in Peru. This project was accomplished after ten years of work, along with pendulum determinations and other scientific works. For the high-latitude arc, another expedition led by Pierre Louis Moreau de Maupertuis went to Lapland the following year. They measured an arc of about 1°, close to the Arctic Circle. Bouguer published the results of the Peruvian measurements in his classic work *La Figure de la Terre,* in which he plainly proves that the length of a meridian arc increases with increasing latitude, and he gives the value of the ellipticity as derived from a comparison of three arcs, one in Peru at 2° South Latitude, one in France at about 47° North Latitude, and one in Lapland at 60° North Latitude. The accuracy of Newton's theoretical calculations was therefore confirmed. Furthermore, Bradley communicated the results of his determinations of terrestrial gravity, derived from the length of a pendulum which vibrates in one second, and the effects of the attraction of mountains on the vertical.

MASKELYNE, SUCCESSOR TO BRADLEY

Nevil Maskelyne, Astronomer Royal at Greenwich, observed in 1774 the direction of a plumb-line on either side of a mountain in Perthshire, in order to determine, by comparison with the attraction of the whole earth, the earth's density and consequently its mass. For the former he found the value of 4.5 times the density of water, whereas Newton, basing his work only on general considerations, had already found a value closer to the true one. Henry Cavendish, more than twenty years later, was able to obtain more exact measurements, making use of the attraction of two heavy balls instead of the attraction of mountains.

In order to realize the plans of his predecessor Halley, Maskelyne was sent by the British government to the island of St. Helena to observe the transit of Venus and also to verify the existence of a small parallax of Sirius which seemed to appear in Lacaille's observations at the Cape. The weather prevented observation of the transit, and a faulty instrument, a zenith sector used for this purpose, interfered with the observations of Sirius. But other expeditions were sent throughout the world by various nations, not only for the transit of 1761 but also for the one of 1769, in order to solve the important problem of determining the "astronomical unit" with the greatest possible accuracy. The results agreed more with the predictions of Lacaille than with those of Halley, although considerable deviations were found, especially in the results obtained from the first transit. For the second transit, more accurate measurements gave a value for the parallax of the sun between 8″ and 9″. Later all these observations were discussed by J. F. Encke, who deduced a parallax of 8.57″.

On his trip to St. Helena, Maskelyne made many observations to try out the various methods which had been proposed for the determination of longitude at sea. He preferred the method of measuring with the sextant the distances of known stars from the moon. After his return to Greenwich he proposed to the Navy the adoption of this method and, to facillitate its acceptance, he prepared tables which he published annually in the *Nautical Almanac*.

About the same time the English watchmaker, James Harrison, succeeded in making a portable clock which could withstand the sea despite the motions of the ship and the considerable variations in temperature. This was the "marine chronometer" which he was able to perfect after a long labor of thirty years. He gave it to Maskelyne to test on a trip made to the island of Barbados in 1763. Maskelyne was able to determine the longitude of Barbados within 1', while the method of lunar distances entailed inaccuracies of 4'. In this way one could say that the difficult problem had been solved; Harrison received rich rewards for his labors, and prizes were also given to astronomers like Leonhard Euler and Tobias Mayer for their theoretical investigations of the motion of the moon.

TOBIAS MAYER, OF GÖTTINGEN

Tobias Mayer, director of the Observatory of Göttingen and professor at the same university, also a diligent and accurate observer, invented some practical methods for correcting instrumental errors in observations. He improved Lacaille's tables of the sun and compiled a catalog of about a thousand zodiacal stars, whose proper motions he determined by comparing the positions given by Roemer and by Lacaille. He made theoretical and practical studies of the moon to contribute to the solution of the problem of longitude and to study the moon's physical surface. He traced a detailed selenographic map and gave a complete geometric explanation of the various librations of the moon, establishing with precision the position of its axis. Mayer, starting with the theoretical works of Euler, compared the latter's lunar tables with observations, and he published new tables in 1752, together with instructions for their use in the determination of longitude at sea. He also revised the theory to improve the coefficients which appeared in the equations, and he computed still newer tables more precise than his previous ones, which won him one of the prizes offered by the British government.

While such progress was being made in the field of observational astronomy, other important developments resulted from Newton's discoveries in the theoretical study of the motion of celestial bodies, that is, in that branch of astronomy which is customarily called "celestial mechanics."

III : THE MODERN ERA

13 : Newton's successors

ON THE BASIS OF NEWTON'S WORKS AND DIS-
coveries, the planetary motions began to be quite well established
at the beginning of the eighteenth century. However, there was still
the general problem, as yet unsolved, of determining the planetary
positions at any time on the basis of universal gravitation, together
with further development of theory and calculation, and of comparing these positions with the actually observed ones. Such information
would have made it possible to compute, for the different planets,
the "ephemerides," which are so useful and necessary even for everyday purposes. As is well known, the general problem cannot be solved
by rigorous mathematical methods in the simplest case of three
bodies which mutually attract one another, and therefore it is necessary to use successive approximations. These bring good results, especially in the case of the solar system where the mass of the sun is so
much greater than, and therefore prevails over, the sum of the
masses of all the planets, so that the latter can be almost neglected.
The problem is further simplified by the fact that the orbits of the
planets and their satellites are nearly circular and not much inclined
to the ecliptic.

Many astronomers have occupied themselves with the theory of
the moon, which is complicated by the relative closeness of our
satellite. The planetary theories are less involved because of the
much greater distance of the sun from the planets. Consequently in
the problems of celestial mechanics the theory of the moon is treated

by itself. Voltaire's book "The Elements of Newton's Philosophy" spread Newton's ideas abroad and favored their development, which followed from the work of great mathematicians such as Euler, Clairaut, d'Alembert, Lagrange, and Laplace.

LEONHARD EULER

Leonhard Euler, born in Basel (Switzerland) in 1707, started to study theology, but he was led to the mathematical sciences by Jacques Bernouilli. He then devoted himself entirely to such sciences and applied them particularly to theoretical astronomy. He was invited to St. Petersburg to collaborate with the Russian Academy of Sciences, then recently founded, and later transferred to the Academy in Berlin. Afterwards he returned in 1766 to Russia, where he had been invited by the empress Catherine II. He lived until 1783; he was blind for the last seventeen years, during which his extraordinary scientific activity never diminished, not only in the field of theoretical astronomy but also in other wide fields of the mathematical sciences. In the former it seems that he was the first to note that as a consequence of the law of universal gravitation a planet does not describe an ellipse around the sun, but both sun and planet describe ellipses around their common center of mass. The same is true for a planet and its satellites. Thus the center of mass of the earth-moon system moves along the ecliptic, and the center of the earth will be above or below the ecliptic depending on whether the moon, whose orbit is inclined to the ecliptic, is respectively below or above the ecliptic. He was also one of the first to discuss the difficult problem of the moon by trying to solve the problem of three bodies. His conclusions are in his *Novae Tabulae Motuum Solis et Lunae* and *Theoria Motus Lunae*, published in St. Petersburg in 1753. Several years earlier he had completed a general theory of the motions of planets and comets. He applied these new methods to the comets of 1680 and 1744 and thus opened up new paths in this field of research.

ALEXIS CLAUDE CLAIRAUT

Alexis Claude Clairaut of Paris, a precocious genius, was nominated at a very early age to the Academy of Sciences. After having taken part in the expedition to Lapland led by Maupertuis, he finished his classical work on the shape of the earth. Since the return of Halley's comet was expected in 1758, Clairaut calculated the perturbations of the comet caused by the major planets, Jupiter and Saturn, which it had closely approached in its course. As a result he found the date of its perihelion, which he calculated with an error of plus or minus one month. The comet was in fact seen again on Christmas Day, 1758, one month and a day before the date predicted by Clairaut, thus confirming the brilliant prediction of Halley.

JEAN LE ROND D'ALEMBERT

A formidable rival of Clairaut was Jean le Rond d'Alembert, so called because he had been abandoned at birth on the steps of the church St. Jean le Rond in Paris. He made some remarkable contributions to mechanics and discovered a dynamic principle which bears his name; he also contributed to mathematical physics. In the astronomical field he made investigations of the precession of the equinoxes and of the nutation of the earth's axis, demonstrating the agreement between the theory of these phenomena and the observations of Bradley.

In the problem of three bodies and in particular in the theory of the moon, his researches led him to oppose Euler and Clairaut, and this discussion served to improve the work of all three scientists. They were working at the same time, though almost independently, on the problem of three bodies, applying it in particular to the moon and encountering the same difficulties as had confronted Newton. One could imagine, as Clairaut thought, some insufficiency of the law of universal gravitation, though Clairaut himself noted that if no terms were omitted, the motion of the apogee derived from the theory agreed well with the observed motion. D'Alembert obtained even more accurate results and published a complete theory of the moon, furnished with tables, in the first volume of his *Récherches sur Différents Points Importants du Système du Monde*. Clairaut perhaps was the most successful in his representation of the real motions of the moon, making use of Lacaille's observations and attaining a remarkable degree of accuracy.

The classical methods of Euler have always remained the fundamental ones, even in modern theories like the one of Hill. Euler in fact developed also the method for the treatment of the perturbation which he had already indicated in his first lunar theory, and which is known under the name of "variations of the elements or parameters." When one considers the perturbations, one can no longer consider the planetary orbits as ellipses with the sun at one of the foci. Instead, at different epochs there are ellipses with variable elements, which determine their form and position in space, so that the planets in the course of time actually describe open curves which can no longer be considered closed. Euler considered the perturbed planet as covering arcs of an ellipse with ever varying elements, in order to represent its complicated motion at any time. He showed how the elements of the various successive ellipses can be calculated, if the position of the perturbing planet is known. One can then establish with sufficient accuracy the positions which the planet will assume in the course of time. But the complete explanation of lunar and planetary perturbations became manifest a few years later through the work of two other celebrated mathematicians, Lagrange and Laplace, whose discoveries led to deeper knowledge of gravitational theory and explained away the last non-uniformities in the motion of the celestial bodies.

JOSEPH LOUIS LAGRANGE

Joseph Louis Lagrange, or Lagrangia, descended from a French family which had lived in Italy for three generations. When he was very young, he was appointed professor of mathematics in the Artillery School of Turin. After his works came to the attention of Euler, he was introduced by Euler to the Academy of Berlin. At twenty-eight years of age, in 1764, he won the prize offered by the Paris Academy for research on the problem of lunar libration, by devising new methods for the treatment of the most lofty speculations of dynamics. Shortly afterward he won another prize for a theory of the satellites of Jupiter. In connection with the differential equations of the perturbed motion of a satellite, he discussed the attractive forces of the sun and the other satellites and came to consider the problem of six bodies. The most noteworthy of his various discoveries is that of the invariability of the mean distance of the planets from the sun. Euler had already surmised that the non-uniformities of the motions of Jupiter and Saturn, because of their mutual attraction, would be averaged out after a long period of time. In the particular conditions of the planetary system all the changes to which the planetary orbits are subjected from the mutual attractions are periodic, and therefore the system by itself does not tend toward its destruction but may last forever.

When Euler returned to St. Petersburg, Frederick II wished to have a worthy successor at his court, and he appointed the "greatest mathematician of Europe," Lagrange. Lagrange accepted and spent twenty-one years in Berlin. He tackled the problem of libration, preparing material for his *Mécanique Analytique*, which was published when he was asked by Louis XVI to become a member of the Paris Academy. This work is considered one of the most beautiful mathematical works after the *Principia* of Newton; he perfected the law of universal gravitation, carrying it to the limit of its great possibilities.

PIERRE SIMON LAPLACE

Pierre Simon Laplace, born in Normandy in 1749, was introduced very early to the French scientific world by d'Alembert. He acquired fame with his important discovery of the invariability of the mean distance of the planets from the sun with a hypothesis which was later generalized by Lagrange. Of the numerous perturbations which affect the motion of the moon, there still remained to be explained the acceleration of its mean motion. Halley had first suspected it from a comparison of ancient Babylonian observations, recorded by Hipparchus, with observations of Albatenius and modern ones. The velocity increases 10" every century. Since it could not be explained by Newton's law, Laplace supposed first that gravity was not transmitted from one body to another instantaneously, but in a finite time, like sound and light. But after he had had occasion to note, during his studies of Jupiter's satellites, that the secular variations in the eccentricity of Jupiter's orbit cause a secular variation in the mean motions of the satellites, he applied this result to the moon and was able to discover that the acceleration observed by the astronomers must be due to the secular variation of the eccentricity of the orbit of the earth. Modern investigations have modified Laplace's results and have brought new elements into the complete explanation of these non-uniformities.

The fundamental work of Laplace is his *Mécanique Céleste*, which as a sequel to Newton's *Principia* gives mathematical expression to the calculation of the motions of the celestial bodies. After his death, a second edition was published (1829-1839). When this was out of print, the government of Louis Philippe had the *Oeuvres de Laplace* published in seven volumes. Celestial mechanics is found in the first five, in the sixth is the *Exposition du Système du Monde,* and in the seventh the theory of probability.

Laplace had planned to collect in his treatise the theories which formulate the effects of universal gravitation on the equilibrium and motions of the solid and fluid bodies making up the solar system and similar systems scattered throughout the immensity of the sky. Astronomy, in fact, is a great problem of mechanics where the elements of motions are arbitrary parameters. The solution of the problem depends upon the accuracy of the observations and the perfection of the analysis. It is necessary, Laplace affirms, to banish all empiricism, which no longer has any place in astronomical tables. He was almost able to reach this goal.

The first part of the work contains methods for the calculation of the translational and rotational motions of the celestial bodies, the theory of elliptical motion in its first approximation, the discussion of the form of celestial bodies, and the theory of tides. He discusses further the precession of the equinoxes, the libration of the moon, the shape and rotation of the rings of Saturn and their permanence in the plane of the planet's equator, and the principal non-uniformities of the planets, in particular Jupiter and Saturn, which seem to contradict the law of gravity. In the second part, which begins with an enthusiastic dedication to Napoleon Bonaparte, citizen first consul, he considers in particular the perturbations of the motions of the planets and comets around the sun, of the moon around the earth, and of the satellites around their respective planets. He thus attained the greatest accuracy then possible in astronomical tables.

Although Laplace in his treatise forgets to mention the works of his predecessors, nevertheless it cannot be denied that his contribution to the foundation of celestial mechanics was very great. The investigation of the shape of a rotating fluid in equilibrium occupied his attention for many years. The results of his many studies of this subject, conceded by him to be "one of the most interesting points in the system of the world," are included in his *Mécanique Céleste* and are one of the more notable proofs of his genius. Laplace discussed the subject from the point of view of a gradual aggregation and cooling of a mass of matter, and he proved that the form finally assumed by this mass is an ellipsoid of revolution whose equator is determined by the primitive plane of the maximum areas. Laplace's studies on the subject of attractions have remained classical, for he introduced two powerful analytical methods for the treatment of physical problems, the "coefficents of Laplace" and the "potential function." He reduced the forces of nature to the language of analysis, and laid the foundations of the mathematical and physical sciences.

The well-known theory of Laplace about the origin and formation of the solar system is found in his *Exposition du Système du Monde*, a work which stimulated the progress of scientific thought during the nineteenth century. The theory is explained in a popular manner without the aid of mathematics, and it is like a conclusion of his treatise on celestial mechanics. The procedure adopted by Laplace disguises and hides in the popular exposition all the analytic work previously developed by him. The style is clear and masterful, and the summary of astronomical history which concludes the work is certainly a literary masterpiece. His "Nebular Hypothesis" is discussed in detail and is based on three fundamental facts, at that time without exception in the solar system:

(*a*) The diurnal and annual motions of its components are direct, that is, they take place from west to east;

(*b*) The eccentricities of the orbits of the components are small;

(*c*) The inclination of the orbits to the plane of the ecliptic are also small.

Although the hypothesis is hidden away in a footnote of the *Exposition*—"with the hesitancy and uncertainty which must be inspired by everything which is not a result of observation and calculation"— yet the importance given it by Laplace is immediately evident, from the originality, simplicity, and clarity of the adopted principles. One primordial cause, acting on all the planets, must have produced the three above-mentioned phenomena. Since the planets are separated by relatively large distances, one can admit the existence of more or less dense nebular matter which occupies the whole space until and beyond the orbit of the farthest known planet, Uranus. The formation of the planets would have resulted from the cooling and contraction of the matter. From this an increase of angular velocity follows necessarily, so that at a certain moment the centrifugal force of the outer edge of the rotating nebula overcomes the attraction of the central mass. Thus a first ring would have separated from the nebula, and others successively in a manner similar to what we find in the system of Saturn. From the rotating matter of each ring the satellites would have been similarly formed, since they also lie more or less on the plane of the ecliptic and move in a direct motion. It must be noted that although Laplace mentions Buffon's rough conjecture, it appears that he ignores Kant, who anticipated Buffon's hypothesis up to a certain point.

Laplace's theory, as he himself suspected, cannot be maintained in the light of recent investigations because of dynamical difficulties. The main difficulty is the problem whether a ring of matter of this type would contract into single bodies, and also the fact that the angular momentum of the solar system is distributed 98 per cent to the planets and only 2 per cent to the sun. Yet the ingenious and suggestive hypothesis is still remembered when we speak of the origin of the celestial bodies.

Although Lagrange lived in Berlin and Laplace in Paris, nevertheless their work was always closely connected. They were in continuous correspondence, so that the discoveries and progress of one were used and developed by the other. By means of Laplace's formulas of mechanics, solar and planetary tables were computed and with them it was possible to give the positions of the celestial bodies with generally greater accuracy than preceding tables permitted. The development of celestial mechanics made it possible to compute the masses of the satellites of Mars and Jupiter, and also the mass of Venus. The values of the masses of the moon and the other planets were improved. The irregularities observed in their motions, which seemed to contradict the law of universal gravitation before the time of Laplace and Lagrange, have instead fully proved the accuracy of this law. Ever since their time, the astronomer has been able to go back into the past and forward into the future in determining the positions of the celestial bodies by means of theory and calculation, and to verify the good agreement with observations. Furthermore, changes taking place in the course of the centuries, so minute that they would escape the observer, could be predicted. Naturally a great deal remained to be done, and the progress which has been made since their time is considerable. Yet the foundations of the new science initiated by Newton were and are very basic for future investigations.

14 : observational astronomy: Herschel to Piazzi

PARALLEL TO THE DEVELOPMENT OF CELESTIAL mechanics considerable progress was made in the field of observational astronomy, mostly through the work of a great astronomer who had begun his study for pleasure and a hobby. Astronomical research had been limited, until about the middle of the eighteenth century, to the study of the solar system. Since it was not yet possible to measure the distance of any fixed star, the whole space outside the solar system, which at that time stopped at Saturn, was practically *terra incognita*.

Sir Frederick William Herschel, generally known as Sir William Herschel, born in Hanover in 1738, was by profession a theoretical and practical musician. At a very early age he went to England to practice his profession and he resided there as in a second fatherland. From his faithful sister Caroline, whom he asked to live with him at Bath where he had settled down, we know that the young Herschel read with enthusiasm a treatise on "harmonics," one on optics by Smith, and one on astronomy by Ferguson, and thus he passed from music to the art of building telescopes for observation of the sky.

HERSCHEL'S TELESCOPES

Like Galileo, he built his telescopes himself and made many important discoveries with them. This was the time when the English optician Dollond was perfecting his achromatic lenses, which, however, were rare and expensive. Thus Herschel had to content himself at first with a small "Gregorian" type of reflector with a 2-inch aperture. He soon acquired reflectors of ever larger dimensions, which he laboriously polished by the hundreds, helped by his sister and always obtaining better results. At that time no optical lathes existed and all the work of shaping the parabolic form and polishing the mirror had to be done by hand. One can imagine how much labor and ability were required. Herschel had conceived the ingenious and ambitious plan to go beyond the solar system and discover the structure of the universe. To effect this plan it was necessary to have some point of departure and to have available telescopes of different and ever greater power, in order to observe a volume of space greater than could be observed with the naked eye.

If it is assumed as a first approximation that the stars are of equal luminosity and that their apparent difference of magnitude depends only on their different distances from the solar system, the same star will appear brighter, the greater the area of the mirror of the objective used in its observation. Therefore the brilliance of a star seen through a telescope will be, on the one hand, inversely proportional to the square of its distance and, on the other hand, directly proportional to the square of the diameter of the aperture. For example, if a star observed with a telescope of a 20-inch aperture appears as bright as another observed with a 40-inch aperture, it must be concluded, from the above hypothesis, that the second star is four times as far away as the first. Actually we know that the stars have intrinsic luminosities very different one from another, but still this hypothesis and the hypothesis of a uniform distribution of stars in space, which is also very far from the truth, served Herschel in his first "sweeping of the sky," which he was able to execute, thanks to the powerful telescopes which he had learned to build.

Continuing his work zealously day and night, aside from his regular musical occupations, he provided himself with a much more powerful telescope, of 20-foot focal length, with which he observed Uranus. He had discovered Uranus with his favorite 7-foot reflector, which had an aperture of 6.5 inches.

Later on, in 1785, he began the construction of a reflector with a 40-foot focal length and a mirror 4 feet in diameter. The expenses were paid by the King of England, Herschel's patron. Such a telescope was, for those times, something really exceptional, with its wooden construction mounted in the open air in the garden of

Herschel's home in Slough. The tube could be moved in altitude by means of pulleys and turned in azimuth on wheels which held up the whole construction. A platform, on which the observer stood, was attached where it could follow the upper end of the telescope, where the eyepiece was located. One can well imagine the difficulties and inconveniences under which these observations were made, in the open air and on steps and a platform, up to a height of 50 feet above ground.

EARLY OBSERVATIONS BY HERSCHEL

The discoveries and results obtained by Herschel, with the smaller instruments which preceded the great one, were really exceptional, thanks to his ability and perseverance and the help of his sister Caroline. At first his attention was drawn to the variable stars, especially Mira Ceti, with the idea of understanding and correlating their phenomena with the appearance and disappearance of sunspots. The sunspots led him to consider the possible influence on the earth of the recurrence of solar storms, relating, for instance, the 11-year cycle of solar activity with the variable production of wheat. These were the first attempts at the wide investigations which connect solar with terrestrial phenomena, continued until today in various ways. Herschel noted the typical aspect of the polar caps of Mars and determined the inclination of its axis to the plane of the orbit. He found that because of the similarity of the inclination of Mars' axis with the Earth's, the changes in the climate of Mars must necessarily be similar to ours, and consequently the variations of the polar caps can be explained.

In 1781 in the course of his systematic study of the sky, constantly directed to solving the problem of the structure of the universe, his attention was drawn to a body which at first appeared to him to be a comet. Very soon he noticed that it was a new planet moving outside the orbit of Saturn. In honor of his royal patron he gave it immediately the name *Georgium Sidus*, a name used for some time in England and later replaced by Uranus. Thenceforth Herschel's fame grew rapidly. He was named a member of the Royal Society, and the Astronomer Royal, Maskelyne, invited him to Bath. Invited to Windsor Castle by George III, he accepted the king's offer to become the king's private astronomer and thus he definitely abandoned his career of musician.

STELLAR PARALLAXES AND UNIVERSAL GRAVITATION

The problem which most troubled Herschel was that of determining the annual parallaxes of the stars, that is, their distances, a problem which had already been investigated by his predecessors without success. For this purpose he began systematically to observe the double stars, noting the variations in the relative positions of the two components and demonstrating that they constituted physical systems. Their motion of revolution must be subject, like the solar system, to Newton's and Kepler's laws, although he added that now was not the time to decide the question. Later he again measured the relative positions of several pairs and he was able to confirm his predictions that the two components of a binary system revolve around their common center of mass. Thus developed the great discovery of the extension of universal gravitation beyond the limits of the solar system. This discovery alone would have been enough to immortalize the name of Herschel. He very soon noticed that the presence of double stars could not be attributed to chance, but in most cases the apparent closeness of two stars must actually be the consequence of a physical attraction. This fact hindered Herschel's project of determining the stellar parallaxes by the connection, for instance, of a bright star with one less bright, supposed to be more distant than the first. Now we know that the telescopes of Herschel's time still lacked the necessary precision for the measurement of such minute parallactic angles.

OBSERVATIONS OF CASTOR AND SATURN

In the meantime his measurements of Castor (*a Geminorum*), the well-known system formed by two stars of magnitudes 2.0 and 2.9, actually at a distance of 2″ apart, had proved to him in a succession of observations, which had also been compared to the previous ones of Bradley, that without any doubt the two stars apparently revolved one around the other. Herschel was able to give a first approximation of the complete period of revolution, assuming the motion to be uniform. Herschel's value of 342 years is not very different from the one calculated many years later. On the basis of his systematic observations he published three successive catalogs. He did not regret that he failed to measure the parallaxes, for he believed that the discovery of physical systems of stars was much more important than the discovery which escaped him because of the insufficient instrumental means available.

As soon as he had finished his great telescope in 1789 he directed it toward Saturn, and he was able to admire, in a way never possible before, the five satellites discovered by Huygens and Cassini and also the sixth, Enceladus, which he himself had discovered two years earlier with a smaller telescope. A few days later he discovered the seventh satellite, later called Mimas, which is the closest to Saturn.

STUDIES OF THE MILKY WAY AND NEBULAE

The observation of the sky, executed systematically by Herschel, and the counting of the number of stars in different regions of the Northern Hemisphere led him to establish with greater accuracy and with new results a fact which could be approximately supposed with the naked eye, that is, that the stars are much more numerous in the Milky Way and especially in the equatorial band, whereas they become progressively less dense toward the poles. In Herschel's hypothesis, strengthened by his observations, the space occupied by the stars in those regions of the universe visible and closer to us has approximately the form of a disk or grindstone, whose diameter is five times its thickness. Furthermore the Milky Way, from Scorpio to Cygnus, is divided into two branches, and in the intervening space the stars are relatively few. In the region where the stars are particularly dense he had occasion to notice darker regions, apparently completely devoid of stars, and one could look through them to infinite space. To his faithful helper, his sister Caroline, he immediately communicated his thought that these were real "holes" in the sky. Very much impressed by the size of these dark areas, he examined them attentively without arriving, however, at a satisfactory explanation of their origin. Their origin was discovered later, as we shall see, by Father Secchi and was confirmed by modern photography. They are dark matter which is scattered more or less densely throughout the universe.

The nebulae and star clusters attracted Herschel's attention and, besides the known ones which had been discovered by Lacaille and Messier in France, he found many more in his systematic observations with more powerful telescopes, and he listed them in his various catalogues. Thus he was able to study their various characteristics and forms and also their distribution in the sky, always trying to find a representation of the structure of the universe. Since it was not yet possible to study the physical constitution of the nebulae, he classified them according to their appearance, and he found that they range gradually from the "milky" type, like Orion's nebula, to the "stellar" type. He believed that they all were composed of more or less very distant stars. This idea had been proposed many years before by Immanuel Kant (1755) in his attempt to explain the structure of the universe according to Newton's principles, and also by J. H. Lambert in his "Cosmological Letters," a widely publicized work which produced a great sensation. Lambert finds in the philosophical principles and astronomical observations of all ages similar proofs of the unity and constitution of the universe. The difficulties presented by the observations of Jupiter and Saturn in the interpretation of the stellar motions solved by Lalande and Laplace led him to conclude that a force must exist outside our planetary system which must be subject to another system of higher order, to which our solar system belongs. Lambert makes the hypothesis that there is a spherical star cluster in the universe, dominated by an obscure central body, around which gravitate, together with our sun, all the visible stars. The Milky Way would be a system composed of similar innumerable star clusters. Furthermore, the hypothesis is extended to admit the existence of a still larger system made up of many Milky Ways. These ideas of Kant and Lambert are remarkable, for they foresaw by intuition alone many facts which have been explained today through modern observations.

The hypothesis that the nebulae outside of the Milky Way, later called "extragalactic nebulae," could constitute other systems, other "island universes" comparable to the Milky Way in form and structure, was a very advanced hypothesis, since there was no available knowledge about the distances of such systems.

Herschel, at first, accepted this idea, but later observations of other objects, especially the so-called "planetary nebulae," consisting of a central star surrounded by a nebulosity which certainly did not seem to be of stellar nature, made him change his mind and conclude that there must be a kind of bright fluid, of a nature unknown to us. This was a good prophecy of what was revealed years later by spectrum analysis.

In the distribution of the nebulae and clusters Herschel noted that the former were much more numerous toward the poles of the

Milky Way, whereas the latter were collected close to the equator. He concluded that all these stars must be part of only one system, and thus the existence of "island universes" much more distant than the Milky Way was quite improbable. Even though modern research proves that Herschel's hypotheses must be modified, it is certain that his ingenious conception of a great system moving around a common center of mass, to which our little solar system belongs, made a big step forward in the study of the structure of the universe.

MOTION OF THE SUN

Since the time of Halley it had been known that the stars had their own motions, and Tobias Mayer discovered a way to investigate how the sun, with its solar system, preserves its own motion toward a given point in space. It was desirable to establish whether in the stars surrounding the sun one could discover systematic motions due to an effect of perspective, for example, those which would appear to an observer on the earth who is moving among many sources of light which surround him on all sides and at different distances. The stars in the direction of his motion would seem to go farther apart whereas those in the opposite direction would seem to come closer together. Mayer was not able to establish any motion for the sun from the proper motions which he had available, but Herschel, just using a few proper motions obtained by Maskelyne and Lalande, succeeded in ingeniously concluding that the sun and its system are moving toward a point in the celestial sphere in the constellation of Hercules, which he called the "apex." Twenty years later, in 1805, Herschel restudied the problem with more data and more precise methods of calculation, and he confirmed his previous results, which were but little believed in his time.

"SEQUENCES" METHOD FOR VARIABLE STARS

In the study of variable stars Herschel made no long series of systematic observations, but he devised the simple method of "sequences" afterward employed extensively. This method consists of the determination of the magnitude of the variable and a certain number of comparison stars, more or less bright than the variable, with a given scale. Thus the changes in the magnitude of the variable are immediately evident from the changes which take place in the sequence. For the planets, besides his discovery of some satellites, he determined the period of rotation of Saturn and its rings. He found that the variations in the brightness of Iapetus are regular, since they occur in an interval equal to its period of revolution around the planet. This discovery led him to the conclusion that this satellite and the others revolve around Saturn just as the moon revolves around the earth.

CONSTITUTION OF THE SUN

Already, in 1774, Alexander Wilson of Glasgow, from his systematic observations of sunspots, had noticed that as the spots approached the edge of the sun they changed their form. This fact could be explained as an effect of perspective, if one supposed that the umbra or nucleus of the spots was at a lower level than the photosphere, like the bottom of a funnel which widens into the penumbra up to the level of the photosphere. About twenty years later Herschel confirmed these observations, and as a result of his other observations he elaborated a theory of the constitution of the sun which was standard until the advent of spectroscopic investigations. In Herschel's theory the light of the sun was given out by the "photosphere," which surrounded the solid dark nucleus. This nucleus was visible only through a tear in the photosphere, such as would appear in the umbra of the sunspots, but the penumbra could be a lower gaseous layer made luminous by the overlying photosphere. In Herschel's words the sun is the primary star of our system, probably inhabited like the other planets by beings adapted to the special conditions of that enormous globe. The discoveries and works of Herschel and also his fame hide somewhat the work of other astronomers of his time who, nonetheless, made notable contributions to observational and theoretical astronomy.

HERSCHEL'S CONTEMPORARY ASTRONOMERS

In Italy the Jesuit Father R. Boscovich (1711–1787) was among the first to teach Newtonian mechanics. Being also a very expert observer, he measured a meridian arc between Rome and Rimini. In France J. B. Delambre (1749–1822) succeeded Lalande in the chair of astronomy at the Collège de France. He also measured a meridian arc, between the parallels of Dunkerque and Barcelona.

which was to serve as the basis of the new metric decimal system. He computed tables of the motions of Uranus and the satellites of Jupiter, and won the prizes offered by the Academy of Sciences. His greatest work is his "History of Astronomy," in six volumes, which includes everything which had been done from primeval times to his immediate predecessors. This book was circulated widely.

The German astronomer, J. Schroeter, made at that time many physical observations of the planets and the moon. His two volumes on the moon contain many precise data on the surface details, whose physical conditions he attempted to investigate.

GIUSEPPE PIAZZI

The most famous astronomer of Herschel's time is without doubt Father Giuseppe Piazzi, born in Ponte in Valtellina (Northern Italy) in 1746. A Theatine monk, he first taught philosophy in the college of his order and only relatively late in life did he begin to consider astronomy. The Bourbon government of Naples, after he had been professor of "sublime calculus" at Palermo, sent him abroad to prepare for the founding of two observatories, one at Naples and the other at Palermo. He stayed three years at the observatories of Paris and Greenwich and he had occasion to visit Herschel at Slough, where he broke an arm falling from one of the high wooden ladders at the side of the great reflector.

Afterward he returned to Palermo and bought for the new observatory a vertical circle made by Ramsden, a masterpiece of mechanical craftsmanship of that time, and other instruments which he had erected on the tower of Santa Ninfa at the Royal Palace. His first thought was to undertake a new and more accurate determination of the positions of the many fixed stars, for he believed stellar catalogs to be the basis and foundation of astronomical science. After twenty years of hard work and sleepless nights he was able to publish his monumental work containing the position of 7646 stars, under the title: *Praecipuarum Stellarum Inerrantium Positiones Mediae Ineunte Saeculo Decimonono ex Observationibus Habitis in Specula Panormitana ab Anno 1792 ad Annum 1813*. With this catalog which found great favor among the astronomers of the time and their successors and which was awarded a prize by the Institute of France, Piazzi was able to prove that the proper motions of the stars are not the exception but the rule. He thus opened up a new field of research, and he discovered a star with a most interesting proper motion, 61 Cygni. Its distance from the earth was determined by Bessel several years after the death of Piazzi, who had vainly tried to measure the distances of the Pole Star and Vega.

On the night of January 1, 1801, while Piazzi was performing his systematic observations at the Ramsden Circle and was awaiting the meridian transit of a seventh-magnitude star previously catalogued by Lacaille, he noticed a new star before it. Without suspecting its nature he measured the co-ordinates, but the next evening he found that they had changed. On the following nights he was able to confirm the discovery of a "wandering star," perhaps a comet, perhaps a planet. It was not possible for him or for his assistants to observe it with any other telescope except the transit instrument, but he was able to continue his observations until the star came close to the sun, that is, until the middle of Feburary. If this body were a planet, the example of Uranus had shown that it was possible to compute a first approximate circular orbit even if the arc of the presumably elliptic orbit was very small. But the body discovered by Father Piazzi and observed for 41 days, covering a geocentric arc of only three degrees, was now lost among the innumerable stars, and the astronomers were very interested and anxious to find it again. We know that Napoleon discussed with Laplace on the field of battle the name to be given to the tiny planet if it were ever found again. To Piazzi's faithful friend, Barnabas Oriani, he also praises the discovery, expressing pleasure that it had been made by an Italian.

15 : the times of Gauss, Bessel, and Struve

KARL FRIEDRICH GAUSS

MEANWHILE IN GERMANY, THE YOUNG ASTRON-
omer and mathematician, Karl Friedrich Gauss, later called *mathe-
maticorum princeps,* had already had some occasion to study the problem of the proper motions of the stars. He thought of applying his
own solution to the new star discovered by Piazzi. By considering
three complete observations as far apart in time as possible, he could
establish with three pairs of co-ordinates (right ascension and declination) six equations, which theoretically would be enough to determine the elements of the orbit. The problem was thus treated in
a general way as had never been done before. The method permitted a determination of the elliptic orbit of the planet with an
accuracy which could be increased by considering, besides the three
fundamental observations, all the others available during the period
of visibility of the little planet. For this study Gauss devised the
"method of least squares," which afterward spread so widely, even
outside astronomical calculations. Baron de Zach in Seeberg, after
computing the orbit and the ephemeris, on December 7, 1801,
found the lost planet almost exactly in the position predicted by
Gauss.

The "little planet," the first among so many of this swarm of
celestial bodies between the orbits of Mars and Jupiter, was later
called Ceres by Piazzi in honor of the guardian goddess of Sicily.
Since it was possible that other small planets of the same nature

might exist, alert astronomers began to search for them. Olbers in Bremen in 1802 discovered a second which was called Pallas, and later two others were found, Juno and Vesta. Gauss continued to apply his methods and he generalized them in his classic work published in 1809: *Theoria Motus Corporum in Sectionibus Conicis Solem Ambientium.* Nor did the author regret having delayed so long, for he writes in his preface, "the methods first used have been altered so much that between the way in which the orbit of Ceres was calculated and the treatment given in this work there remains hardly a trace of distant similarity."

''ASTEROIDS'' OR ''PLANETOIDS''

By now it was evident that several or many small planets must be revolving around the sun between the orbits of Mars and Jupiter, perhaps the fragments of a larger planet exploded by internal forces. Herschel, who with his discovery of Uranus had extended the limits of the solar system, naturally was very much interested in Piazzi's discovery. In the spring of 1802 he wrote from Slough giving him a report of his observations of Ceres and Pallas and discussing the nature of these new bodies. This gave rise to a brief argument with Piazzi. From the calculations of Gauss, Herschel concluded that the new bodies must be extremely small in comparison to the other planets. For this reason and also because they were outside the zodiac, he did not believe they could be called planets, and since they were not comets they must be a new kind of celestial body. These new bodies, scattered among the fixed stars, are so similar to the stars that they cannot be distinguished from them even with a good telescope. From their "asteroidic" aspect Herschel proposed the name of "asteroids," thus classifying three different types of celestial bodies. The asteroids were characterized by the fact that they had small masses and orbits of small or large eccentricity around the sun, in planes inclined at any angle whatsoever to the ecliptic. Their motion could be direct or retrograde, they could not possess much atmosphere, nor even very small tails, and they had neither disks nor nuclei. Herschel added: "If we wanted to call them planets, they could not occupy the intermediate space between Mars and Jupiter with the proper dignity." This sounds like Kepler with his "harmony of the world"! But the more positive Piazzi makes a note at this point in Herschel's letter: "Soon we shall see counts, dukes, and even marquises in the sky!" Herschel's letter ends with a glorification of Piazzi's discovery of this new kind of star, more important than merely the addition of one body, which, "if it were called a planet, would remain in a much inferior position because of its smallness." Piazzi did not agree with Herschel's reasoning. He thought of the new bodies as "wandering stars," which could be called "planetoids" or "cometoids," but not "asteroids." According to his opinion, the only characteristic which distinguished them from comets and planets was their eccentricity and inclination, so that if they all were reduced to the same plane the comets would intersect the orbit of the planets. Ceres then would be a comet, and Pallas a planet. Ceres must be of larger dimensions than Herschel thought, and if the name of "asteroid" was fitting for that planet, the same was true for Uranus.

Later investigations have entirely agreed with Piazzi, and the misnomer "asteroids," although sometimes still used, is being replaced by the designation "minor planets" or "planetoids." Among the many minor planets discovered after Piazzi's time, not one has been found with retrograde motion, as Herschel thought possible. Instead many others, both because of their eccentricity and the inclination of their orbits, represent stages of transition from planetoids to comets, just as Piazzi believed in the case of Pallas. Ceres was found to be larger than Herschel estimated, with a diameter of 475 miles. When he believed that Ceres was so much smaller than Mercury, he had no idea that there was a greater difference between the diameters of Mercury and Jupiter (ratio 1:29) than between the diameters of Ceres and Mercury (ratio 1:6.5).

Piazzi was convinced that the number of these small planets must exceed the four discovered in the first decade of the nineteenth century. At the age of seventy, while observing Vesta, the fourth of these planets, he wrote as follows: "During the past month and part of the present I have been observing Vesta. Its light seemed to me so twinkling and alive, like that of the stars. Might it be in a state of combustion?" Later research has excluded this possibility, but it has led to the discovery of the variability of the light of many planetoids and of the difference in albedo from one to another.

BARNABAS ORIANI

A close bond of friendship and mutual esteem linked Father Piazzi with Barnabas Oriani, who in the same period left marked impressions in all the fields where astronomical research was active. He was born in 1752 of humble parents and was received very young into the order of the Barnabites. He was admitted to the Observatory of Brera (Milan) when Lagrange was retiring. Oriani's greatest work is concerned with the theory of Uranus, whose orbit he computed after the planet had covered a heliocentric arc sufficient to determine the orbit precisely, following the observations made from 1781 to 1783. He knew that he had to wait several years to perfect his theory. In the meantime he observed the planet accurately, and in 1787 he wrote:

> The tables of the new planet which we made two years ago have furnished such accurate positions that they rarely deviate from the observed positions more than 20″. Yet the planet in four years has covered only a very small part of its course, and in order to say anything about the absolute perfection of the tables it is necessary to compare observations for eighty years. The body must be observed at the principal points of its orbit, that is, at the apsides, at the nodes, and at its mean distance from the sun.

While waiting for new calculations he made some formulas for the correction of the elements of the orbit. Later, on the basis of Laplace's theory, he computed the perturbations which Jupiter and Saturn produced on Uranus, treating first the secular perturbations, then the periodic ones, excluding the lesser planets.

Oriani inspired and counseled Plana and Carlini in their immense work on the theory of the moon. He had met Piazzi at Brera in 1789 and from that time he was his most faithful friend. From their long and interesting correspondence we see the nobility of their spirit and the good will and care with which Oriani helped Piazzi in his first steps and during all his astronomical career.

It was desired by the astronomers of the time that the original observations made at the Observatory of Palermo be published in their entirety, and various proposals were suggested. Oriani hoped that the "Insititute of Science and Art" would include these observations in the volumes of its annals. But since this project was delayed, Oriani generously proposed to his friend Piazzi that he be allowed to publish them at his own (Oriani's) expense. For various reasons the project was not realized until later, under the auspices of the astronomer von Littrow, in the "Annals of the Observatory of Vienna."

OBSERVATORIES: EQUIPMENT AND METHODS

Ever more precise astronomical observations, executed more and more systematically, began to bring astronomers outside the realm of the by now narrow solar system. Greater accuracy was now necessary, more than ever before, in order to begin the measurement of the universe which surrounds us. In the years which follow the work of Herschel and Piazzi, we shall see how this was accomplished through the merit of their successors, and also through the extraordinary progress in the field of optics, precision mechanics, and physics in general.

In the eighteenth century there were relatively few observatories of great importance, and most of the observational work was done in the observatories of Paris and Greenwich, which had been founded in the preceding century. Toward the end of the eighteenth and the beginning of the nineteenth century, observatories multiplied rapidly, not only in Europe but throughout the world. These observatories constituted a vast network of observation centers which began to distribute among themselves the great task of the study of the sky in two hemispheres, with an ever increasing accuracy thanks to the continual progress acquired in the technical construction of instruments and the corresponding progress in theory and methods of calculation. Men began to notice that observatories located in populated districts were inconvenienced by the unclearness and general unquietness of the atmosphere due to dust, smoke, and variations in the density of the air. As a consequence of the daily heating of the buildings and the radiation from illuminated streets at night, the lower strata of the atmosphere were perturbed. All these factors made the images unsteady and indistinct. The observatories were equipped with instruments even more precise and complicated: no longer are the telescopes constructed with long tubes of cardboard or wood resting on shaky supports, but solid metal mounts are provided for meridian or equatorial circles, which are equipped with thread micrometers and finely graduated circles; no more is timing dependent on irregular clockwork motions, poorly controlled, but pendulum clocks and high precision chronometers are used.

The long calculations necessary to correct the observations and to obtain the best results were made easier by logarithmic tables, computing machines, and the method of least squares. This last method had been used, as we mentioned before, in the calculation of orbits by Gauss, who, independently of Legendre, had devised the method at that time. Actually, Father Boscovich had already proved in 1770 that when observations are available in a larger number than necessary, if as many equations are established as there are unknowns, the most probable value is the one which reduces to a minimum the absolute sum of the deviation of each observation from the average. Gauss and Legendre, starting from this concept, applied their "method of least squares"—so called because the sum of the squares of the residual errors must be reduced to a minimum—to the determination of the most probable orbit of a celestial body, that is, the orbit which best fits all the observations. They also generalized this method for use in combined observations of different "weight," that is, of greater or lesser reliability resulting from the instruments employed, the good or bad observing conditions, or the ability of the various observers.

From the time of Gauss and Legendre this method has found wide application in astronomy, physics, and generally in all determinations where known and unknown causes of errors must be taken into account. When the new planet of the solar system, Uranus, was discovered, the calculations of its orbit became relatively easy, because it could be safely assumed that the orbit was nearly circular and very little inclined to the plane of the ecliptic. But Ceres, having a large eccentricity and an inclination of ten degrees, made necessary a search for a general method which, based on a few observations of a very small arc of the orbit, would permit the determination of its orbit accurately enough to find the planet again after its conjunction with the sun. Therefore one can understand the importance of the *Theoria Motus* of Gauss, where he solved one of the most interesting and difficult problems in astronomy.

Father Piazzi was the first to prove irrefutably the existence of the "proper motions" of the stars, that is, the annual individual motion of each star, projected on a plane perpendicular to the

line of sight. For all stars this motion is a very slight angular measure, because of their great distances. It can be measured only
with very precise observations, separated by many years. Piazzi discovered that the star 61 of the constellation Cygnus has a large
proper motion, one of the largest now known. He also proved the
possibility of measuring the distance of the star, since its large
proper motion indicated the relative closeness of the star to the
solar system. His attempts to measure the parallax of the Pole Star
and Vega, that is, the angle in which one would see from the star
the radius of the earth's orbit, prepared the way for Friedrich Wilhelm Bessel, who was able to determine the first parallax, and thus
the first distance, of the very star 61 Cygni.

FRIEDRICH WILHELM BESSEL

The King of Prussia wanted to establish a new observatory
in Königsberg, and in 1810 he called young Bessel to direct it.
Bessel understood immediately the necessity of building instruments
of high precision, in order to be able with the greatest possible
accuracy to establish the astronomical constants, such as precession,
aberration, and refraction, as well as the true position of the stars
at any given instant. While waiting to initiate his program of observations, Bessel discussed the famous observations made by Bradley
at Greenwich from 1750 to 1762 with which, as we have said,
Bradley discovered the aberration of light. Thus in 1818 Bessel was
able to publish his work entitled *Fundamenta Astronomiae pro Anno
MDCCLV Deducta ex Observationibus Viri Incomparabilis, James
Bradley in Specula Astronomica Grenovicensi per Annos 1750–1762
Institutis*. The reduction methods used by Bessel were compiled in his
Tabulae Regiomontanae, which were extremely useful for practical
astronomical calculations. Having obtained for the Königsberg observatory a new meridian circle from Reichenbach, Bessel was able
to undertake the great task of determining the positions of all the
stars down to the ninth magnitude in the zone of the sky included
between 15° south and 45° north declination. In twelve years he
made 75,000 such observations, assisted by F. Argelander, director
of the observatory of Bonn. We may recall that we are indebted to
the latter for an atlas still widely used today, known under the name
of the *Bonner Durchmusterung*, which includes all the stars of the
Northern Hemisphere down to the eleventh magnitude.

With the meridian circle we can measure, as is well known, differences in the co-ordinates (right ascension and declination) of the stars which cross the meridian in succession. The smaller the differences, the more precise are the co-ordinates. When it is desired to measure the differences in co-ordinates of the stars which are included in the field of the telescope, as in the case of double stars, we use the equatorial equipped with a thread micrometer. In order to obtain good results with this method it is necessary that the equatorial follow the diurnal motion very accurately, a feat which was not possible in Bessel's time, and that the micrometer threads be illuminated. To eliminate these difficulties, since he wanted to take very exact measurements of the proper motions and double stars, Bessel had Fraunhofer construct in Munich a "heliometer" of rather large dimensions. The heliometer had been invented several years earlier at almost the same time in France and in England, and it is in substance a double-image micrometer. In fact, the objective of an equatorially mounted telescope is cut in half so that the sectional plane passes through the optical axis of the lens; and the two half-lenses, mounted on separate metal mounts, can move next to each other parallel to the line of section. The amount of shift of each half-lens, with respect to the position where they form a complete lens, is measured by a micrometer screw. Each half-lens forms a complete image of the celestial body at its focus. When the two half-lenses are not displaced, there is obviously only one image at their focus, but when the optical centers of the two half-lenses are shifted by the micrometer screw, the image becomes double and the distance between the two images is equal to the distance between the centers of the two half-lenses. This instrument is thus a micrometer adapted to measurements of small angles in general. It was called a heliometer because it was believed that it could be used to measure the diameter of the sun with great accuracy.

With the new heliometer Bessel measured, during one whole year, the angular distance of the binary system 61 Cygni from two faint neighboring comparison stars. These stars do not have as large a proper motion as 61 Cygni and thus must be farther away from the solar system. At the end of 1838 Bessel was able to announce that 61 Cygni had described in the sky in the course of a year a very small apparent ellipse, the image of the path of the earth around the sun. In other words, he had succeeded in determining the first "annual parallax" of a star. His result was 0.30", equal to a distance of 11 light years, which is very close to the value adopted today based on numerous determinations. Thus Bessel was able to solve the age-old problem which had so troubled his predecessors since Copernicus and Galileo. Although the heliometer was gradually abandoned, in 1839 Thomas Henderson at the Observatory of the Cape of Good Hope announced that one of the brightest stars of the Southern Hemisphere, α Centauri, had a parallax of almost 1", that is, a distance of 4 light years, the smallest known today. Immediately afterward Friedrich Wilhelm Struve at the Observatory of Pulkovo determined the parallax of α Lyrae (Vega).

The remarkable precision obtained by Bessel in his micrometer readings made with the heliometer enabled him to determine the distances of Saturn and Jupiter from their satellites and thus to find the mass of the planets. In his *Astronomische Untersuchungen* he gives the results of his observations and compares them with the theory, concluding with more precise tables than any others on the motion of these satellites. Furthermore, he obtained from the workshop of the Brothers Repsold of Hamburg a new meridian circle with new improvements, among them a method for the determination of the "nadir" and thus the "zero" of the vertical circle. He was able to observe the coincidence of the micrometer threads with their image reflected in a mercury mirror, when the instrument was pointed straight downward in the direction of the nadir. The use of this high-precision instrument enabled Bessel to clarify a fact of great importance. He had suspected, as early as 1834, that the proper motions of certain stars, as for instance Sirius and Procyon, are not uniform. As the result of an extended series of observations, made with the new meridian circle, Bessel was able to announce the discovery that these stars must in reality be double, having one or more invisible companions, and that the suspected irregularity is due to the orbital motion of the luminous and dark components, the latter being invisible, around the common center of mass of the multiple system.

The great technical skill and the precise instruments at Bessel's disposal enabled him also to make important progress in the measurement of our globe. By means of the pendulum he determined the intensity of the gravitational force; he measured astronomical coordinates and made triangulations in East Prussia. The remarkable results obtained by Bessel are undoubtedly due to the prefect construction of the astronomical instruments of his time, but also, as he himself writes in the preface of his *Untersuchungen* (Researches), to the facts that his investigations were always directed to a definite and immediate goal, in a more precise manner than had ever been possible before, and that he tried to improve the circumstances of observation and eliminate all possible causes of errors. He always believed that the reduction by the observer himself of the results of the observations made was an essential condition for success in all astronomical research.

FRIEDRICH WILHELM STRUVE

Not less important and renowned was the work of Friedrich Wilhelm Struve, the first of a well-known family of astronomers which still exists today. Born in Altona in Germany in 1793, he emigrated as a young man to Russia, where he made his home. He first devoted himself to classical studies, but he soon turned to astronomy and became director of the Observatory of Dorpat (Latvia) and professor in the university there. Procuring a meridian circle from Reichenbach and Ertel and a celebrated refractor with a 9-inch aperture from Fraunhofer—the masterpiece of this great mechanic and expert in optics—he was able to rival Bessel's observations in the new era of positional astronomy. We have already noted that William Herschel discovered the binary nature of many double stars, but for about fifteen years thereafter there was no progress in this important field. Only his son, John Herschel, took it up again and measured Castor, whose orbital motion predicted by the great Herschel had already been verified by young Struve.

From that time (1819) Struve initiated in Dorpat regular observations of double stars, measuring the angles of position and the distances of the brighter components with respect to the lesser ones. The following year he published his first catalog of double stars. This was only the beginning of an enormous work which began to interest a great many astronomers. The number of measurements was increased, and the true orbits of the double stars were determined from their motion around their center of mass. Having set up in Dorpat the new refractor of Fraunhofer, after two years of observation Struve published his *Catalogus Novus Generalis Stellarum Duplicium et Multiplicium*, which was a milestone in astronomical history. From this work it became clear that the duplicity or multiplicity of a star was evidently not exceptional. He thus proved the existence of true systems of stars governed by the same law of universal gravitation as controls the sun and its planets. Proceeding in his program, which was constantly expanded, Struve determined the position angles, the distances, the magnitudes, and the colors of a great number of stars, which he gathered together in 1837 in his classic work entitled *Stellarum Compositarum Mensurae Micrometricae*, followed fifteen years later by another entitled *Stellarum Fixarum Imprimis Duplicium et Multiplicium Positiones Mediae*, where he also gives the proper motions calculated from the oldest observations. To the study of the structure of the Galaxy, Struve made considerable contributions, in addition to those made by Herschel in both hemispheres, concerning the distribution of the stars with respect to the galactic equator.

The year 1833 brought a great change in Struve's life, when he was called by the Emperor Nicholas to build and direct the great central Observatory of the Russian Empire, near the village of Pulkovo, not far from St. Petersburg. This was indeed a great observatory, in its conception and in its actual equipment of new precision instruments. It was constructed according to the experience obtained at Paris and Greenwich, but it was geared to the study of the fixed stars rather than of the solar system. Following the ideas of Bessel, the Observatory of Pulkovo was also furnished with a great zenith instrument, especially adapted to observations in the prime vertical, which, as Bessel had demonstrated, are particularly suited for the determination of the constants of aberration and nutation and of parallaxes.

Struve also directed and executed measurements of a Russian and Scandinavian meridian arc which extended for no less than 25°, from the mouth of the Danube to the Arctic Ocean. He also determined the difference of longitude between Pulkovo and Altona and between Altona and Greenwich. We have already mentioned how difficult these determinations were at the time of Galileo and until the day when Harrison invented and constructed the first marine chronometer. With such a clock, which in a first trip from England to Jamaica in 161 days ran an error of $1^m 5^s$, and with the rapid improvements which followed, the method of determining longitude by carrying the time of the first meridian to various places became common practice among navigators and geodesists. Struve also used this method in a first expedition, in which as many as 68 chronometers were transported 16 times across the Baltic. In a second expedition 42 chronometers passed 16 times across the North Sea and the Thames. Later the transmission of time by telegraph and radiotelegraphy replaced the transporting of chronometers. Following these first precise determinations of longitude there arose the problem of whether the "prime meridian" should be established at Pulkovo or Greenwich. There is no doubt that Struve's sympathies were with Russia and that the great new imperial observatory had obscured the fame of Greenwich, but Struve, as a true astronomer, knew well the tradition behind the English Observatory and Flamsteed, Halley, and Bradley, and he decided immediately for Greenwich.

To Struve we owe new and accurate determinations of the constants of aberration, precession, and nutation, and, as we have mentioned, of stellar parallaxes. The perfection of the instruments which he had built for Pulkovo by the famous artisans of his day enabled him to make such remarkable progress that other European observatories followed his example. At Pulkovo he had the satisfaction of leaving as his successor his son Otto. We shall see later on how this illustrious family, which began its fame with Friedrich Wilhelm, has continued, with no less energy and intelligence than its head, to cultivate successfully the science of the heavens.

16 : the birth of astrophysics

By "ASTROPHYSICS" WE MEAN THAT BRANCH OF astronomy which is concerned with the physical characteristics of celestial bodies, that is, their luminosity and spectroscopic peculiarities, their temperature and radiation, the nature and condition of their atmosphere, surface, and interior, their qualitative and quantitative composition, and finally all the phenomena arising from these physical conditions.

From the day that Galileo turned his telescope to the sky it was possible to study the physical surface of the sun and planets. About two centuries later people began to apply the spectroscope and spectrum analysis to the study of the stars, and thus it became possible to study the physical nature of the universe. To these two epochs the progress in astronomy in general can be traced, and in particular the very remarkable progress in astrophysics. In fact, without the telescope, the spectroscope, and the conquests of atomic physics, this program would not have been possible. Galileo initiated the first of these epochs, and Father Secchi was born at the beginning of the second and soon became, as we shall see, a pioneer in astrophysical research.

SUNSPOTS AND SOLAR ACTIVITY

We have already spoken of the astronomical discoveries of Galileo which opened the way to the physical study of the solar system and of the first discoveries of the nature of sunspots. During the total eclipses of the sun there had been seen, ever since ancient times, both the corona which surrounds the solar globe like a luminous aureole of variable aspect, and the prominences which surround certain points of the sun's surface like great flames. But only during the eclipses of the nineteenth century were the details of the corona and prominences made evident. The first observers—Cassini, Lalande, and others—maintained that the appearance and disappearance of the sunspots were not subject to any law. But Horrebow, toward the end of the eighteenth century, after having observed sunspots for several years, announced that their manifestations were probably governed by a period of time. Only later, in 1843, did the apothecary Schwabe, of Dessau, state the existence of a ten-year period in the frequency of the spots. Schwabe had begun his observations with the idea of discovering a planet inside Mercury's orbit, and for thirty-three years he made systematic observations which led him to his discovery. At first it did not attract much attention, but after Humboldt had published it and placed it in a better light in his *Cosmos*, everyone recognized its truth and importance; and the former pharmacist, now famous, used to say: "I can compare myself to Saul, who went out to find his father's asses and found a throne!" alluding to the sunspots in place of the intra-Mercurial planet.

At the Berlin scientific congress of 1828 Humboldt gave a first impetus to research on terrestrial magnetism under the leadership of Gauss. With the magnetometers devised by Gauss, the first magnetic observatory was founded in Göttingen in 1833. In 1851 Lamont, director of the Observatory of Munich, was able to establish a periodic variation of the terrestrial magnetism, from his own observations and from those of Göttingen. He had discovered superimposed on the diurnal variations of the declination of the magnetic needle another variation of longer duration, slightly more than 10 years. A few months after the announcement of the discovery, Sir Edward Sabine, unaware of Lamont's conclusions, undertook similar investigations with magnetic observations made in Canada. He considered the irregular perturbations of terrestrial magnetism, the so-called "magnetic storms," and found that they attained a maximum frequency and intensity every 10 years. He was also the first to note the coincidence of this period of terrestrial magnetism with the sunspot period indicated by Schwabe.

R. Wolf, in Berne, while making a statistical study of sunspots from the time of their discovery until 1850, deduced a more precise duration of 11.11 years for the cycle of solar activity, with a variation similar to that of the light curves of certain variable stars, where the rise from minimum to maximum intensity is more rapid than the descent from maximum to minimum. The discovery of the relationship between the manifestations of solar activity and of terrestrial magnetism brought hope of discovering other correlations in the climatic conditions on the earth. Sir William Herschel took the first step in this direction, attempting, for example, to correlate the period of solar activity with the periods of greater or lesser production of wheat, but his results, which seemed to prove in some way the existence of such a relation, have not been confirmed by later investigations. Nevertheless similar investigations are still in progress.

In the field of solar physics the above-mentioned discoveries were followed in 1860 by those of Carrington and Spörer: the "equatorial acceleration" of the sun, determined from the movement of the spots at various latitudes, the shift in latitude of the spots in the course of a cycle, and the determination of the inclination of the solar equator to the ecliptic. In the very first determinations of the sun's rotation, made by various observers, sizable disagreements had been evident, and as far back as 1630 Father Scheiner had showed that different spots gave different periods and furthermore that the spots farther from the solar equator moved with a slower angular velocity than the closer spots. For more than two centuries the discovery of Father Scheiner was not investigated, until C. H. F. Peters in 1855, following observations made at the Observatory of Capodimonte in Naples, explained that the spots have irregular proper motions, in intensity as well as in direction, and then he explained the above-mentioned differences of the periods of rotation derived from different sunspots. Carrington in England and, independently, Spörer in Germany, discovered that the sun, or at least its outside visible envelope, does not have one period of rotation alone. It does not rotate as a rigid body, but with gradually increased angular velocities from the equator to the pole. In other words, the period of rotation of the sun about its axis is shortest at the equator and increases with increasing latitude.

Besides the sun, the only bodies of which it was possible to make observations and discoveries of a physical character were the remaining bodies of the solar system. These were studied by Gian Domenico Cassini and by the disciples of Galileo, who determined the various particulars presented by the surfaces of certain planets, the periods of rotation, and the flattening at the poles. After Huygens' discovery of the real configuration of Saturn's rings, other observations in the nineteenth century established its complex constitution. In 1857 Clerk Maxwell explained the existence of the rings, theoretically, imagining that they were formed by thin layers of innumerable corpuscles, each of which described its own orbit around the planet like one of so many minute satellites. These corpuscles must be so numerous that they appear as a continuous whole which reflects the light of the sun to us.

The first observations of comets made with the telescope had already shown that they are formed of extremely rarefied cosmic matter, especially in the tail. The head or nucleus generally appears denser and thicker. There was proof of the very small density of the tail when in 1819 the earth, according to Olbers' calculations, was very probably enveloped in the tail of the comet of that year and also in the tail of the resplendent comet of 1861. It had been noted that as the comets came closer to the sun they became larger, especially the tail. Olbers recognized that the tail was an emanation from the nucleus which became brighter and renewed itself the closer the comet came to the sun. But nothing could be said at that time about the chemical composition, concerning which Olbers had already made some hypotheses.

THE PARSONSTOWN TELESCOPE AND NEBULAE STRUCTURE

Meanwhile, particularly in England, people tried to continue the tradition and pioneer work of Herschel in the construction of larger reflectors with the hope of coming closer to the celestial bodies in order to know them better. In 1845 William Parsons, third Earl of Rosse, was able to construct a gigantic metal mirror 6 feet in diameter and 52 feet in focal length. The laborious experiments to find the best alloy and to polish the reflecting surface were made by the laborers of his feudal estate of Birr Castle at Parsonstown in King's County. The "leviathan of Parsonstown" was mounted that year between two large walls, which limited the field of view to one hour of right ascension on both sides of the meridian, in order to give better stability and easier access for the observer to the Newtonian focus. The great telescope revealed immediately the structure of the nebulae and star clusters. Since the time of Galileo it had been believed that the nebulous masses of the sky would be resolved by more powerful telescopes into myriads of stars. In the third month of the telescope's use Rosse discovered a real spiral nebula near the tail of the Great Bear. In the hazy contours he could perceive a delicate spiral structure of almost geometrical precision. It was the first appearance of this characteristic structure of stars and nebulous matter and it was to open the way to new and important research and speculation on stellar evolution.

FRAUNHOFER LINES

Wollaston in 1802 substituted for the round pinhole, used by Newton and his successors, a long narrow slit so that the emission of light might be examined through a prism. He observed that the solar spectrum was cut by seven black lines which he believed designated the limits of the various colors. But it was Fraunhofer, the celebrated student of optics at Munich, who discovered in 1815, by means of a slit, prism, and telescope, that the solar spectrum is marked by thousands of dark lines, which today bear his name. Fraunhofer counted 600 and drew 324, measured their relative distance, and assigned letters of the alphabet to the principal lines. He extended his research to other celestial bodies and found that the spectra of the moon and planets possessed the same lines as the spectrum of the sun, whereas the spectra of some of the brightest fixed stars presented different characteristics. In the spectra of Sirius and Castor he saw only three wide, dark lines, two in the blue and one in the green. The spectrum of Pollux resembled that of the sun entirely, as did the spectra of Capella, Betelgeuse, and Procyon. One solar line, indicated by Fraunhofer by the letter D, seemed especially intense in the spectra of the latter four stars. The position of this line coincided with the well known yellow emission line produced by the light of incandescent sodium vapor, which could easily be reproduced in the laboratory. Spectrum analysis, the foundation of astrophysics, is based on the correspondence of these radiations. Not until forty years after Fraunhofer's discovery could the physical significance of these lines be explained, when several experimenters, among them, Sir John Herschel, began to establish the correspondence between the dark absorption lines and the bright emission lines.

KIRCHHOFF'S LAW

Gustav Kirchhoff, professor of physics at the University of Heidelberg, went to the root of the problem, and he established his well known general law which states that the ratio between the emission and absorption powers for rays of the same wave length is constant for all bodies at the same temperature. The same characteristics obtained from the emission spectra of the various laboratory substances are found in the celestial spectra, which are mostly absorption spectra. Kirchhoff was then led to the important conclusion that terrestrial elements other than sodium—iron, magnesium, calcium, copper, zinc, and the like—must be present in the sun in greater or lesser degree. With great precision he drew a map of the solar spectrum which was printed by the Berlin Academy in 1862 in three shades, in order to give an idea of the different intensities of the lines. Kirchhoff's conclusions spread abroad rapidly and their importance was well appreciated. A beginning had been made in the knowledge of the physical constitution of the sun and stars.

The fundamentals of spectrum analysis are credited equally to Kirchhoff and his colleague, the chemist Robert Bunsen, but the application to the study of celestial bodies and especially of the sun is the work of Kirchhoff. With these applications modern astrophysics begins. Its importance in the knowledge of our universe can be well appreciated when we think that this branch of astronomy leads to experimental verification of the physical and chemical constitution of the celestial bodies and their evolution. Astrophysics provides irrefutable proof of the unity of matter and the superior order of the whole universe.

FATHER ANGELO SECCHI

Pioneers in this field of research were Father Angelo Secchi and Sir William Huggins. The former, exiled from Italy with the Jesuits, finished his astronomical studies at Georgetown Observatory near Washington, so that when he returned home in 1849 he was nominated director of the Roman College Observatory. He rebuilt it completely and equipped it with new instruments adapted for the purpose which he explains clearly in one of his papers, almost at the conclusion of his long and important accomplishments:

In these last years there has arisen a branch of study never considered before, the physical study of the celestial bodies. If we except the work of the Herschels, who never had a real well-ordered observatory, these studies have been cultivated only sporadically and by very few amateurs. Even the Herschels themselves disappeared from the scene after Sir John's immortal expedition to the Cape of Good Hope. Thus physical astronomy was an almost abandoned field when we were called to direct the Roman College Observatory, and we have resolved to devote ourselves to it. This decision has governed all our later studies and the very choice of the instruments for the new observatory. This study was once believed unnecessary and someone has even said that at the College we do not cultivate astronomical science at all, but physics instead. There are even some persons who have refused to be called astronomers, as if Galileo and Herschel, who spent their lives in such studies, were not astronomers. But time has justified us and we can say without blushing that now in our traces there have arisen elsewhere physical observatories for the sole purpose of studying the celestial bodies, as in Oxford, in Berlin, in Paris itself, in Calcutta, and in other places. This physics of the celestial bodies was then in its infancy and it has grown in the twenty-five years of the work of this observatory, which has had some place in its development.

These words clearly show that from the beginning Father Secchi had chosen this new promising field of research. As yet with inadequate means, he had turned his attention to the sun, measuring the intensity of solar radiation with a thermoelectric pile, first during the eclipse of 1851 and then directly from the solar image at the telescope. The thermoelectric pile had previously been used by Henry at Washington to determine the temperature of a sunspot, which he found to be less than that of the photosphere. Father Secchi occupied himself instead with the determination of the ratio between the solar radiation at the center and at the edge of the disk. For this he obtained photographic images in daguerrotype. He was thus one of the first to apply photography to astronomy, particularly in the various phases of the eclipse of that year (1851). Furthermore, on the image of the sun projected by his Cauchoix refractor he noted deviations in the galvanometer of the pile, and he proved that the radiation at the center of the disk is almost double the radiation at the edge.

The study of comets had always been cultivated at the Roman College, especially by Father De Vico, who became famous in 1835 because he was the first to discover Halley's comet. Continuing the study of comets, Father Secchi discovered in 1853 a comet with a multiple nucleus. He also found in 1852 the two fragments into which Biela's comet had broken in its appearance of 1846 and he saw a faint star through the nucleus of one of the fragments, proving in this manner the tenuousness of cometary matter.

He communicated his discovery to the scientific world as follows:

> The morning of August 16, 1852, at 3:30 a.m. (civil time) the comet came into the field of my telescope, but I almost lost the discovery, since it then directly covered a star of ninth to tenth magnitude. The comet could only be seen as a light veil of fog which surrounded the star. Knowing however that there was no notable nebula in that position, I fixed attentively the position of the star and a few minutes later I saw the little star shifting and thus I was sure I had found the comet. In the next few days I had no more doubts, for I found the second part.

Shooting stars were also a subject of research at the Roman College. In those days it had not yet been exactly decided whether they were caused by a meteorological phenomenon of atmospheric origin or by a cosmic phenomenon. From his studies Father Secchi realized that shooting stars must be of cosmic nature, and therefore every year regular observations were made of the radiant points, which prepared the way for the great discovery of Schiaparelli. In possession of new larger instruments, such as the Merz 10-inch refractor of 13-foot focal length, Father Secchi observed Saturn and the rings, noted the dimensions, and determined the luminosity of the various parts. At the same time as Bond and Lassell he found that the inner ring is nebulous and he was the first to declare that the surface of the rings is flat. He also determined the apparent magnitude of the disk, the flattening, and the eccentricity of the rings. From 1860 to 1863 he made many drawings of the variable features of Jupiter's surface and noted that great perturbations took place in its atmosphere, similar to our storms. Because of the fine quality of the Merz lens he was able to observe and follow certain spots on the Medicean planets and to determine their diameters, their periods of rotation about their axes, and their different reflecting powers of sunlight. Father Secchi followed the planet Mars also, especially during the opposition of 1859. He discovered two configurations of red color, dark and permanent, between the two large continents. He called them "canals," a term accepted later by Schiaparelli. He ascertained the eccentric position of the polar caps with respect to the pole, a fact which was confirmed later. He believed that these caps were clouds and not masses of snow and ice, as has been established by later observations. He applied the spectroscope to the study of the planets and he showed that in addition to the lines which indicate the presence of steam, there are other characteristic zones, especially toward the red. This led him to the conclusion that their atmosphere was "not yet cleansed and had elements different from ours."

On Mars, again with spectroscopic observations, he noted the almost permanent transparency of the atmosphere, a fact confirmed later by Schiaparelli. Furthermore, he observed that Uranus and Neptune present discontinuous spectra. Such an appearance is produced by the presence of bands of the same character as those of Jupiter and Saturn, but much more intense, produced by substances in their atmospheres which could not then be identified. Secchi's studies of the moon were made with drawings and photographs. The drawings were to emphasize the features of the most important craters, the principal one being called *Copernicus*. Of this he made measurements and a detailed drawing, with the idea that any variations which might appear with time could be easily recognized. By 1859 Father Secchi had already published a complete set of photographs mainly for the purpose of studying the theoretical conditions of celestial photography. Thus he was able to establish the incapacity of the existing refractors for photography, since the visual objective was corrected for the human eye and not for the violet region of the spectrum to which the photographic plate is sensitive. Therefore, since no objectives corrected for photography were then in use, it was necessary to resort to reflectors for good results.

After the first experiences and observations of Fraunhofer, G. B. Donati, of Florence, undertook on a larger scale the investigation of the spectra of the stars. He used a large 16.5-inch burning-glass, preserved today in the Museum of the History of Science in Florence, a precious piece which had been used for physical experiments by the Accademia del Cimento. He also used a spectroscope constructed by G. B. Amici, with which he observed and described the spectra of 15 stars, giving their most important absorption lines. He published these important results in the Annals of the Florentine Museum in 1862. The next year L. M. Rutherfurd, of New York, made an attempt to classify the stellar spectra.

News of these observations came to Father Secchi in Rome and gave him the idea of undertaking similar investigations with the Merz refractor, adapting to it a spectroscope also made by Merz. Meanwhile the French astrophysicist Janssen was in Rome and had with him a small spectroscope which Father Secchi asked him to attach to his Merz equatorial telescope. Together they made observations of the spectra of certain bright stars, and communicated the results to the Paris Academy. These confirmed not only the existence of spectral lines but also their identification with those produced by known elements on the earth. With the improvement of spectroscopes for this particular use Father Secchi began to notice the difference in the various types of stellar spectra, while in Italy and other countries interest in this type of research became ever more widespread. In England Sir William Huggins, who built an observatory for himself near his house on Tulse Hill, understood, like Father Secchi, the importance of this new branch of astronomy and in fact he wrote:

> It was just at this time that the news came of Kirchhoff's great discovery (1859) of the true nature and chemical constitution of the sun, from his interpretation of the Fraunhofer lines. This news came to me like the coming upon a spring of water in a dry and thirsty land. Here at last presented itself the very order of work for which in an indefinite way I was looking—namely, to extend his novel methods of research upon the sun to the other heavenly bodies.

Whereas Huggins was minutely studying a few bright stars, Father Secchi wanted to examine many stars, that is, as he himself stated at the meeting of the Tiberine Pontifical Academy in January, 1868: "I wanted actually to see if the composition of the stars is as varied as the stars are innumerable. That was my question, and having had the good fortune to be able to perfect my instrument of observation, I have reaped more bountiful fruit than I had hoped."

The instrument to which he refers is a spectroscope with a slit, sufficiently luminous to permit observations of rather faint stars. He believed that, once a spectral type having certain determinate lines had been recognized in some of the principal stars, the other stars could be examined with simple differential measurements; at the end of 1869 he returned to the optical combination used before by Fraunhofer, which he described as follows:

> The instruments which we have now temporarily mounted for this research consist of a flint prism with a diameter of 6 inches and a refractive angle of about 12°. This is placed directly in front of the objective of the great 9-inch refractor. Reasons of economy have forced us to limit ourselves to this dimension, thus sacrificing more than half the aperture of the same refractor. Nevertheless the results are most satisfactory; the light is much stronger than with a direct vision prism inserted between the objective and the eyepiece, although the dispersion is more than four times greater. The work was done by Mr. Merz of München who tells us, however, that he encountered no small difficulty, and we believe him, for the prism is of rare precision.

For the story of the "prism objective," as this combination is generally called, one must note that after Fraunhofer, who first used a 60° prism attached to a small telescope of 1.2-inch aperture, and one of 37° with a 4-inch telescope, the use of such a combination with the above-mentioned prism must be credited to Father Secchi, who obtained noteworthy results with it. One must not forget, however, that a few months before, L. Respighi, the director of the Campidoglio Observatory in Rome, in his paper entitled "Observations of the Spectra of Stars by Means of a Large Prism Attached to the Objective of the Equatorial of the Campidoglio Observatory" refers to the use of a Merz prism, with a refractive angle of 10° and sides of 5.3 by 4.3 inches, applied to the Merz equatorial of 4.4-inch aperture, to observe the spectrum of the brightest stars. The prism used by Father Secchi has a diameter of 6.4 inches and is perhaps the first to be cast in circular form. At first it was mounted in front of the objective of the great refractor, where it gave "enormous, superb" spectra, but because of the long focal length the light of the fainter stars was dimmed too much. Better results with respect to luminosity were obtained when he used the prism in conjunction with the Cauchoix refractor, the aperture of the objective being the same as that of the prism. This telescope is famous for the numerous observations made by the Jesuit Fathers at the Roman College Observatory and especially for the observations on the "colors of stars" by Father Sestini. With the Merz prism objective, applied to this instrument, Father Secchi obtained "a result superior to that of the great equatorial, with respect to intensity, although not equal in dilation, as would be quite natural." The most salient point confirmed by his investigations was "that the stars are very numerous; yet their spectra can be reduced to a few well-defined and distinct forms which, for the sake of brevity, we shall call *types*. The examination of the stars has occupied us for several years; and all the principal stars and most of the others have been examined, almost 4000 in all, because besides the principal stars all the surroundings were examined."

SPECTRAL TYPES

This was the discovery of the well known spectral types; the three principal ones are the white-blue, yellow, and red, to which is added a fourth type defined by Father Secchi as "rather bizarre and varied. At first glance one could believe that it results from the third by the suppression of certain dark lines." And finally, there is a fifth type which comprises stars with bright emission lines. This first classification was soon universally adopted because it was so practical and because it was immediately supposed to correspond to the various stages in the successive evolutions of the celestial bodies. The study of the spectra of the stars, thus outlined by Father Secchi, led right away to very important results. He writes in his book *The Stars*: "If one will apply to this study the great reflectors, like the one of Lord Rosse, the silver-coated glass of Paris, the one of Lassell, not to mention the great refractors of Washington, Porro, etc., they will certainly reveal unsuspected marvels, especially if they are located in opportune places, as for instance on Mt. Etna or other high mountains, where the atmosphere is very pure. The astronomers must not insist on remaining in the capital cities or in their surroundings, where the atmosphere, besides its denseness, is cluttered up with a thousand dirty things and absorbing vapors." Father Secchi already foresaw the great modern reflectors located on mountain tops.

SIR WILLIAM HUGGINS

Huggins, on his part, began his investigations on stellar spectra in collaboration with W. A. Miller, professor of chemistry at King's College, London. After having made a diagram of the spectra of 26 terrestrial elements and the spectra of a few stars, in 1863 he concluded that "the stars, while differing the one from the other in the kinds of matter of which they consist, are all constructed upon the same plan as our sun, and are composed of matter identical at least in part with the materials of our system." In fact, he was able to identify by direct comparison of celestial and terrestrial spectra the presence of certain elements and their characteristic grouping of lines, as for example hydrogen, iron, sodium, and magnesium. At the same time, while studying the spectra of the nebulae, Huggins made another important discovery and thus resolved a much debated question. It had been generally supposed that the nebulae were nothing but star clusters, so far away from the earth that they could not be resolved even by the greatest telescopes existing in those times. Sir William Herschel had been convinced that many of Messier's *nébuleuses sans étoiles* could be resolved into star clusters, but he had also discovered that, even with increased power of the optical means, many of such nebulae could not be resolved into stars. It was Lord Rosse, as we have mentioned, who discovered their spiral form and Huggins who proved with the spectroscope that some nebulae cannot be considered as clusters of many fixed stars, conceived as so many "suns," but must rather be regarded as enormous masses of luminous gases or vapors. In fact, he had observed that the spectra of certain nebulae consist of a few bright lines, that is, emission lines, for they are emitted by incandescent gases. Nitrogen was the only element among those investigated by Huggins which presented bright lines close to those of the spectra of the nebulae. However, he noted that other lines, though rather intense in the spectrum of nitrogen, were not visible in the spectra of the nebulae. He concluded in a daring hypothesis that the appearance of only one line in the spectrum of a nebula might indicate a form of matter, as yet unknown to our analysis, more elementary than the form of nitrogen.

Father Secchi in 1868 declared that no visible Doppler effect could be discovered in the stellar spectra, but Huggins, in possession of a spectroscope of higher power, demonstrated that the Fraunhofer lines present in the spectrum of Sirius showed a small displacement relative to the corresponding lines of laboratory spectra, that is, a Doppler effect, equivalent to a velocity of 30 miles per second along the line of sight. Several years later he was able to give the velocity in the direction to or from the sun of 19 and 11 stars, respectively. In 1880, using "dry" photographic plates for the first time for astrophysical purposes, Huggins was able to photograph on the same plate a terrestrial spectrum and the spectrum of a star, one next to the other. He was thus able to determine directly the velocity of a body along the line of sight in miles per second.

Only later, as Huggins himself says, did the use of photography become general, when H. C. Vogel, at Potsdam, extended and perfected the spectroscopic method of measuring the velocity of stars along the line of sight and made it common practice. With a new spectroscope designed by Zöllner, Vogel obtained the first spectroscopic proof of the rotation of the sun, by comparing the spectra of the two opposite edges, east and west, and he thus confirmed the existence of the Doppler effect. Vogel also proposed an extension of the spectral types of Father Secchi, to take into consideration the various characteristics of the spectra revealed by photographs. Although his classification was not adopted, the fundamental principles have found application in the classification now in common usage.

RESEARCH IN SOLAR PHYSICS

It is certainly to the credit of Father Secchi that he considered research in solar physics to be among the most important researches for the progress of astrophysics. The sun is the star closest to us and the only one of any appreciable diameter whose entire surface we can see. All other stars, even through our most powerful instruments, are mere luminous points which must always be studied as a whole without any possibility of detail. Father Secchi well understood that from a spectroscopic study of the sun conclusions might be drawn about its physical characteristics which might later be extended to the stars and make evident the relation which must exist between them. Thus from the study of the constitution of the solar system it has been possible to pass to the study of the sidereal constitution of the universe.

All the investigations of Father Secchi in solar physics and those of his predecessors and contemporaries are collected in his work *Le Soleil*, published in two volumes in a most accurate edition by Gauthier-Villars in the years 1875–1877. The first volume contains general information on solar phenomena, more detailed information on the surface and atmosphere, and data on eclipses. In the second volume are treated the solar prominences, that is, the eruptions which take place at the edge of the sun, the sun's temperature, and its radiations. Then, considering the sun as the center of the solar system, he examines the problem of its origin. He studies further the aspect and the constitution of comets and shooting stars. The treatise closes with a last chapter which discusses how our sun is related to the fixed stars and how the stars may all be considered as suns. The work was at first written in Italian, but, urged by his friends, Father Secchi translated it into French with the help of Father Larcher. In the preface, which ends with the verse of the eighteenth Psalm, *in Sole posuit tabernaculum suum Altissimus,* he clearly explains the scientific and religious purposes for which he studied the sun so thoroughly:

> Many peoples of antiquity adored the sun, an error perhaps less humiliating than many others, because this body is the most perfect image of the Divine Being, the instrument used by the Creator to communicate to us almost all his benefices in the physical order of things. Although in our eyes the sun is nothing but a simple creature, yet its study is one of the loftiest to which scholars can dedicate themselves. The history of the conquests made in this inexhaustible field will always be one of aims most worthy of our attention and most suited to edify our spirit.

Father Secchi seems to have understood well the importance of the study of the sun because of its close connection with all the manifestations of life on the earth. He writes in the same preface:

> The contemplation of the works of God is one of the noblest occupations of the spirit, and it is the main purpose of the study of nature. But this study often brings us to useful results which we would not cast aside. The study of the sun, for the moment, does not seem to give us this advantage. Whatever our research may be and the knowledge we may acquire, we will never have the power to control the influence of the sun; nevertheless, the effect of this body is too closely linked with the phenomena of life, heat, and light to render useless our attempts to investigate the nature of its effect. And besides, who knows but that a close correlation may exist between certain solar phenomena and some terrestrial phenomena, which it would be important to foresee with some certainty?

In this case also Father Secchi foresaw the great development attained by such study in a few years, with so many important results.

The original contributions made by Father Secchi in his pioneer work on solar physics are very remarkable. They were integrated and extended during his own times, or immediately afterward, by many astrophysicists of various countries. All the opinions expressed on the nature of sunspots, observes Father Secchi, depend on the conception of the nature of the sun and the status of its inner mass. If we compare the sun to liquid red-hot lava, we are naturally led to believe that the spots are formed by solid, dark slag which floats on the surface. If we assume instead that the outer layer is gaseous, constituted more or less like the clouds which are formed in our atmosphere, the name "slag" can be used only very improperly, because then the matter under consideration will not be solid. We may think that the spots are gases shot out from inside the body of the sun, which are cooled by expansion, and, falling to the external surface, produce less bright regions, which appear dark by contrast. Before favoring these or other hypotheses, he continues to examine all the data furnished by observations. One must note that the concept was already clear in his mind that the sunspots represented regions of lower temperature than the surrounding photosphere. This concept, as we shall see later, was confirmed by comparing the spectra of the spots and photosphere. C. A. Young, at Princeton, years later, investigated the spectra of the spots with very powerful spectroscopic means, and discovered that the spectrum of the umbra was not uniformly dark, but instead could be resolved into a large number of very close lines. We know today that these are the "bands" which indicate the presence of molecular matter.

OTHER STUDIES OF SUNSPOTS

At the same time as Father Secchi, an accurate and systematic study of sunspots was concluded by R. C. Carrington, who had built a private observatory at Redhill in Surrey. From a long series of observations and drawings of the solar surface, he drew conclusions of great importance: the law of rotation of the sun at various latitudes, the existence and direction of systematic currents, the distributions of spots on the surface of the sun, and the position in space of the solar equator, with new precise data. To him the surface of the sun, called the "photosphere," looks as if it were covered by an enormous number of small luminous granules of all dimensions but of widely differing form, the oval form predominating. The spaces between granules form a darker background without being entirely black.

The visual observation of this structure was confined photographically for the first time by P. J. C. Janssen, founder of the Meudon Observatory, near Paris. In 1879 he announced the presence of a real *réseau photosphérique*, which he obtained from exposures of one- to three-thousandths of a second with a photographic apparatus which could take a series of photographs in short intervals of time, on the principle of cinematography, which it preceded. Janssen also made evident, in his photographs of a partial eclipse of the sun, that not the least distortion of a granule could be detected, and thus he proved the absence of any atmosphere on the moon. The more luminous granules which constitute a "granulation" in the photosphere are, according to Father Secchi, nothing but the extremities of columns of very hot gas which climb from the underlying solar surface, which is generally less luminous. The appearance of pores and the formation of spots, which indicate a strong disturbance in that region of the sun, sometimes extend far beyond the limits of the region occupied by the spots and their penumbra. Of what nature are these perturbations?

Hervé Faye, of the French Academy of Sciences, attempted, in Father Secchi's time, to propose a theory of the constitution of the sun, even arguing with Father Secchi. Contrary to Herschel's theory, Faye was the first to advance the hypothesis that the sun can be considered as a thermal machine radiating heat from its surface. Faye writes:

> The firebox is the very mass of the body, furnished at its origin with a tremendous quantity of thermal energy which is fed by the progressive contraction of the entire mass. The source of cold is celestial space, the condenser is the photosphere, the regulating means is the natural invariability of the temperature at which the chemical combinations are produced and destroyed. The machine functions by rising and falling currents which carry vapors and solid and cold substances. The way in which the heat is transported from the center to the surface lies in the fact that these solid or oxidized substances require from the central layers, in order to dissociate, a quantity which their vapors carry upward to the photosphere, where they reproduce themselves by combination."

For Faye the sunspots are cyclones, but against this hypothesis Secchi observes that if a vortical motion existed in all the spots, the penumbrae would always show a curvilinear structure around the nucleus, which is only rarely observed. Of the three hundred spots which Secchi observed in the course of one year, only seven or eight appeared to have the well-defined spiral structure which is necessary to explain a vortical motion. Furthermore this structure never lasts longer than a day or two, but the spots themselves may last a long time after having lost their spiral form. From this fact Secchi drew his first conclusions: these phenomena cannot take place in a solid body, but must be produced in a fluid mass, whose fluidity is similar to that of a gas, so that the constitution of these phenomena must be compared to the formation of flames or clouds. The particulars of the penumbra show clearly that the dark mass does not invade the luminous matter, but instead the luminous matter precipitates itself onto the dark regions, and often the bright mass seems to float on the darker mass which constitutes the nucleus. Later observations with the spectroheliograph confirm that in general the cyclonic motion does not exist in the spots at the level of the photosphere.

The observation of the splitting of the spots, which often happens in the nuclei in the form of eruptions which surmount and break them, is attentively followed by Father Secchi, who is thereby strengthened in his opinion that such wide, rapid, and complex movements on the surface of the sun could never take place in any solid substance. He therefore concludes that the photosphere must be composed of an elastic fluid similar to our gases and that the spiral motions sometimes visible in the sunspots rather resemble the cyclones of the terrestrial atmosphere. These vortices are more frequent during the period of formation of the sunspots; afterward the motions which produce them soon become more regular and produce currents which, according to his observations, converge toward the center of the nucleus of the spots. Once it is established that the nucleus is composed of a dark mass surrounded by photospheric matter in the gaseous state, must one conclude that such a black mass is solid? For Secchi there is no doubt that it is gaseous, but out of respect for differing opinions he proposes to institute other investigations "to persuade his adversaries."

At that time (1857) Warren de la Rue, who had been among the first to use photography for celestial observations, was commissioned by the Royal Society to construct an instrument, the "photoheliograph," with which the sun could be photographed every day. Thus photographic documentation, in addition to visual, of the variations in solar activity date back to that time. De la Rue also obtained stereoscopic photographs of the spots and faculae, and ascertained that the faculae are located in the upper part of the photosphere, since the spots appear as holes in the penumbra which is at a lower level than the surrounding regions. Thus the discovery of Wilson was confirmed, and Secchi, after a suggestion of Faye, determined the "parallax of depth" of the spots, that is, the apparent shift of the depression of the surface during the rotation of the sun. Another student of the sun, Samuel P. Langley, about ten years later, made his marvelous and well known drawings of the spots and other details of the solar surface, from which we can better understand the structure of the spots and the phases of their evolution.

ORIGIN AND APPEARANCE OF SOLAR SPECTRUM

Using spectroscopes with several detached prisms, built by Hofmann and Merz, or direct-vision spectroscopes built by Amici, Father Secchi extended the investigations of Ångström and Kirchhoff on the spectrum of the sun. He proved that the absorbing layer, which produces the Fraunhofer lines, must be of small depth, noting at the moments of the second and third contacts of a total eclipse of the sun the reversal of the hydrogen lines in the chromosphere and, an instant before the appearance of the dark Fraunhofer lines, the continuity of the spectrum except for some sodium and magnesium lines which also appear reversed. From this observation he concludes that it is the layer, observed at that moment, which partially reverses the dark lines of certain metals, as the "pink layer" reverses the hydrogen lines. This "reversing layer" does not have power strong enough to make the lines bright in the full light of the sun, and thus it produces only a partial reversal, so that the contrast which gives rise to the dark rays disappears. Father Secchi discusses all the terrestrial experiments which might shed light on the origin and appearance of the solar spectrum and concludes that the formation of the Fraunhofer lines, wide or narrow, well-defined or diffuse, depends upon the conditions of temperature and pressure which predominate in the layer where the phenomenon of absorption takes place. This notion agrees fully with modern research and theory.

In 1862 Janssen built an observatory at Montmartre to investigate how sunlight is absorbed by the earth's atmosphere. With a spectroscope of great dispersion with five prisms, he succeeded in resolving the dark bands into narrow lines, which became more intense as the sun became low on the horizon. Thus he was able to establish that these lines were of atmospheric origin, and consequently he called them "telluric lines." Later he discovered that such lines are due to bands of water vapor present in the earth's atmosphere. Always intent on investigating the effect of the absorption of the earth's atmosphere on the spectrum of the sun, Janssen at the advanced age of seventy years had himself carried to the top of Mont Blanc for the principal purpose of finding out whether oxygen was present in the sun. He made the ascent in winter when the influence of water vapor in the atmosphere is reduced to a minimum. His observations implied the absence of oxygen in the sun; later observations have established its presence.

OBSERVATIONS OF ECLIPSES

The importance of total eclipses of the sun for the direct and spectroscopic study of the phenomena which appear when the disk of the sun is covered did not escape Father Secchi, who took advantage of all possible occasions to widen his research of solar physics. The eclipse of 1860, total in Spain, was the first during which he was able to observe the nature of the red "prominences" or "protuberances," that is, the great eruptions of hydrogen which had been noted during the most ancient eclipses. The first scientific observations were made during the eclipse of 1842, without, however, any sufficient explanation of the phenomenon. Father Secchi went to the Desierto de las Palmas near Castellón de la Plana, close to the east coast of Spain, where he made very important observations, having conceived the idea of photographing the direct image of the sun covered by the moon. Warren de la Rue had gone to Rivabellosa on the west coast with the Kew heliograph, which magnified the sun's image through the eyepiece. Both observers, despite the uncertainty of the luminous intensity of the prominences and consequently of the correct exposure, obtained good results. Comparison of the photographs of Father Secchi and De la Rue leads to the following conclusions: (1) that the prominences are real objects and not light effects, as some people believed; (2)

that the prominences belong to the sun; and (3) that the corona is real, more developed at the equator than at the poles, and at 45° latitude more than at the equator itself.

The solar eclipse of August 18, 1868, total in India, was observed by Janssen with spectroscopic observations of the prominences. He related that he had been struck by the great brightness of the emission lines of the prominences and that he thought it would soon be possible for him to see them even without an eclipse. The next day, in fact, he succeeded in making those memorable and historic observations which have given astronomers a new method for observing the prominences in broad daylight. With the slit of the spectroscope aimed radially, partly at the disk of the sun, partly outside it, he explored a portion of the edge, observing the line Hα (C of Fraunhofer). He described as follows what he was able to see:

> I was investigating a region of the western edge, when all of a sudden I noticed a small red line, very bright, of height from 1' to 2', which constituted the exact continuation of the dark line C of the solar spectrum. As I shifted the slit of the spectroscope in order to explore the region, systematically, the line continued changing in height and brightness in its various parts, thus presenting great variability, both in height and brightness in the various regions of the prominence.

About a month later he wrote:

> It was on August 19 that I made this discovery and consequently I can say that for me the real eclipse took place on that day and not on August 18. Since that date I have been able to sketch, day by day, the form, the location, and the constitution of the prominences of the sun, which until that day had been visible only during eclipses.

The report of Janssen's discovery was read at the meeting of the Académie des Sciences in October, 1868, and was followed immediately by a communication from Sir Joseph Norman Lockyer who claimed the same discovery, made at the same time in England with a high-dispersion spectroscope. Father Secchi immediately afterward succeeded in repeating the observations of Janssen and Lockyer by setting an enlarged slit tangent to the edge of the sun. Thus in 1869, with L. Respighi, he began a regular series of observations day by day of the "spectroscopic images of the edge of the sun," which were thenceforth published regularly in the "Memoirs of the Society of Italian Spectroscopists."

CHARLES A. YOUNG

In the total eclipse of the following year (1869) the American astrophysicist, C. A. Young, was able for the first time to prove the gaseous nature of the corona by observing in its spectrum the green emission line, of which he determined the approximate wave length 5304Å. He identified it with the nearby chromospheric line (wave length 5317Å). The latter, the instant before totality, is very brilliant in the spectrum of the edge of the sun, but it disappears a few seconds after the onset of totality, when the much weaker line of the corona becomes visible. In view of the small dispersion used at that time, it is no wonder that the two lines were confused. Only during the eclipse of 1898 were they distinguished and separately identified by Lockyer. In the eclipse of 1869 Young, on the basis of theoretical considerations, tried to see the "flash spectrum," which he actually observed for the first time the next year during the eclipse visible in Spain. He described the phenomenon as follows:

> Just previous to totality, I had carefully adjusted the slit tangential to the sun's limb at the point where the second contact would take place, and was watching the gradual brightening of 1474 (the green corona line) and the magnesium lines. As the crescent grew narrower, I noticed a fading out, so to speak, of all the dark lines in the field of view, but was not at all prepared for the beautiful phenomenon which presented itself when the moon finally covered the whole photosphere. The whole field was at once filled with brilliant lines, which suddenly flashed into brightness and then gradually faded away until, in less than two seconds, nothing remained but the lines I had been watching. The slit was very close, and the definition perfect.

From this observation he concluded that all the absorption, which produces the Fraunhofer lines, has its origin in a thin layer, a few hundred miles deep, located above the photosphere, which he called the "reversing layer."

Like Secchi, Young made some magnificent and interesting drawings of prominences, and also photographs. He wrote a well known and much appreciated book about the sun, which has been translated into several languages. He was the first to use the diffraction grating in astronomical spectroscopy, and he determined the sun's period of rotation from the shift of the lines at the two opposite edges. Convinced that the thermopile was an unsatisfactory instrument for measuring solar radiation in the various regions of the spectrum, he invented the "bolometer," an electric thermometer based on the principle of the Wheatstone bridge. He explored and diagrammed with it the infrared region of the spectrum as far as wave lengths ten times larger than the region of the visible spectrum. Named secretary of the Smithsonian Institution in Washington, he founded there an astrophysical observatory for the main purpose of measuring the quantity of heat transmitted by the sun to the earth, in order to find out if it were constant and how it influenced meteorological conditions on the earth.

SIR JOSEPH NORMAN LOCKYER

A contemporary of Young and Langley, Sir Joseph Norman Lockyer began as an amateur to have an interest in astrophysics. Having specialized in the study of the sun, he was called to direct the Observatory of Solar Physics at South Kensington in 1885. Just as Huggins had had the collaboration of the chemist Miller, Lockyer had the collaboration of the chemist Frankland. One of his most important discoveries was that of the spectrum of prominences and the possibility of observing them in full sunlight. As we have said, his discovery was simultaneous with Janssen's. Continuing these investigations, he found that the prominences arise from a gaseous envelope surrounding the sun, which he called the "Chromosphere." In 1881 he completed and published his celebrated observations, from which he announced how certain lines of iron increased notably in intensity during the transition from the spectrum of the electric arc to that of the spark. The study of the "enhanced" lines, as is well known, is of fundamental importance in modern astrophysics. Mainly from the study of the spectrum of the chromosphere, Lockyer derived his theory of the dissociation of the elements at the high temperatures of the stellar atmosphere. Thus in his treatise *"Chemistry of the Sun"* he supposes that the lines H and K of the violet region of the solar spectrum are due to the dissociation of calcium, and he shows that they gradually become more intense as the electric charge increases. These ideas can be easily translated into the modern theory of ionization. Observing the spectrum of prominences, he noted the bright yellow line D_3, and he surmised from its behavior that it could not be produced by any element recognized on the earth. Therefore he attributed it to a new gas, which he called "helium." For nearly thirty years it was believed that this gas could be found only in the atmosphere of the sun and earth, until in 1895 Sir William Ramsay discovered it also in the radioactive minerals.

TACCHINI AND RICCÒ

To the school of Father Secchi belong two other Italian astrophysicists, Pietro Tacchini and Annibale Riccò. The former was born in Modena in 1838, twenty years after Father Secchi; the latter also in Modena in 1844. Together with their master they present three beautiful, serene, and interesting scientific figures, passionately and enthusiastically dedicated to their work, which they faithfully followed all their lives. They gathered such a mass of observations and results that today, in the light of new discoveries and new powerful means of observation, the quality and quantity of their work reveal them as pioneers.

At the very beginning of his astronomical career Tacchini formed scientific ties with Father Secchi, which developed into a deep, devoted friendship and a continuous collaboration, almost daily, lasting until the premature death of Secchi. At the Palermo Observatory Tacchini's daily observations of the sun made him realize the necessity of a well-organized national collaboration in order to follow the multiform and variable phenomena presented by the sun. He also understood that all these phenomena combined, which he comprised under the name of "solar meteorology," are the origin of various terrestrial phenomena. His wise hypotheses about the influence of solar eruptions on the appearance of the northern lights in the upper terrestrial atmosphere, which he so cautiously advanced and so often mentioned in his letters to Father Secchi, today have well-confirmed experimental and theoretical foundations. The remarkable maximum of solar activity in 1870, accompanied by many luminous northern lights on the earth, redoubled the work in Rome and Palermo and gave Secchi and Tacchini the idea of establishing a special institution with the special purpose of following, from various Italian observatories and with the same criteria, the activity of the sun, and with the more general purpose of research on the physics of the sky. Since the instrument used for such work is almost exclusively the spectroscope, the organization founded in 1871 was called the Society of Italian Spectroscopists; its well-known "Memoirs" still continue today under the new title of "Memoirs of the Italian Astronomical Society." It is indeed one of the greatest glories of Pietro Tacchini that he intensely desired and affectionately initiated such an institution, which was the first of its kind in the world and which gave a forceful incentive to research on the physical constitution of the stars. Only twenty-three years later, in the United States, Hale founded the *Astrophysical Journal,* and among his first collaborators were Tacchini and Riccò.

Tacchini made various expeditions outside Italy to observe celestial phenomena. The first was his expedition in 1874 for the occasion of the transit of Venus across the disk of the sun. This transit was much anticipated by astronomers, because it was expected that the many expeditions scattered throughout the globe could obtain data for establishing a precise value of the distance of the sun from the earth. At the Padua Observatory Tacchini prepared the necessary instruments; he chose his collaborators, first of all Father Secchi, who for reasons of poor health was not able to accompany him. The chosen location was about 150 miles north of Calcutta, in Muddapur in Bengal, and his companions were Alessandro Dorna, director of the Turin Observatory, Antonio Abetti, then astronomer at the Padua Observatory, and Father Lafont, director of the College of Saint Xavier in Calcutta.

In 1882 Tacchini observed a total eclipse of the sun in Egypt, and in the following year, together with some French astronomers, another one on Caroline Island, a coral reef in the Pacific. There he had occasion to observe some prominences of white color; most prominences are of a bright red color, due to hydrogen. As we now know, the white is essentially due to calcium vapors. At the death of Father Secchi, Tacchini undertook the direction of the Roman College Observatory and provided it with the most powerful instruments built in Italy.

Riccò, director of the Catania Observatory, and its station on Mt. Etna, took Tacchini's place as editor of the "Memoirs of the Spectroscopists," where can be found all his numerous regular observations of sunspots and prominences. He demonstrated their various characteristics and the zone preferred by the prominences, variable with the eleven-year cycle of solar activity. Since the Catania Observatory was also equipped for geophysical observations, Riccò turned his attention to the study of the relation between sunspots and the perturbations of terrestrial magnetism. From a goodly number of observations he proved the existence of a retardation of the magnetic perturbation on the earth of 45 hours after the passage of the spots across the central meridian of the sun. This corresponds to an average velocity of propagation of the corpuscles producing a magnetic perturbation of 650 miles per second. Having provided the Catania Observatory with a photographic telescope, he collaborated on a photographic map of the sky for which he undertook the zone of $+47°$ to $+54°$ declination, and he commenced the publication of the corresponding catalog. It can be said that the first period of the rise and development of astrophysics closes with Riccò. From his death in 1919 begins, with the use of the great reflectors, sun towers, and wide-dispersion spectrographs, a new epoch, which has been rich in discoveries, observations, and practical and theoretical research in this branch of astronomy.

17 : nineteenth century astronomy and celestial mechanics

AFTER THE OBSERVATIONS OF BRADLEY AND Bessel the feeling grew that it was necessary to determine the position of the fixed stars with the highest possible accuracy and to arrange them in great homogeneous catalogs to be used for the study of their proper motions, of star streams and their distribution, as well as for reference in the determination of the positions of the planets.

ARGELANDER

One of the pioneers in this field was a student of Bessel, Friedrich W. A. Argelander, born in 1799 in Memel in East Prussia, of a Finnish father. After having assisted Bessel in his meridian observations of zones from 15° south to 45° north declination, he was made director of the new Bonn Observatory. He procured a Pistor meridian circle, with the intention of undertaking a project of great importance in extending the knowledge of the starry sky. His result is the well-known *Bonner Durchmusterung* of the northern sky, that is, a "review" or list of all the visible stars down to the ninth magnitude, and also many of the tenth magnitude, included between the North Pole and 2° south declination. To have an idea of the vastness of the work it will be enough to say that the number of catalogued stars is 324,198, all marked on celestial charts, of the highest usefulness and still employed today.

The *Bonner Durchmusterung* was extended by E. Schönfeld to part of the Southern Hemisphere as far as 23° south declination, and to 43° south by J. M. Thome, director of the Argentine National Observatory, in the *Cordoba Durchmusterung*. Sir David Gill, Astronomer Royal at the Cape of Good Hope, completed the review of the southern sky photographically, and J. C. Kapteyn compiled a catalog containing 400,000 stars. Since in these reviews the positions of the stars are only approximate, Argelander realized the necessity of determining the precise co-ordinates of most of the stars contained in these catalogs, and he divided the work among the various observatories of the world, adopting a uniform system. In 1867 Argelander presented his project to the *Astronomische Gesellschaft*, the German astronomical society of international character, founded in Heidelberg in 1863. After long laborious years the unification of all the catalogs was finished, under the name of the society itself. It was published by the participating observatories of the various nations, and it contains the stars of the *Bonner Durchmusterung* as far as the ninth magnitude. This very noteworthy and important work on the position and distribution of the stars in the Galaxy was to be even further extended by photography.

PHOTOGRAPHIC MAP OF THE SKY

Sir David Gill was the first to propose, in 1886, the idea of an international organization which would assume the task of making a photographic map of the whole sky, accurate and on a large scale. The brothers Paul and Prosper Henry, of the Paris Observatory, had meanwhile designed a photographic instrument for reproducing the Milky Way, whose great number of stars made visual observations impossible. The following year, under the auspices of the French Academy, fifty-six representatives of seventeen nations met at the Paris Observatory to lay plans for the great new astronomical undertaking. They defined the type of photographic telescope to be used, and assigned to each of the participating observatories a region of the sky to photograph. Each was to make two sets of photographic plates: the first for a catalog of stars to the eleventh magnitude, to be followed by micrometric measurements for the position and magnitude of every star contained in each plate; the second for the actual map of the sky, including stars to the fourteenth magnitude, which was to be enlarged to form the celestial atlas. Eighteen observatories scattered throughout the world undertook the task: Greenwich, the Vatican Observatory, Catania, Helsingfors, Potsdam, Oxford, Paris, Bordeaux, Tolouse, Algiers, San Fernando, Tacubaya, Santiago, La Plata, Rio de Janeiro, Cape of Good Hope, Sidney, and Melbourne. Some of them for various reasons failed in their task. The final success of the work, however, was not compromised, for other observatories filled the gaps and gave assistance. Hyderabad took the place of Santiago, Cordoba of La Plata, Perth and Edinburgh of Rio de Janeiro. Oxford helped in the reductions of the Vatican, and Naples collaborated with Catania in reductions and calculations. In Italy, through Tacchini's influence, Catania Observatory was chosen because of the purity of the sky, and the zone between 46° and 55° north declination was assigned to it. Half a century of continuous work, organized and initiated by Riccò, was finally completed by A. Bemporad and G. A. Favaro with a total of 320,275 stellar positions, contained in eight volumes of sixty-four parts. To the reobservation of the fundamental reference stars, as a supplement to those of the catalogs of the *Astronomische Gesellschaft*, almost all the Italian observatories contributed: Arcetri-Florence, Padua, Palermo, Turin, and Campidoglio-Rome. The work of Catania is all the more notable in that (by contrast with the other participating observatories) only this observatory and that of Helsingfors published, in addition to the rectilinear co-ordinates of each star, also the equatorial co-ordinates (right ascension and declination) so that the catalog is immediately usable. This celestial map is believed to contain 100 million stars, and the catalog of all stars to the eleventh magnitude inclusive includes about 6 million. By repeating this great work, in fifty or one hundred years, we shall have most important elements for the calculation of proper motions and eventual intermediate variations.

SOLAR PARALLAX

The preceding chapter mentioned the Italian expedition to India, directed by Tacchini, to observe the transit of Venus across the solar disk in 1874. It seemed unquestionable at that time that with photography, the heliometer, and the spectroscope it would be possible to determine with precision the transit of Venus, as seen from a number of stations scattered throughout the earth, at different points of the solar disk and thus to obtain a value for the parallax of the sun, affected by only a small average error. The major civilized nations carefully prepared numerous expeditions. One of the most fervent champions of the method already proposed by Halley was another astronomer royal, George Biddell Airy, who assumed the direction of the Greenwich Observatory in 1835. Several years before the two transits of Venus across the sun in this century (1874 and 1882), Airy had opened the discussion in the Royal Astronomical Society on the most appropriate methods of observing them. On the basis of earlier experience with the transits of 1761 and 1769, it was hoped to reduce the uncertainty in the observation of the transit which was produced by the disturbing phenomenon called the "black drop." There were five British expeditions: to Egypt, to the Hawaiian Islands (Sandwich), to the island of Rodriguez in the Indian Ocean, to Christchurch in New Zealand, and to the island of Kerguelen (or Isle of Desolation) in the southern Indian Ocean. Many observers were trained for months at Greenwich under the general direction of Airy; a model was even built for practice in observing the transit. For various reasons, among them the unforeseen effect of the illuminated atmosphere of Venus, the results did not come up to expectation. The existence of the atmosphere was known, appearing as a luminous ring, but no one believed that it would disturb the observations so much that it would lead to such marked differences in the determinations of the transits. Even photography brought no better results. No less important was a similar project undertaken in Germany, with five expeditions for the transit of 1874 and four for the transit of 1882, sent to various parts of the world under the direction of A. Auwers, president of the Academy of Sciences of Berlin, who assembled all the numerous observations in six huge volumes. These expeditions determined the external and internal contacts of Venus with the edge of the sun. Wide use was made of the heliometer, with which the distance of Venus was measured directly from the edge and center of the solar disk. All the results obtained from the transits of Venus with so much labor and trouble were found to be considerably inferior to the accuracy obtained more easily with the method of the planets, or better still, of the minor planets.

In the "great opposition" of 1877, since Mars was then relatively close to the earth, Gill thought of using the method of the "diurnal parallaxes," proposed by Airy several years before. This method consists of making observations of the positions of the planet at hour angles as far apart as possible. For this purpose Gill went to Ascension

Island (in the Atlantic Ocean), where he obtained a good value for the parallax of the sun. On the other hand, since 1872 J. G. Galle had been suggesting the determination of the solar parallax by observing the minor planets, which in their orbits come very close to the earth. They have the advantage over Venus and Mars that they present a point disk and also, because of their great number, frequent favorable oppositions. Gill, who had already tried the method with the minor planet Juno on the occasion of the transit of Venus observed from Mauritius (Indian Ocean), made a more complete attempt with the minor planets Iris, Victoria, and Sappho. However, instead of measuring their diurnal parallaxes, he wanted to combine observations made from stations as far apart as possible.

This project implied a wide collaboration of several observatories with identical instruments. Heliometer measurements were made by Gill and Finlay at the Cape of Good Hope, by Elkin and Hall at New Haven, and by Peter in Leipzig. Among the various observers there was also Auwers who, besides participating in the observations of Victoria with Gill, reduced the computations of the exact position of the comparison stars, from meridian observations made in a large number of observatories. For Victoria a triangulation was also added, made with the heliometer, to determine the systematic errors which affect the meridian observations. All the discussion of this remarkable work is published in two large volumes of the Annals of the Observatory of the Cape, where the resulting value of the solar parallax is 8.804″ with a small average error of 0.005″. In current use this value has been rounded off to 8.80″.

The superiority of the method of the minor planets was thus fully shown, as well as the importance of international collaboration and the organizing capacity of Gill. He well deserves the credit also for the determination of stellar parallaxes, that is, the distance of the stars, by a direct trigonometric method. Using the heliometer in collaboration with Elkin, he determined the parallaxes of several bright stars—Sirius, Canopus, α and β Centauri—and of some stars with pronounced proper motions. He was thus able to discover that α Centauri is one of the nearest stars to the solar system, having a parallax of 0.75″ with a probable error of 0.01″. In collaboration with Finlay and De Sitter he made other measurements with a heliometer of greater power and thus established the distance from the solar system, and the high luminosity, of some of the brightest stars, like Canopus and Rigel.

THE DISCOVERY OF NEPTUNE

The most sensational discovery of the nineteenth century which demonstrated the great progress of celestial mechanics was the discovery of a new important member of the solar system. As early as about 1820 the anomalous motion of Uranus had led to unforeseen difficulties in the correlation of old observations with modern ones, so that Bessel expressed his opinion to Humboldt that the time would come when the "mystery of Uranus" would be solved by the discovery of a new planet. The elements could be calculated from its effect on Uranus, and eventually verified by its effect on Saturn. A student of St. John's College at Cambridge (England), John Couch Adams, in 1841 at the age of twenty-two turned his attention to the problem; and two years later, working on his doctoral dissertation, he attempted a first approximate solution of the problem by computing a circular orbit with a radius equal to twice the mean distance of Uranus from the sun. This result seemed to bring theory and observation together, and after Adams had obtained from the Astronomer Royal Airy the observations of Uranus made at Greenwich, he was able to find another more accurate solution for the mass, the heliocentric longitude, and the elements of the orbit of the hypothetical planet, which he communicated to the Greenwich Observatory in October, 1845.

Entirely independently of Adams, Urbain Jean Le Verrier, Arago's successor as director of the Paris Observatory, in June, 1846, presented to the Academy of France his second paper in which, having assembled the most reliable observations of Uranus, he compared them with the theory expounded in his first paper. He came to the conclusion that it was impossible to represent the observed motion of Uranus without admitting the presence of some outside force. The hypothesis that the law of universal gravitation was no longer exactly valid at the remote distance of Uranus should be discarded, for too many proofs had been assembled that it was valid even beyond the solar system. There remained only to admit the presence of another unknown planet, located on the ecliptic at twice the distance of Uranus. The problem was therefore the same as that which had already been solved by Adams, and in fact Le Verrier found that there was only one region of the ecliptic where the disturbing body might be found in order to satisfy the observed irregularities in the motion of Uranus. He concluded that on January 1, 1847, its heliocentric longitude would have to be about 325°, but he gave no elements of the orbit or mass of the planet. The position assigned by Le Verrier differed by only 1° from that of Adams, in the papers which the latter had transmitted to the Greenwich Observatory seven months earlier. In August of the same year Le Verrier presented to the Academy of France his third paper, which contained the elements of the orbit of the new planet. In England, at Cambridge Observatory, the search for the planet was begun at the end of July, 1846, three weeks before the planet was in opposition, and the observations continued for two months in the zodiacal region having its center on the ecliptic at 325° longitude and extending 15° in longitude in both directions from the central point, and from 5° north latitude to 5° south latitude. Since there was no map of that region in England the search was rather difficult, but nonetheless the planet was actually observed during those first nights in August. However, its motion was not detected and therefore the planet was not discovered.

On September 3 Adams communicated to the Astronomer Royal a new solution to the problem which brought a small decrease in the distance of the planet, with a consequent better agreement between theory and observation. The search in the sky, entrusted to Rev. J. Challis, director of the Cambridge Observatory, was still proceeding slowly. Meanwhile Le Verrier communicated his major conclusions to Johann G. Galle, assistant to J. F. Encke at the Berlin Observatory and later director of the Breslau Observatory, in a letter dated September 18, 1846:

> As you will see, sir, I prove that it is possible to satisfy the observations of Uranus only by introducing the effect of a new planet, hitherto unknown; remarkably enough, there is only one position on the ecliptic which can be attributed to the disturbing planet. The following are the elements of the orbit which I assign to this body.

He gives the elements of the planet and then proceeds:

> The present position of this body shows that we are now, and will continue to be for several months, in a favorable condition to discover it. Moreover, the size of its mass permits the conclusion that the size of its apparent diameter is more than 3″. This diameter is of such a nature that it can be distinguished, in good telescopes, from the false diameter bestowed by various aberrations on the stars.

Having received this letter on September 23, Galle spoke about it to his director Encke, who did not seem very enthusiastic about Le Verrier's proposal; he was even doubtful of Le Verrier's results. Nevertheless Galle, helped by a young student, H. L. D'Arrest, was able to consult that same night a new celestial map of Bremiker, printed but not yet published, of precisely the twenty-first hour of right ascension; and he quickly discovered the planet by comparing the charted stars with those in the sky. The body was followed as much as possible that night, but neither from its disk nor its motion could one be certain that it was really the new planet. The following night Galle was able to establish its motion and he wrote to Le Verrier: "The planet whose position you indicated really exists," and Le Verrier communicated the discovery to the Academy and wrote to Galle:

> I thank you heartily for the speed with which you informed me about your observation of September 23 and 24. Thanks to you, we are now definitely in possession of the new world. The pleasure I felt in seeing that you found it less than 1° from the position which I had indicated is a little disturbed by the thought that if I had written to you sooner, four months ago, we would then have obtained the result which we have just achieved. I shall communicate your letter next Monday to the Academy of Sciences. The Bureau of Longitudes here has decided in favor of "Neptune," with a trident for its symbol. The name of "Janus" would imply that this planet is the last one in the solar system, and there is no reason to believe that this is so.

Thus the name and the symbol were conferred on the planet within a week after its discovery. Galle had suggested the name of "Janus," the mythological predecessor of Saturn. Very interesting to us is the observation of Le Verrier that Neptune might not be the outermost planet.

The news of the discovery of the planet arrived in England September 30. Until then the analogous work of Adams was known only to a few individuals and nothing had been disclosed abroad. Consequently, when the official astronomers, to whom Adams had communicated results almost identical to those of Le Verrier, made known their inconclusive and belated research, there arose much heated discussion. It soon died down, however, and there remained only respect and admiration for the two valiant theoretical astronomers who, unknown to each other, and quite independently, had solved a problem whose solution was believed impossible. The first determination of Neptune's orbit had been made by Adams, using the observations of Challis of August 4 and 12, before the official discovery and the subsequent one of October 13. In November, 1846, Le Verrier published in the *Connaissance des Temps* his *Recherches sur les mouvements de la planète Herschel (dite Uranus)*, where he gives all the analytical and numerical procedures which he used for the discovery of the disturbing body. In the following years at the Paris Observatory Le Verrier undertook the immense task of revising the theories of Mercury, Venus, the Earth, Mars, Jupiter, Saturn, Uranus, and Neptune, calculating tables of their motions. Adams made an important analysis of the more complicated and laborious parts of this undertaking, published in the Annals of the Paris Observatory.

THE MOTION OF THE MOON

Adams, who was later named director of the Cambridge Observatory, presented to the Royal Society in 1853 his celebrated paper on the secular acceleration of the mean motion of the moon. Halley was the first to discover this acceleration, by comparing Babylonian Observations of eclipses with those of Albatenius and modern times. Newton mentions this discovery in the second edition of his *Principia*. Later, as we have said, Laplace discovered the cause of the acceleration and the problem was thought to be solved. But a detailed and complete theory of the moon, in other words, the calculation of lunar tables which would satisfy all observations exactly, still concerned many investigators—M. C. Damoiseau, Giovanni Plana, director of the Turin Observatory, P. A. Hansen, and C. Delaunay—who all gave new values for the acceleration. When Adams published his paper entitled "On the Secular Variation of the Mean Motion of the Moon," which brought new elements into the very complicated problem, there is no wonder that a long and heated discussion ensued.

The difficulty of the solution of this problem lies in the fact that the sun, in spite of its distance from the earth and moon, influences the orbital motion of the latter as the moon is periodically nearer to or farther from the sun. Furthermore, the angles formed by the line-of-center of the moon and sun and by the line-of-center of the sun and earth are always different. It follows that the attractions of the sun and moon are generally unequal and act in different directions, giving rise to a disturbing action of the sun which produces either an increase or a decrease in the gravitation of the moon toward the earth, sometimes a retardation and sometimes an acceleration of the orbital velocity, and therefore continuous variations in the eccentricity and inclination of the lunar orbit and in the position of its perigee and nodes. In fact, such a complication of inequalities results that they can only be made evident when the effect of disturbing forces is discussed with all the accuracy permitted by analysis.

Delaunay, summarizing the discussion in the *Connaisance des Temps* of 1864, writes as follows concerning Adam's paper:

> The publication of Adam's paper truly marks a memorable step forward, an entire revolution in this branch of theoretical astronomy. His result has therefore been strongly attacked; people did not want to admit it on the basis of apparently exact arguments. Besides, noting that he obtained results which did not agree with observation, they tried to take away from Laplace the credit for one of his greatest discoveries, and they based their reasons on a fallacious and incorrect analysis. But of all these arguments not a single one was right, and the insistence with which they were presented and maintained produced an entirely opposite effect from what was expected. In fact, the verifications of this much-contested result have accumulated so much that it would be difficult to find in the sciences a better established truth than the one which Adams first announced in his paper of 1853. All the objections which have been raised against it have fallen one by one. The analysis which was declared fallacious and incorrect has been recognized as exact. The agreement or disagreement of the theoretical result with the indications furnished by observations has not been considered the criterion of the accuracy of this theoretical result. If the declared disagreement really exists, it must simply be concluded that the cause assigned by Laplace to the solar acceleration of the mean motion of the moon is not the only one which produces the total phenomenon, and in their disagreement there is nothing which can diminish the fame of the discovery of the great French geometer.

With the work of Adams, the labors of astronomers on lunar theory certainly did not cease. Simon Newcomb, in charge of the American *Nautical Almanac*, in 1870 showed that the accuracy of Hansen's lunar tables had been secured since 1750 only by denying all agreement with observations made before that time, so that about 1700 Hansen's tables deviated from observation even more than the table they had replaced. After long and patient work Newcomb came to important results in the representation of the motion of the moon and the four inner planets, and of the orbit of Saturn's satellite, Hyperion. Furthermore, he made noteworthy contributions to the knowledge of the fundamental constants of astronomy. He showed that the secular motion of the perihelion of Mercury is 43″ greater than the theoretical motion calculated from the best values obtainable for the mass of the planets. This disagreement and his theory of the inner planets are very important for the modern hypotheses on gravitation and relativity.

In 1877 George W. Hill, an astronomer on the staff of the American *Nautical Almanac*, published a paper on the motion of the moon's perigee, where he applied new methods of analysis and calculation. Instead of using polar co-ordinates referred to a fixed axis, he adopted rectangular co-ordinates referred to moving axes, from which he obtained differential equations, in simple algebraic form, very simple to solve by infinite series. One of the greatest difficulties which had been encountered in the earlier theories is that the lunar perigee has a continuous motion, so that it cannot be calculated as a fixed ellipse which would represent with sufficient approximation the actual orbit of the moon for any given interval of time. The merit and importance of Hill's new method were soon recognized, but although he had worked to prove its usefulness he did not have time to formulate a lunar theory. Nevertheless his ideas found practical application, thanks to E. W. Brown, director of the Yale Observatory at New Haven, who completed the new theory and computed its corresponding tables.

SOLAR SYSTEM

In the period of Airy, Auwers, and Gill we must note in the field of celestial mechanics the important and brilliant work of Airy on the long-term inequalities in the motions of the Earth and Venus, which won him the gold medal of the Royal Society in 1832. He had suspected the possible existence of this inequality from examination of the errors in Delambre's solar tables and comparison of the Greenwich observations. The precise determination of these inequalities required much laborious work; we can understand the importance of the announcement made by Airy to the Royal Society: "Thus terminates one of the most laborious investigations that has yet been made in the planetary theory . . . I believe that the paper now presented to the Royal Society contains the first specific improvement in the solar tables made in this country since the establishment of the theory of gravitation."

As we have already mentioned, the irregularities in the motions of Procyon and Sirius had made Bessel suspect that they were double stars. He wrote to Humboldt: "I am convinced that Procyon and Sirius constitute real binary systems, formed by a visible star and an invisible one. There is no reason to suppose that luminosity is an essential characteristic of cosmic bodies. The visibility of innumerable stars is no argument against the invisibility of infinite others." Auwers, in an exhaustive discussion of the meridian observations of Procyon made in twenty observatories from 1750 on, proved that its motion is orbital and thus confirmed Bessel's hypothesis. He computed the period as 39.4 years, and also computed the other elements of the orbit. Only later (1896), did J. M. Schaeberle succeed in discovering with the refractor of the Lick Observatory, the companion of Procyon at a distance of about 4.5″, and of the thirteenth magnitude. A similar investigation was begun for Sirius by Auwers in 1861, and a year later, on January 31, the American optician, Alvan Clark, Jr., while testing a new objective of 18-inch diameter which he had constructed, discovered the hypothetical companion of Sirius in the exact location required by the theory. It must be remembered that a good determination of the orbit of Sirius, made by C. A. J. Peters, already existed. But Auwers' investigation, which lasted a good six years, is more complete, for it is based on 7000 meridian observations in right ascension and 4500 in declination.

During the study of the first observations of Sirius and Procyon, Auwers acquired a thorough knowledge of the old catalogs, and he exposed the systematic errors and imperfect corrections as well as the importance and usefulness of such precious material. For Procyon, he himself corrected a set of observations from Greenwich and Palermo. Well known is his *Neue Reduction der Bradley's sehen Beobachtungen aus den Jahren 1750 bis 1762*. The stars of Bradley were reobserved at Greenwich in 1865 and in this manner the "Auwers-Bradley" proper motions were obtained, which constitute the foundation of almost all the basic work on the motions of the stars and their statistical relationships. S. Newcomb's constant of precession, H. Kobold's research on the solar apex, and J. C. Kapteyn's discovery of the two streams of stars and his determination of the laws of luminosity and density of the stellar system are only a small part of the great progress which stems from the precise observations of Bradley and the patient and intelligent reductions of Auwers, whose catalog and proper motions were published in 1888 by the Academy of Sciences of St. Petersburg. This work led him to complete a fundamental system of stellar location and proper motions, which were used as the basis of the catalogs of the *Astronomische Gessellschaft*. Other similar fundamental catalogs, in good agreement with Auwers, were later compiled by Lewis Boss and Newcomb.

Another important result of Gill's observations with the heliometer was that of the determination of the elements of the satellites and mass of Jupiter. The longitudes of the satellites are easily deduced from the observations of their eclipses, but the latitudes are more difficult to derive. Measurements with the heliometer had been made by Bessel and others, but the satellite had always been referred to the edge or to the center of the disk. Gill adopted instead the method of measuring the distance and the position angles of the satellites with respect to one another, referring these later to fundamental stars. The discussion of the vast material collected by Gill and his associates was used by W. De Sitter, director of the Leiden Observatory, for his elaboration of the theory of the satellites and for the calculation of their elements and masses.

New horizons in celestial mechanics were opened at the end of the nineteenth century, when Henri Poincaré, professor at the Sorbonne, proved that the series generally used in the calculation of perturbations are not convergent, but semiconvergent. At first the terms decrease rapidly then increase again over long intervals of time. The various periodic terms in the movement of the planets, which are sufficient for ordinary cases, remain approximately valid, but no conclusion can be drawn about the final stability of the solar system because use of the above-mentioned series is not permitted beyond certain limits of time. Considerable interest was aroused by Poincaré's investigations on the possible forms of equilibrium of liquid rotating masses, which led Poincaré to the discovery of the "pear-shaped" form of equilibrium. The possibility of recognizing the first stages in the separation of a satellite from its central body or the evolution of a double star explains this interest which leads to speculation about the origin of the celestial system. There were many such investigations following the school of Poincaré.

A few weeks after the discovery of Neptune, a satellite was discovered by William Lassell, who had left the business world for a successful career in astronomy. He rivaled Herschel and Lord Rosse in constructing four large reflectors, and he built one with a mirror of 25-inch aperture and 20-foot focal distance, on an equatorial mount. With this fine instrument he discovered Neptune's satellite, whose existence he confirmed with accurate observations. Two years later, in 1848, at the same time as G. P. Bond in the United States, he discovered the eighth moon of Saturn, very faint, which was called Hyperion. In 1851, after a long study, he stated that there were two other satellites of Uranus (Umbriel and Ariel) inside those which Herschel had discovered in 1787. The largest telescope constructed by Lassell, also on an equatorial mount, on the island of Malta, measured 49 inches in aperture and 34 feet in focal length. With it he observed nebulae and satellites, and he compiled a catalog of 600 new nebulae. His mirrors were metal and, unlike those of Lord Rosse, formed of an alloy containing a little arsenic in addition to copper and tin, and consequently they possessed a higher reflecting power.

THE STRUVES

The head of the astronomical family of the Struves, Friedrich Wilhelm, was succeeded by his son Otto as director of the Pulkovo Observatory. He had already won the gold medal of the Royal Astronomical Society for his determination of the constant of precession, in which he included the proper motion of the solar system. Following William Herschel, he found a value not far removed from the value known today for the annual motion of the sun. The third generation was represented by Otto's sons, Hermann and Ludwig Struve. Hermann moved the old observatory of Berlin from the Encke Platz in the middle of the city to the park of Neubabelsberg and remodeled it completely. From his many observations of Saturn's satellites he computed their orbits, their masses, the position of the equator, and the form of the planet. Ludwig Struve was professor of astronomy at the University of Kharkov and died in 1920.

Georg Struve, son of Hermann, followed in the fourth generation. He was the official observer at the Neubabelsberg Observatory and also studied the systems of Saturn and Uranus, making many accurate observations of their satellites. He died in 1933 at forty-seven years of age. Otto Struve II, son of Ludwig, represents the same fourth generation. He emigrated to the United States and was appointed director of Yerkes Observatory as successor to E. B. Frost in 1932. In 1939 he founded the McDonald Observatory in Texas.

SCHIAPARELLI

In the field of planetary observations remarkable discoveries and progress were made by Giovanni Virginio Schiaparelli, director of the Brera Observatory in Milan from 1862 to 1910. In 1877, when Mars entered one of its "favorable oppositions," Schiaparelli wanted to test whether the 9-inch Merz refractor, with which he had been successfully observing double stars, would give good results also in the study of the surface of planets. He wanted to verify for his own satisfaction the well known observations of the features of Mars and its atmosphere. The good quality of his telescope and excellent atmospheric conditions permitted him to describe in great detail the southern hemisphere of the planet, which was then clearly visible, and part of the northern one. Thenceforth he continued carefully to observe the planet in its later oppositions, and his results are assembled in seven papers published by the Academy of the Lincei.

In the first paper, which refers to the observations made during the opposition of 1877, Schiaparelli determined the fundamental topographical data, that is, the direction of the axis of rotation, and the position of the southern polar cap. He also established the coordinates of certain fundamental points, with which he was able to complete the topographical description by drawing the surrounding regions, and he thus mapped all the features of the planet. These are described in detail by Schiaparelli who, following the custom of his predecessors, adopted from poetical geography and mythical archeology a wide nomenclature to distinguish similar formations from one another. Therefore in his nomenclature, which has been generally adopted, the euphonious names which evoke so many connotations indicate a mass of detail whose connection or relation could not be remembered otherwise—for example, if numbers or letters of the alphabet were used.

With great detail Schiaparelli recorded his observations of the physical nature of Mars and the facts or questions concerning the constitution of the planetary surface and its atmosphere, as well as the

variation in size of the southern polar cap and its nature, the mete-
orologic processes which take place on the surface of Mars, and the
limit of visibility of the measured objects. His maps of the planet are
richer in detail than all previously published maps, for the excellent
optical qualities of his telescope revealed to him small details which
had escaped the larger telescopes. During the opposition of 1879–
1880 Mars had just passed its summer solstice and its surface did not
present the obstacles which in the first opposition had made difficult
the exploration of the regions north of the equator. In the opposition
of 1881–1882, although the apparent diameter of the planet had
noticeably diminished, Schiaparelli gathered some information of
great interest.

> None of the dark lines, schematically called 'canals,' was missing
> this time . . . Effects probably of solar nature laid bare an
> enormous amount of detail not even suspected during the pre-
> vious oppositions. The wide regions, which in 1879 appeared
> as indeterminate mists and seemed to belong to the so-called
> 'seas,' were resolved into most complicated intricacies of pure
> lines. Then the curious and unforeseen 'gemination' of the so-
> called 'canals' was revealed.

Even if the "gemination," that is, the doubling of the canals, as
has been confirmed later, is probably nothing but illusion and optical
combination due to the arrangement and the greater or less clarity
and astigmatic effects of the observations of the details on the surface
of Mars, still it is certain that Schiaparelli's observations are very
important and have been the source of and incentive to further investigations. In the opposition of 1886 he began to use the new 18-
inch refractor, with which he obtained a preliminary conception of
all the boreal regions almost as far as the pole, where the white pre-
cipitations were then of small area.

Schiaparelli's observations of Mars established a precedent and constituted the beginning of a systematic study undertaken by his contemporaries and successors, both visually and, as we shall see later,
photographically. Thus, also with the help of the spectroscope, many
consequences were derived, and clarifications of the observed phenomena. Nevertheless we must confess that our present means of
observation, both visual and photographic, are inadequate to un-
ravel the mystery of the constitution of Mars.

The periodicity of the phenomenon of cosmic meteors, and the meteoric systems which have one or more radial points in the sky, had attracted the attention of astronomers, among others Schiaparelli, who diligently observed the meteor showers during certain August nights of 1866. He believed that the meteors traveled in well-defined orbits, and he studied the effects of the attraction of the earth and the causes which might influence the visibility and the number of the meteor showers. Retracing their possible origin, he established an undoubted relationship between comets, shooting stars, and meteorites. This idea was not new at that time, since it was natural to suppose that the meteoric stars which approach us in showers must come from disintegrating bodies in the depths of space. But it is to Schiaparelli's great credit that he investigated the transformation of such a cluster as it entered the sun's sphere of influence, and proved that for every rarefied cloud of matter, both continuous and discontinuous, the law of attraction necessarily determines the transformation of that formless mass into a thin and very long stream bent along a curve, which close to the earth is not very different from a parabola, and in general resembles a prolonged conic section.

The number of such streams or swarms may be quite large. The particles are so scattered that their orbits can cross without interruption and change course like river beds. The current, after its passage at perihelion, becomes always more diffuse, and, as it passes close to a planet, it may be affected so violently that it breaks up and some particles may take up a new orbit and become independent meteors. To prove this theory, Schiaparelli calculated from the apparent position of the radiant point and from the velocity of the meteor shower called "Perseids" (because it appeared in the constellation of Perseus in 1866) the elements of the orbit traversed by this swarm. He found a remarkable and certain coincidence with the elements of the third comet of 1862, which had a period of revolution of 121 years. Also for the Leonids which in November, 1866, had presented a magnificent shower of shooting stars, Schiaparelli calculated the elements of the orbit and proved that they coincided with those of the first comet of 1866, discovered by W. Tempel, which was at perihelion in January and had a period of revolution of 33 years. This new discovery removed all doubt of the connection between comets and meteors and of the nature of the meteoric orbits in space. We must conclude therefore that the comets, under the dissolving power of the sun or some other body of the solar system, often may lose and abandon along the orbit some part of themselves. The splitting and successive disappearance of Biela's comet, followed by the magnificent showers of fire in 1872 and 1885, have splendidly confirmed the work and hypotheses of Schiaparelli.

EDWARD C. PICKERING

In the epoch preceding the more recent one when larger instruments and new methods of experimental physics have been applied to the study of the sky, a great advance in the knowledge of both celestial hemispheres was accomplished by Edward Charles Pickering, director of the Harvard College Observatory in Cambridge, Massachusetts, from 1876 to 1919. In this observatory, thanks to Pickering and his successor Harlow Shapley, we can find the recent history of any region of the universe which we want to investigate. In America for Pickering, as in Italy for Father Secchi, there were those who criticized a physicist as director of such an important observatory, but the times were now ready, as we have seen, for the development of astrophysics. Pickering understood the need for systematic work on a large scale, for which the help of many collaborators is indispensable, and by his influence and authority he gathered considerable private funds for the construction of instruments and for the maintenance of a large staff for the purpose. His first program was the determination of the magnitude of all the brightest stars included in the *Harvard Photometry*. This work was extended to the Southern Hemisphere when Pickering established a station at Arequipa in Peru. The work was effected visually with his meridian photometer, by comparison of the magnitudes of the various stars with certain fundamental ones.

G. P. Bond, Pickering's predecessor, had foreseen the possibilities of photographic application, for in 1850 he had photographed α Lyrae and noted the advantages that this new method could bring to stellar photometry. His results induced Pickering to adopt this new method, thus determining "photovisual" magnitudes by means of filters and orthochromatic plates in order to arrive as close as possible to the visual magnitudes. The rapid progress in the manufacture of photographic plates and of instruments with wide-field photographic objectives gave Pickering the idea of assembling a vast collection of photographs, extended over a period of time, so as to constitute as complete a "history of the sky" as possible. In addition to direct photographs, in order to catalog the stars and obtain their magnitudes, the spectra were photographed with the prism objective.

Many discoveries of new stars, minor planets, variable stars, and other interesting bodies were made by such photography in both celestial hemispheres. For the study and classification of the stellar system Pickering had the valuable aid of his collaborators, Mrs. W. P. Fleming, Miss A. C. Maury, and Miss A. J. Cannon, who brought to completion a work of fundamental importance, the *Henry Draper Catalogue* (so called in honor of the New York pioneer in stellar spectroscopy), published in the Harvard Annals. In the catalog there are given, in addition to the approximate co-ordinates referred to the equinox of 1900, the photometric, visual, photographic magnitudes of about 225,000 of the most luminous stars, and the spectra of each star. The spectra are indicated by letters of the alphabet in what is commonly called by astronomers the "Draper Classification." This is a derivation, and more detailed division into various classes, of the first classification into types by Father Secchi. The study of the spectra, photographed with prism objectives more powerful than those of Father Secchi, a method which is indeed an improvement over simple visual observations, for the purpose of recognizing the type spectrum and the Fraunhofer lines, led to a designation of the various spectrum classes by the various letters of the alphabet. In the progressive study of such classes we can establish, as is well known, a spectral "sequence" in which the letters of the alphabet are no longer in their usual order, but nevertheless they are still retained to designate the various types of spectrum until further observations and research can bring a more rational classification.

The importance of the Harvard Observatory collection of photographs covering the whole sky has become steadily more apparent in the course of time. Of each "new" star or variable which is discovered, the history can generally be found. For example Eros, discovered in 1898, was found on the Harvard plates during its important opposition of 1894, and thus important data were available for the determination of its orbit.

With Schiaparelli, Pickering, and their schools we can say that an astronomical epoch comes to a close. A new one begins, in which the great development of technical methods and a more extensive use of physical means, and also an ever-widening international collaboration have led to modern advances, especially toward concepts of stellar evolution and the structure of the universe.

18 : location, equipment, and methods of some modern observatories

THE SCIENCE OF OPTICAL AND MECHANICAL constructions has made so much progress in recent times as a result of the invention of more marvelous and complex machines that its possibilities for helping man in his new conquests, both practical and spiritual, seem unlimited. In the investigation of the sky, which proceeds so slowly because of the magnitude of the task and the insufficiency of the means, the fundamental problem has always been that of magnification with powerful optical means in order for the human pupil to gather the greatest possible quantity of the faint light which comes to us from the celestial bodies, or in order to fix it on photographic plates.

REFRACTORS AND REFLECTORS

From the time of Galileo and Newton until half a century ago the competition between mirrors and lenses was very close. It seemed, however, to be resolved in favor of lenses because they do not deteriorate with time, and the refracting telescope is easier to build and more convenient to use. The advantages of reflectors are (1) the much lower cost of the mirrors; (2) the possibility of increasing their dimensions, since they do not have to be built with optical glass, but only with a good homogeneous piece of glass; (3) a better central definition of the image due to the absence of chromatic aberration, so that for equal focal lengths one can increase the aperture and thus the luminosity of the catoptric objective compared to the dioptric objective; and (4) it is also possible to use different focal lengths with different types of mounts, like those of Newton and Cassegrain, or other combinations. On the other hand, the first metal mirrors made of bronze soon lost their reflecting power, because of oxidation, even if some arsenic had been added to brighten them. As for the later glass mirrors, it was often necessary to renew the silver coating, not to mention the inconvenience to the observer to have to climb, in the most common Newtonian combination, to the top of the telescope to make observations.

However, in the construction of astronomical objectives, a limit of the aperture was soon reached. About half a century ago this limit appeared quite considerable, but now it seems very modest, though it has never been superseded. In 1840 G. B. Amici, director of the Florence Observatory, had constructed two achromatic objectives, one of 11, the other of 9½ inches, with very remarkable optical properties. They were used for many years by G. B. Donati, W. Tempel, and Antonio and Giorgio Albetti, and other similar objectives of not much larger dimensions were built by European and American opticians. The aperture was gradually increased to the present maximum of 40 inches. George E. Hale, the first director of Yerkes Observatory (connected with the University of Chicago) had the opportunity in 1893 to acquire two glass disks for an objective of 40-inch diameter. This glass had been ordered three years before for a telescope which was to be erected on Mt. Wilson in California, a strange coincidence, considering what has happened since. Because that project could not then be carried out, Hale, having obtained the necessary funds from Charles T. Yerkes, purchased the disks and entrusted the work to the optician Alvan Clark, while the equatorial mount was built by Warner and Swasey. The work was successfully completed in 1897 and the powerful refractor in its large dome with moving floor has rendered great contributions to astronomy. The objective, as is customary with astronomical objectives, is made of two lenses: the outer one of crown glass is double convex; the inner lens, separated from the outer one by approximately 8 inches, is of flint glass, plano-convex. The total weight of the objective is about 500 pounds. The glass disks were furnished by Mantois of Paris, and they are exceptionally pure and transparent.

Ever since that time reflectors have become predominant. The optical work has been perfected and means have been found to coat the mirrors with aluminum instead of silver. Meanwhile no further attempts have been made to build objectives larger than 40" in diameter. Glass blocks of increasingly larger dimensions (40, 60, 100 inches) were melted with relative ease; and the problems of grinding the parabolic surface which forms at its focus the image of the celestial bodies, as well as the problems of optical tests for gradual correction of the errors during the grinding, were successfully resolved, all to the required degree of accuracy. But the glass used for these mirrors, of the same constitution, if not perfection, as the optical glass used for lenses, presented the drawback of being too easily distorted by variations in temperature, so that the care exercised during the grinding of the reflecting surface became partly useless. Furthermore, the very thin layer of silver deposited by a chemical process similar to that used for ordinary mirrors, but naturally on the front of the mirror and without any protection, deteriorated and became rapidly oxidized, because of exposure to atmospheric changes during observations, and thus frequent recoatings were required. Despite these difficulties, the remarkable progress attained with such mirrors, which were exploring the depths of the heavens, enhanced the hope that the difficulties in building mirrors of even greater dimensions could be overcome. Mirrors of small aperture, compared to the above-mentioned dimensions in the United States have been built of pure quartz, which can resist temperature variations. For larger dimensions, up to the maximum of 200 inches attempted for the Mt. Palomar Observatory, considerable difficulty was encountered in melting pure quartz. But the problem could be solved by making the great glass disk out of pyrex, which is commonly used in glassware to be employed at high temperature and which consists mostly of quartz.

In addition, the method of aluminum coating gradually took the place, with considerable advantages, of the old method of silver plating. By electrolysis a very thin layer of aluminum is deposited on the parabolic surface of the astronomical mirror. This procedure, not new in itself, only recently has found practical application for this particular purpose, and it is now always employed for astronomical mirrors. The mirror to be coated is enclosed, after being properly cleaned, in a tank in which a high vacuum can be created and in which a wire of very pure aluminum is wrapped around some tungsten coils. An intense electric charge causes the aluminum to evaporate and to be deposited on the surface of the mirror. This process has two great advantages over silver coating. First, the bright surface is very resistant and does not deteriorate easily; it may be washed with soap and water to restore its original lustre, a method not possible with silver coating. Second, the reflecting power of the aluminum surface (equal to or a little less than that of the silver surface) for the radiations included in the visual spectrum from red to violet is much superior in the violet region. Furthermore, the silver layer is actually transparent to the ultraviolet, whereas the aluminum reflects a good percentage of it. Therefore, if we want to photograph stellar spectra with a combination of astronomical mirrors like the reflector, the instrument necessary for the purpose, the spectrograph, will give the whole spectrum from ultraviolet to red only if the mirrors of the reflector are coated with aluminum. Silver-coated mirrors completely absorb the first ultraviolet radiations. The great advantage in the use of aluminum- rather than silver-coated mirrors is thus evident and has already brought important results.

As astronomical telescopes have been gradually improved, the problem of the usable visual field has always existed. If we look through one of the original telescopes of Galileo, we are astonished that he could make so many discoveries with such a limited visual field, which is actually only a little larger even in the ordinary modern telescopes which are corrected along the optical axis. When photography took the place of almost all visual observation, the necessity and possibility of the use of photographic objectives for photographing the sky immediately led to considerable progress. In a short time, concurrent with improvements in photographic processes, objectives were built, especially for celestial photography, with combinations of four, six, and more lenses, which encompassed a much broader field than that of the ordinary telescope amounting to a few minutes of arc. On sufficiently extended areas, up to 20° or 30°, such marvelous photographs have been obtained with lenses that reflectors would seem to have been completely superseded.

THE SCHMIDT TELESCOPE

But reflectors are destined to be still dominant, or more accurately a combination of the two has come about. The story is as follows: In 1930 Bernard Schmidt, optician of the Bergedorf Observatory (Hamburg), invented a combination of a concave mirror and a "correcting plate" which, constructed and tested, solved successfully the problem of field; it competed with the best photographic objectives and actually surpassed them in the dimensions of the field, just as the parabolic mirror has surpassed the objective. The new Schmidt telescope, which Americans call the "magic camera," consists of a spherical mirror with a correcting plate in front of it located at the center of curvature. A spherical mirror cannot make all the parallel rays which come from the stars converge in one focus alone, because the rays on the peripheral zones of the mirror are reflected closer to the surface than the central rays. The image of the celestial bodies thus cannot be well defined, and for this reason the parabolic form had been adopted. But the intermediate plate of Schmidt has the function of bringing all the rays exactly, or almost exactly, to the same focus, by slightly bending the incident rays close to the center of the mirror, while the peripheral rays are bent outward; hence they all are reflected from the mirror at such varying angles that they converge at the same focus. The correcting plate is generally flat on one side and has different and complicated curvatures on the other, calculated mathematically and reproduced by able opticians. It is very thin, and its curvature is so small that it can be discerned only by optical tests. By means of this correcting plate the central image of a star is as well defined as that given by a parabolic mirror. The great advantage of this system, however, is that because of its geometrical properties it gives celestial images at several degrees from the axis almost as fine a definition as that of the central images. Therefore the field becomes as useful as in the photographic objectives. The Schmidt telescope is an improvement over them, because of the absence of residual coloration of the images, the dimensions in which it can be built, and the ratio of the focal distance to the aperture, which may even become unity, thus giving the instrument great light-gathering power.

We may say that the Schmidt telescope, born in Germany, has emigrated to the United States, in the sense that more Schmidt telescopes have been built here than in Europe, by professional builders and also amateurs. The largest one yet built was for the Mt. Palomar Observatory, where is found its greater companion, the 200-inch parabolic mirror. The aperture of the spherical mirror is 72 inches and the aperture of the correcting plate 48 inches with a ratio $f/2.5$. In Italy, at the Arcetri Observatory, a Schmidt telescope was built with a pyrex mirror of 21-inch aperture, a correcting plate of 12 inches, and a ratio $f/3$.

A modification of the Schmidt telescope, which may have various useful applications, was invented in 1941 by D. D. Maksutov, of the National Optics Institute of Moscow, and independently, two years later, by A. Colacevich at the Arcetri Observatory. In this new model the Schmidt plate is replaced by a spherical meniscus with edges concentric to those of the spherical mirror. The meniscus corrects the spherical aberration of the mirror. This new type of telescope can take the place of the Schmidt, since it gives a wide field, well corrected also for very large apertures. It has the advantage of easier construction and a shorter telescope tube. Both types have a curved field which may be flattened conveniently with a suitable lens. The reflectors with a parabolic mirror, which permit, by sacrificing the field, large linear scales on the photographic plates, and the reflectors with a spherical mirror and correcting plates, giving a wide field and high luminosity, have made great progress in the investigation of the sky out to distances much farther away from the solar system than those attained before.

TELESCOPE MOUNTINGS

Fine optical parts would not be well utilized if they were not mounted in an appropriate manner and with perfect mechanisms, in order to follow the celestial bodies very accurately in their apparent motion across the celestial sphere, during the long exposure which the astronomer must make to impress the light of faint stars on photographic plates. Although it is generally true that the mechanical part has always preceded the optical part in the sense that difficulties could be solved more easily for the former, it is no less true that the progress in devices, especially electrical ones, has brought about a real revolution in this field. The driving clock with a weight controlled by a pendulum or a centrifugal-force regulator, used until a few years ago to drive the telescope so as to counteract the rotation of the earth, has been replaced by electric motors controlled with extremely high precision in various ways, as for instance by a quartz crystal made to vibrate at constant frequency by an electric current furnished by electronic tubes. It is the same principle as that used in the frequency controls of radio stations or in quartz clocks which rival in accuracy of timekeeping the astronomical pendulums kept at constant pressure and temperature. By the application of devices similar to those used for the transmission of orders in battleships, machines are built today capable of rapidly directing the largest telescopes toward a given celestial body, whose co-ordinates, of course, must be known. They can keep the body exactly in the field of the guiding telescope during the photographic exposure, which may last several hours, correcting the possible and inevitable irregularities in the motion of the instrument and the variations in atmospheric refraction.

PHOTOGRAPHIC PLATES

Optical and mechanical progress was followed by progress in the preparation of photographic plates. This presented two main problems: first, to devise very sensitive emulsions which would obtain successively fainter celestial bodies without an excessive increase in the exposure, and which, at the same time, would have a "grain" so minute that the details—for instance, the thin Fraunhofer lines— would not be lost; second, to be able to photograph the widest possible region of the spectrum from ultraviolet to infrared. These problems have been solved for the most part in the scientific laboratories of the large companies which manufacture photographic plates, now generally available on the market, and new studies and improvements have been added to the field of scientific photography, which today finds so many technical applications.

SPECTROGRAPHS

Research in solar physics has led to the invention of new instruments, like the "spectroheliograph" and the "coronagraph," bringing very important results, along with the first applications of cinematography to the study of the sky. Celestial phenomena are generally too slow to make cinematography feasible, but solar phenomena, especially the prominences and the corona, may be recorded continuously. It is therefore possible to follow their motions and variations with a special cinematographic adapter applied to solar towers and coronagraphs.

In the construction of spectrographs for the study of stellar spectra, prisms or diffraction gratings are used. The improvement in optical glasses and polishing has led to the construction of prisms and prism objectives of considerable dimensions. Liquid prisms have also been used successfully, for instance by J. Evershed. After the discovery of diffraction phenomena by Father Grimaldi, gratings were built for the first time by Fraunhofer, when in 1821 he conceived the idea of using a whole series of equidistant slits, instead of only two slits, as had been done previously to produce the interference phenomenon. His first grating consisted of a silver thread wound on a brass frame. Naturally he took great care to have the spacings between turns exactly equal, a necessary condition for pure spectra. Later Fraunhofer succeeded in making gratings by engraving many parallel equidistant lines on glass plates. He managed to engrave 7500 lines to an inch. After him, L. M. Rutherfurd in New York was the first to engrave on silver-coated glass plates, the "reflection gratings," that is, gratings which produce the spectrum by reflection instead of by transmission. These are the gratings generally employed today in astrophysics. He was able to engrave the gratings also on a metal mirror surface instead of on a glass plate, and more precisely on a plate of an alloy, like that used for the mirrors in reflectors, which after polishing attains a high percentage of reflection. The metal surface has the advantage of being easier to engrave, since it is not as hard as glass, and therefore the diamond point used to trace the many lines is worn down less.

Henry A. Rowland, of the Institute of Physics at Johns Hopkins University in Baltimore, began to be interested in spectrum analysis in 1881. He realized the necessity of good diffraction gratings, and after studying the problem he devised a procedure for making on a lathe screws of constant pitch, an essential condition for the construction of a good grating. He thus attained very high accuracy in the construction of reflection gratings on flat surfaces and succeeded in tracing 100,000 lines to an inch. He also thought of using, instead of a flat surface, a concave surface, for he discovered that such a grating can give a "normal" dispersion, with a special mount, and is always in focus in a determined line, without the use of lenses to gather the image of the spectrum. The many gratings built by Rowland, widely employed in astrophysical research, usually have 15,000 lines to the inch.

The technique for obtaining good gratings, even today, despite the great progress of precision mechanics, is rather difficult. Gratings are built in the shop of the Mt. Wilson Observatory on a machine made by C. Jacomini. With this machine was made, for instance, the grating used at the solar tower of Arcetri which has a ruled surface of 4 x 4.4 inches, with 15,000 lines to the inch, therefore a total of 66,-000 lines. The form of the lines traced by the diamond was chosen in such a way that the light is concentrated mostly on one of the spectra of the first order, a fact which makes it particularly adapted for observations with the spectroheliograph. More recently gratings have been built on aluminum-coated glass, with high reflecting and resolving power.

With these powerful means of light dispersion the modern astronomical spectrograph is constantly being perfected by the use of various combinations of lenses, mirrors, prisms, and gratings, kept at constant temperature, and with adapters for obtaining terrestrial comparison spectra of various kinds.

MEASUREMENTS OF LUMINOSITY AND RADIATION

It is also necessary, in order to measure accurately the intensity of the light distributed in the various regions of the spectrum, to "calibrate" the plates taken by the telescope with spectrophotometric procedures. The precise measurement of the intensity of light which comes from a celestial body, either globally or from the different regions of its spectrum, is another of the fundamental problems of modern astronomy. At first visual photometers of different types, based on various principles, were used, but now most of these measurements are made indirectly either by photography or photoelectric cells. The photograph of a celestial object or its spectrum presents, since it is always an impression in black and white, a more or less intense blackening according to the luminosity. It is from this blackening that the astronomer must derive his measurement of the absolute or relative intensity of the celestial body or of the various regions of its spectrum. Visual photometers had been employed in physics, and others were developed in which thermopiles or photoelectric cells were substituted for the human eye. For astrophysical needs "microphotometers" have been constructed and perfected; in these the element sensitive to the difference in blackening can be the eye, or more conveniently, the thermopile or the photoelectric cell. With the latter the greater or smaller differences of intensity, visible on the impressed photographic plate, are revealed and recorded. They are also compared with standard light sources, which are used so that from time to time the photographic emulsion, temperature, developer, and so forth to which the plates are subjected, may be controlled.

A special photographic technique has thus been developed in a few years, and it has already rendered great services in permitting us to follow with precision the light variations of variable stars and the diverse variations which occur in stellar spectra. It is also possible to measure the quantity of light emitted or absorbed by the emission or absorption lines present in the spectra and thus to evaluate the quantity of atoms which produce the various spectral lines in the outer atmosphere of the stars. Thermopiles, used in microphotometers or radiometers extremely sensitive to infra-red rays, are employed at the focus of the larger telescopes. They serve to measure the calorific radiations which come from the individual stars or planets. We thus have the elements with which to derive the temperature of those stars, or the temperatures which prevail in the different regions of the planets, under various conditions of solar illumination. Photoelectric cells sensitive to various radiations may now be applied, instead of a photographic plate, to the focus of the telescope, in order to determine the variations in magnitude of the celestial bodies. Great progress has been made in this field with the use of sensitive galvanometers and electrometers and suitable amplifiers.

MEASUREMENTS OF STELLAR DIAMETERS

"Interferometers" have been successfully introduced in astronomical measurements to determine the very small diameters which some of the brightest and nearest stars may present, but because of their enormous distances they have so far escaped all direct measurement. A. A. Michelson was the first to think of this application of his interferometer. After his experiments in the laboratory he was invited to Lick Observatory on Mt. Hamilton in California to test his method by measuring the diameters of Jupiter's satellites. These average about 1″ and are therefore too small to be measured without systematic error by a micrometer applied even to the largest telescopes. Michelson's first interferometer consisted of two movable slits in front of an 11-inch objective. In order to make good measurements it is necessary to have considerable calm in the atmosphere. During a stay of three weeks on Mt. Hamilton, Michelson was able, in only four nights, of which only one offered perfect atmospheric conditions, to determine the diameters of the Medicean planets. His results were very close to the average of numerous micrometer measurements affected by a considerable mean error, a fact which brilliantly demonstrated the success of the new method. He predicted that with the system of two movable slits applied to the 40-inch objective of Yerkes

Observatory it should be possible to measure stellar diameters much less than 1″. In his well-known book *Light Waves and Their Uses*, Michelson wrote in 1907:

> The nearest of these stars, as before stated, is so far away that it takes several years for light from it to reach us. They are about 100,000 times as far away as the sun. If they were as large as the sun, the angle they would subtend would be about one-hundredth of a second. A forty-inch telescope can resolve angles of approximately one-tenth of a second, so that, if we were to attempt to measure, or to observe, a disc of only one-hundredth of a second, it would require an objective whose diameter is of the order of forty feet—which, of course, is out of the question. It is, however, not altogether out of question to construct an interference apparatus such that the distance between its mirrors would be of this order of magnitude.
>
> But it is not altogether improbable that even some of the nearer stars are considerably larger than the sun, and in that case the angle which they subtend would be considerably larger. Hence it might not be necessary to have an instrument with mirrors forty feet apart.

The predictions of Michelson have been completely verified in the course of later years. J. A. Anderson, of Mt. Wilson Observatory, with an eyepiece interferometer, that is, with the two slits placed at a certain distance in front of the eyepiece instead of the objective, discovered that Capella (α Aurigae) is a double star with its components, in 1920, 0.05″ apart. In the same year Michelson and F. G. Pease constructed a 20-foot interferometer, which they attached to the 100-inch telescope at Mt. Wilson. The light beams emanating from Betelgeuse (α Orionis), gathered by two mirrors placed at the extremity of a rigid metal beam 20 feet long, were received at the Cassegrain focus of the reflector. There the disappearance of the interference fringes was observed by bringing together or separating the mirrors. The diameter of α Orionis came out 0.047″, on the assumption that the disk of the star is uniformly luminous. This triumph of modern observational methods was followed by the measurements of the diameters of seven other red giant stars, whose diameters corresponded in general very well with those calculated theoretically. Furthermore, it has also been discovered that the diameter of Betelgeuse seems to be variable, from 0.047″ to 0.034″, a fact which may correspond to the variation in luminosity of the probably pulsating star.

Electronic tubes, used as in television, promise important applications for some particular research. We see how the great progress in the construction of telescopes is rivaled by the invention and the construction of numerous accessories which complement the telescope in its modern investigation of the sky.

OBSERVATORIES: LOCATION AND EQUIPMENT

As such rapid progress was accomplished in the construction and engineering of astronomical instruments, it was necessary to provide mountings for them in localities and buildings adapted to the purpose for which they were to be employed. In Europe the observatories, more or less ancient, are being modernized; or annexes are being erected in localities far from populated districts. In the United States, with the help of generous benefactors, observatories have been founded which are now famous in astronomical history, both for the means at their disposal and for the astronomers who have worked or who are working there, and for the many very important results attained.

To cite only a few of the most famous observatories which possess the largest instruments, we may mention Lick Observatory on Mt. Hamilton in northern California, founded in 1888 at 4212 feet above sea level, with its 36-inch refractor and 36-inch Crossley reflector, named after the donor, and the first of the large mirrors made of silver-coated glass. J. E. Keeler, who was director of Lick Observatory, made his well known photographic catalog of nebulae with this reflector, and W. W. Campbell, who succeeded him in 1901, made many measurements of stellar radial velocities.

The construction of Yerkes Observatory, planned and directed by Hale, was begun in 1895 and completed two years later. The site was chosen about one hundred miles from Chicago, on the banks of Lake Geneva near the village of Williams Bay in Wisconsin. The plan, as Hale writes, shows the influence of Lick Observatory and of the astrophysical observatory of Potsdam. The building has the form of a Roman cross, designed in such a way that the three domes which project above it do not interfere with one another. The great dome which houses the 40-inch refractor is located at the westernmost end, and at the extremities of the arms of the cross are two other lesser

domes. With the 40-inch refractor, S. W. Burnham has made many
observations of double stars (published in the most important extant
catalog of double stars), and E. E. Barnard has made measurements of star clusters, faint nebulae, comets, and satellites. The great
refractor may easily be used for visual, photographic, and spectroscopic observations, employing the "Bruce" spectrograph and the
"Rumford" spectroheliograph, so named after the donors of these
remarkable accessories. One particular characteristic of the observatory—one which was later considerably developed at Mt. Wilson—is
the establishment of a spectroscopic laboratory, in which the solar and
terrestrial phenomena may be experimentally reproduced within certain limits. Apparatus for producing sparks between metal poles in
the air, in a vacuum, and in liquids, and for producing electric arcs
is used together with spectroscopes in order to study the radiations
of metal vapors under various physical conditions, especially of temperature and pressure. For studies in solar physics, since great dispersion and hence spectrographs with considerable focal lengths are
needed, Hale had a horizontal telescope constructed in which the
solar light is directed by means of mirrors.

Then, too, the steadily increasing dimensions of modern instruments made necessary a careful choice of the localities where they
were to be used. Newton in his treatise on optics wrote:

> Even if the theory of telescope construction develops so as to
> be completely practical, nevertheless there are certain limits be-
> yond which the telescope cannot be useful. In fact, the atmos-
> phere, through which we observe the stars, is in perpetual agi-
> tation, as we can see from the trembling of the shadows cast by
> high towers and from the twinkling of the stars. The only rem-
> edy would be a quiet atmosphere, as for example what we might
> find on the highest mountain tops above the great layers of
> clouds.

Newton could not have been an alpinist, for otherwise he would
have known that steadiness of images is often lacking on mountain
tops, even though greater transparency of the atmosphere is gained by
the great height. Nevertheless the quoted passage is quite remarkable
if we consider what is being done today, whereas the medieval astronomer was generally content to make his observations perched on a
rooftop. Even the first observatories of the eighteenth century were
located in the highest parts and sometimes even in the attics of

public buildings. The oldest observatory in Italy, that of Bologna, founded in 1725, was actually erected on the tower which overlooks the university building. Very soon, with the rapid growth of city centers and their nightly illumination which brightens up the sky, such observatories became ill adapted to astronomical tasks.

The proximity of heavily populated districts with their night lights causes much disturbance both in visual and in photographic observations. The latter, for example, made even with telescopes of average power, are clouded after long exposures because of the light diffused in the atmosphere. It would seem that the removal of observatories from populated areas should suffice to eliminate this inconvenience, and also that of the disturbance or general agitation of the atmosphere due to dust, smoke, and variations in the density of the air resulting from the daily heating of buildings, and from streets with their nightly illumination, which disturbs the lowest layers of the atmosphere. In fact, in the open country, preferably covered with rich vegetation, there are very considerable advantages, but for the astronomer in search of a serene and purer sky, even this is not enough. It is well known that the atmospheric strata close to sea level are the densest, and that with increasing altitude the atmosphere becomes more rarefied and the sky becomes bluer. If it were possible to remove ourselves from the surface of the earth as far as the highest level of the atmosphere, or even to get altogether beyond it, then without the diffusion of solar light in the particles of air, we would see the resplendent sun shining in a sky dark as night. Therefore we can understand that the astronomer would gain in visibility and in the perfection of the image which he observes through the telescope, not only by leaving the populated centers but by raising himself above sea level. This has been done for some important observatories, notably those which employ the world's largest telescopes.

The Italian astrophysicists Tacchini and Riccò in 1890 made an attempt to erect a high-altitude observatory on the highest peaks of Mt. Aetna at 9676 feet above sea level, and to mount an equatorial of dimensions rather large for that time. But the eruptions and volcanic emenations prohibited any profitable work.

MT. WILSON AND MT. PALOMAR

In the United States Hale, in his search for better atmospheric conditions than Chicago had to offer, after a careful investigation chose one of the summits of the Sierra Madre in southern California for a large new observatory to be erected through the munificence of Andrew Carnegie. On top of Mt. Wilson, 5714 feet above sea level, numerous instruments have been erected since 1904, at first only for research in solar physics, but then later for all astrophysical research. Two solar towers, a 60-inch reflector, and finally in 1918 the 100-inch Hooker reflector are the principal instruments of this famous observatory. Much work has been accomplished since that year with the powerful instrument, and new discoveries have been possible in regions of the sky made accessible by its great light-gathering power. Meanwhile the nightly illumination of the ever-growing cities which are located at the foot of Mt. Wilson, especially Pasadena and Los Angeles, makes itself felt in the long-exposure photographs taken with the 100-inch reflector. Without saying that this effect prohibits observations, it is certain that for a more powerful instrument it was necessary to look for a more suitable location.

For the continuation of research on the structure of the universe and the physical constitution of the stars and nebulae, it was desirable to increase the power of the telescopes even more. Hale, this time with the help of the Rockefeller Foundation, in the last years of his life began the project of constructing a 200-inch reflector, which after nearly fifteen years of work was completed in 1948. The search for a location suitable for such a powerful instrument was long and detailed. Many astronomers were sent with special instruments to various regions of the United States where the atmospheric conditions might be better than those on Mt. Wilson. The choice fell on Mt. Palomar, also in California, about ninety-five miles southeast of Mt. Wilson, and some fifty miles northeast of San Diego. Its altitude is a little more than that of Mt. Wilson, and Mt. Palomar has the further advantage of being a widely extended ridge, whose summit is a high plateau well covered with vegetation, whereas Mt. Wilson is rather steep, a fact which causes convection currents which rise and fall on the mountain sides, perturbing the nearby atmospheric strata. A Schmidt-type reflector is now functioning at Mt. Palomar and another one with a 70-inch mirror is under construction. With the former, interesting observations and discoveries of novae and supernovae have already been made.

THE 200-INCH REFLECTOR

At this date there can no longer be any doubt of the success of the great undertaking and of what we hope to obtain from the great telescope. It was certainly to Hale's great credit to foresee, on the basis of previous experience, how far modern engineering could go, and to obtain a grant of several million dollars from the Rockefeller Foundation in order to begin, in 1928, studies and tests for the construction of the new telescope. Only one part, actually, was really difficult and required preliminary tests, although the American opticians felt confident they would reach their goal in one way or another: this was the vital organ of the telescope, the great 200-inch mirror.

It is not important to the astronomer, as it is to the biologist, to magnify the objects which he examines, but rather he always has to try to see—or better, to photograph—more of them in the far-off regions of space. It is necessary to have lenses or mirrors of large dimensions in order to gather the largest possible amount of the little light which comes to us from the stars or nebulae. Ordinary glass, used until a few years ago for the construction of astronomical mirrors, is subject to expansions that alter the surface during even relatively small changes in temperature, the stellar images which are formed at the focus being distorted. Quartz, one of the constituent elements of glass, is on the other hand insensitive to temperature differences, so that if the mirror could be made exclusively of melted quartz, the great drawback would be avoided. A famous American inventor, Elihu Thomson, had already constructed some quartz mirrors of small dimensions in the laboratories of the General Electric Company, and it was decided to attempt the melting of a great massive block of pure quartz.

Special equipment was set up in the great factories of General Electric in Lynn, Massachusetts, for this purpose. For eighteen months almost a thousand dollars a day were spent in various experiments as the pure quartz at very high temperature was poured bit by bit into an oven where the disk was being gradually formed in successive layers. But the layers cooled irregularly, and at the end of eighteen months the engineers had to admit that it was not possible to accomplish the task in this way. They then thought of resorting to pyrex glass, as has been mentioned before, which has a coefficient of expansion only one-third that of ordinary glass. The work was assigned to the Corning Glass Works, in New York State, and the engineers began work at once. First there was melted a 120-inch mirror, necessary for the grinding of the surface, tentatively spherical, eventually parabolic, of the great 200-inch mirror. To diminish the total weight of the large mirror they thought of making the back in the form of a honeycomb, instead of a solid block. Another difficulty was the cooling of the great block from 3000° C, the melting temperature of pyrex, to ordinary temperatures, by a few degrees a day. Any sudden change in temperature had to be avoided, as it would have irremediably damaged the homogeneity of the mirror.

For an entire month the Corning workers heated sand and chemical substances in the oven to make sixty tons of melted pyrex. Finally the great day of the melting arrived, which assumed the importance of a ceremony, as happens in the melting of great bells, in the presence and with the benediction of ministers of God. This was March 25, 1934. Great crucibles containing the melted mass of pyrex were transported and poured every two minutes into the oven where the cast of the mirror was located. Everything seemed to be proceeding without incident, when some dark masses were observed floating in the melted glass. They were parts of the cast which were to form the cavities in the back of the mirror, which because of the intense heat had been detached from the bottom. It was decided to continue the fusion but to undertake another immediately, holding this first disk as a reserve. At the end of the same year the second disk was melted in perfect condition. It was then hermetically sealed for a good ten months in the oven to cool gradually down to the surrounding temperature. To obtain the very slow cooling, it was necessary, with special thermostats, to regulate the decrease from the oven temperature at the moment of the melting to normal temperature. Then it happened that in New York State in the spring of 1935, there were floods which seriously threatened the oven in which the mirror was sealed and all the electric equipment in the basement. Engineers and workers of Corning Glass worked desperately day and night to construct dikes with sacks of sand and they succeeded in avoiding disaster. Finally, at the end of ten months, they were able to remove the magnificent glass disk from the crucible which contained it and prove that the disk was optically perfect in all its parts. The director of the Corning Glass Works then exclaimed with a sigh: "I guess we can telegraph the Coast. Dr. Hale can have his mirror."

With every precaution, in a railway car constructed especially for the purpose, accompanied at its departure, during the trip, and at its arrival by the presence and interest of the population, the great disk arrived safe and sound in Pasadena. It was immediately mounted on a large machine where, after long and patient labor, the surface was ground to give it first the spherical form, then the parabolic. The spherical form is approximately that of a sphere with its radius of curvature 110 feet, in which the center of the disk is lower than the edge by about 4 inches. In the middle of the mirror a hole was made, through which the observer or the photographic plate gathers the images of the stars reflected from another mirror placed in the direction of the hole on the upper part of the telescope. The final parabolic curvature which was given to the surface of the mirror, in order that the images may be formed at one focus, was only a little more than a tenth of a millimeter under the spherical curve, but it had to be perfect to the extreme precision of a ten-thousandth of a millimeter. To accomplish this, very fine carborundum was used, and continual optical tests were made with each successive grinding and polishing. In the laboratory the finished mirror furnished overwhelming proofs of the perfect polishing, and it was given the final coat of aluminum which gives it so much light-gathering power for the observation of the stars.

The construction and functioning of a tank more than 200 inches in diameter which would hold the great mirror, and in which the necessary vacuum could be made for the aluminum coating, were not simple undertakings, though they did not offer insuperable technical difficulties. The completed mirror was taken to Mt. Palomar, where its mounting and building were ready. The building is covered by a large rotating dome 140 feet in diameter with an easily opened aperture 36 feet wide, through which the "big eye" examines the various regions of the sky toward which the astronomer directs it by means of perfect electrical movements.

The mounting of the great instrument gave much concern to American astronomers and engineers. There are many types of "equatorial" mountings, and the progress of modern mechanics has been such that there is no problem concerning the necessary strength, rigidity, and precision in their construction. The problem was to choose a type better adapted to the instrument, so that it could be directed towards all parts of the sky visible from the place of observation and so that, at the same time, the weighty mass would not suffer severe flexures. In order to eliminate these flexures, the mounting of the 100-inch reflector of Mt. Wilson is such that when the telescope is resting on the south and north extremities of the polar axis, it cannot look directly at the pole. In the new instrument such an inconvenience is eliminated with the so-called "fork" type of construction. The polar axis at its upper end is fashioned like a horseshoe, and the telescope tube rests in it when it is directed to the pole. By rotating about the secondary axis of declination, and about the primary polar axis, it can attain any region of the sky whatsoever. In order that the north and south extremities of the principal axis, about which the telescope rotates, may not bear down too heavily with their enormous weight on the supports, they are raised by a very thin layer of oil under high pressure, instead of resting on ball bearings. In this way electric motors of small power are sufficient to move the great, heavy mass easily. The open frame which forms the telescope tube is 55 feet long, has a diameter of 23 feet, and weighs about 125 tons.

An electric clock, controlled with the greatest precision by a quartz crystal kept in vibration at constant frequency by an alternating electric current furnished by electronic tubes, serves to make the telescope follow, with very regular motion, the apparent course of the stars in the sky, thus enabling it to make very long photographic exposures. Because of the great size of the instrument, the astronomer observes from a small cabin near the principal focus of the mirror, that is, in the highest part of the telescope tube. Or using a different combination of auxiliary mirrors, he goes to the lowest extremity, obtaining in this case less luminous images but ones on a scale larger than those obtained directly at the principal focus.

The handling of the telescope by modern devices such as those already mentioned enables the astronomer, enclosed in his cabin like the captain of a modern warship in his command station, to transmit by telephone to his assistant, who is about 100 feet farther down at the base of the telescope, the co-ordinates of the star he wants to sight. He is able to follow on appropriate quadrants the movement of the telescope which he must share, while conveniently maintaining his vertical position. Once the star is sighted, that is the celestial field which he wishes to photograph, he begins the exposure, controlling the motion of the telescope, which is generally so perfect that it requires hardly any correction on his part.

The whole enormous mounting, which has required very special work in mechanical and electrical engineering, was constructed by the Westinghouse factory in Philadelphia and transported to the California coast by sea and from there to Mt. Palomar. Four hundred tons, the weight of the entire telescope, may be put in motion with a precision which at a distance of 3 miles will give no greater deviation than an inch. The huge horseshoe which embraces and holds the telescope tube was turned on a lathe 140 feet in diameter, and it required 131 days of labor. At the beginning of the project it was noticed that in the afternoon the sun's rays entered the shop and heated the lathe unequally, producing irregular expansions large enough to introduce errors in the turning. These were on the order of only four-tenths of a millimeter, but easily measured nevertheless. The workshop was then protected with colored glass and the lathe with a screen, to keep the temperature as constant as possible. The progress of the work was observed with appropriate microscopes which brought the surface of the horseshoe to a precision of almost a hundredth of a millimeter.

As has already been noted, the problem of the choice of a location gave much trouble to the Mt. Wilson astronomers. Above all they had to decide whether the new powerful instrument would be better employed in the Northern or Southern Hemisphere. It is true that the southern sky, lacking the observatories which are present in the Northern Hemisphere, is still relatively little known. On the other hand, the comparison of the celestial objects of the two hemispheres and the special investigations which could be made with the new telescope favored placing the telescope in the Northern Hemisphere, where more interesting celestial objects are found, like the nebula in Andromeda, the one in Orion, and the great cluster in Hercules. These nebulae have been well studied already, but a more complete investigation under good meteorological conditions will be very interesting. The latitude and geographical location of Mt. Wilson would certainly have been suitable also for the new telescope, but the objections previously mentioned ruled it out. Meteorological conditions at Mt. Palomar seemed ideal from all points of view, and the site is far enough away from populated districts to exclude disturbances produced by factory smoke or night lights.

The interest which this undertaking has aroused in all kinds of people is evidenced in the numerous publications on the subject appearing all over the world, especially in the United States, where the first results after the great telescope began to photograph the sky were awaited eagerly. To answer a frequent question, we can say that with the large telescope the moon is brought to a distance of 18 miles from the earth, so that if there were centers of habitation we should easily see them; but we know that there is no life on the moon. However, we shall certainly learn something more about Mars than we know now. To make a terrestrial comparison, if the curvature of the earth did not exist, an observer on Mt. Palomar could easily tell the time on the clock of St. Peter in Rome.

But we expect something quite different from the photographs made with the telescope and from the studies in the observatory laboratories. We can now penetrate the universe to a distance of about 500 million light-years; the new mirror will make it possible to push our investigations almost twice as far and to put in evidence ten times as many stars. What new discoveries will be made possible with this gigantic eye? In the constitution of the universe, in the immense quantity of nebulae visible with present-day means, natural principles unknown till now are being discovered. The 200-inch telescope, which has been dedicated to George Ellery Hale, will certainly be able to tell us more and unveil other secrets. Theorists, astronomers, physicists, and mathematicians have already done their utmost but, like the dying Goethe, they ask: "light, more light," and through this marvelous instrument there shall be more light.

OTHER OBSERVATORIES AT HIGH ALTITUDE

Another fine observatory was recently established in the United States. The American benefactor, W. J. McDonald, in his will left considerable funds for the progress of astronomy, and the Universities of Chicago and Texas made an agreement to construct an observatory and to equip it with a powerful instrument. Otto Struve II was the founder of the new McDonald Observatory, established in 1939 at Fort Davis in southwestern Texas, 6790 feet above sea level. The principal instrument is a reflector with an 82-inch parabolic mirror of pyrex, the mechanical part constructed by Warner and Swasey of Cleveland and the optical parts by C. A. R. Lundin.

The use of the instruments devised by Lyot for the observation of the solar corona has seemed more and more necessary; but they have to be located at high altitudes, above 6500 feet, in order to escape the lower levels of the atmosphere which, with their unsettledness and the large amount of diffused light, dim the weak light of the solar corona. Not all high-altitude regions of the earth are favorable, however, for atmospheric conditions depend upon the latitude, humidity of the air, cloud formations, and frequency and intensity of the winds, suitable in some regions and not in others. Lyot used the Observatory of Pic-du-Midi de Bigorre in the High Pyrenees for his observations, which have already brought important results to our knowledge of the solar corona, as we shall see.

This observatory was founded in 1881 for the study of geophysics and later expanded in 1907 for astronomical research. There the sky is of exceptional purity, especially toward the end of spring and the beginning of summer. The observatory is constructed 50 feet below the summit of the Pic-du-Midi, on a small terrace which rises above steep rocky sides. The snows, frequent in spring, purify the air, and a sea of clouds forms for a long period under the peak and prevents the dust, principal cause of the diffusion of light, from rising up to the observatory. In August and September there is generally no snow. In winter and spring the buildings are buried under it, sometimes 16 feet deep. The sun causes some of it to slide onto the roof, where it forms icy overhangs which last until summer. A refractor of 20-foot focal distance, to which are attached the instruments of Lyot, is mounted under a dome provided with a special apparatus which protects its rotational motion from being hampered by the snow. In August and September the observatory can easily be reached by a road which goes to 8530 feet. It generally takes a month to clear away the snow. In winter and spring the road disappears completely and one must go on foot, taking seven to ten hours, depending on the condition of the snow, to reach the observatory, 9380 feet above sea level.

The success obtained by Lyot with his methods at high altitudes has found followers. In Switzerland at Arosa, M. Waldmeier of the Zürich Observatory, instituted some years ago a dependent station at 6724 feet above sea level in the pure atmosphere of that region, where continuous observations are being made of the solar corona and its variations. The United States breaks the record for altitude, having constructed an auxiliary station of Harvard Observatory at Climax, Colorado, near Fremont Pass in the Rocky Mountains, at 11,480 feet. In Czechoslovakia a new observatory has been erected on the Tatra Mountains at 5848 feet, and in Italy the University of Padua now has an auxiliary of its ancient observatory on the plateau of Asiago (province of Vicenza) at 3428 feet, furnished with a reflector with a 49-inch mirror. It is certain that astronomers will continue to look on the highest peaks for the greatest purity possible in the atmosphere "so as not to be disturbed by the shaking of the carriages, or the tolling of the bells," as Father Secchi wrote when he wished for more tranquil places than the roofs of the Roman College, from which he nevertheless made so many famous observations and discoveries.

But even by attaining the highest terrestrial peaks, astronomers are not able to observe the ultraviolet spectrum from luminous celestial sources, especially from the sun, because of the layer of ozone which completely absorbs the solar radiations in the ultraviolet region of wave-length 2840 Å. In very recent times the German war rockets, or V-2 rockets, have been used in the United States for exploring the stratosphere. In one of the tailpieces of the rocket a special spectrograph is attached with a concave Rowland grating. The image of the sun is formed in the slit by a little sphere of lithium fluoride. Exposures, regulated according to the heights attained by the V-2, have been taken automatically up to an altitude of 55 miles. The resulting spectrum is very luminous to 2100 Å and presents, besides the terrestrial atmospheric band, a pair of very intense lines of ionized magnesium at about 2800 Å, a line of neutral magnesium also very intense, neutral silicon, and singly ionized iron. These results are only the beginning of a whole new technique and experimentation, which should lead very soon to many remarkable discoveries.

19 : Hale, Eddington, and twentieth century concepts

DURING THE TWENTIETH CENTURY THE CON-tinued progress of theoretical and technical means, the power of the instruments, the number of scientists and observatories, the easier and faster exchange among the various nations (when they are not at war) of the discoveries and results obtained, and well-organized international cooperation have led to new and important concepts of the structure of the universe and of the evolution and origin of stellar energy. Actually it is difficult neatly to distinguish research in astronomy from that in astrophysics; and it is not easy amid the great number of accomplishments to attribute to this or that investigator the credit for a discovery, or a new method of investigation, or the amassing of important results. Certainly there are some leaders whose names remain indelible in astronomical history and whose fame increases with time. But there are so many deserving names that it is difficult to record them all adequately. We shall try to give an over-all glance at the results obtained in relatively recent times up to the present, without pretending to give the complete picture either of the subject-matter or of the persons.

GEORGE ELLERY HALE

George Ellery Hale and Arthur Eddington are two figures of first importance in the modern era, very different in their activities and in their accomplishments, especially in astrophysics. Hale provided powerful means of observation used by a multitude of astronomers, his collaborators and followers. Eddington ingeniously foresaw consequences of experiment and theory which can be said to have opened the way to a new and modern conception of the structure of the universe, important not only from the scientific point of view, but also from the philosophic.

In 1889 Hale, at the Harvard Observatory, made the first attempts to construct the "spectroheliograph," which he subsequently perfected in his small private observatory at Kenwood near Chicago. Two years later he obtained the first photographs, on ordinary plates, of the solar prominences, using the two intense spectral lines of calcium in the violet region (H and K), for he intuitively thought that they would be the most suitable for revealing monochromatic images of the sun in that gas, which is so abundant there. In June, 1892, after having improved his instrument, he was able to obtain photographs of the whole disk of the sun, in the light of those same lines. The photographs showed the appearance and distribution of areas more or less luminous in the various regions of the solar surface, corresponding to the greater or lesser intensity of the lines. In the same year H. Deslandres, director of the Meudon Observatory, devised his "velocity spectrograph," which was developed later into the spectroheliograph. An English astrophysicist, J. Evershed, also devised and constructed a similar instrument not long after Hale's invention.

It is interesting to read in Hale's autobiographical notes how he was led, from an eager and strong desire to study natural phenomena, to specialize in solar physics:

> . . . I bought Lockyer's *Studies in Spectrum Analysis* and began the observation of flame and spark spectra and their comparison with the spectrum of the sun. At last I found my true course, and I have held to it ever since.
>
> In passing, however, I must emphasize the advantages I gained from my earlier work in other fields. It gave me a broad interest in many branches of science and taught me something of their mutual dependence. It led me to read *The Origin of Species* and initiated a lasting desire to study evolution. It taught me to regard the sun as a typical star, a link in the long chain of evolution, and thus helped me to avoid becoming exclusively a specialist in solar research. And it was the source of all the work I have done in helping to develop such institu-

tions as the National Academy of Sciences, the California Institute of Technology, the National Research Council, and the International Research Council (now the International Council of Scientific Unions). I still look with delight at rotifers and other microscopic objects, and realize that the marvels I saw through the little microscope of my boyhood days are as astonishing as any revealed in the heavens by the largest of telescopes.

At his observatory in Kenwood, Hale made important studies of the spectra of prominences and sunspots. He identified the ultraviolet lines of hydrogen in the Balmer series and numerous lines of other elements in the eruptive prominences. He measured the displacements of the line Hα and compared them with the H and K lines of calcium and with the D₃ line of helium. The spectrum of the sunspots interested him very much, and he was thus preparing himself for the discoveries which he was to make much later with more powerful instrumental means at his disposal. In the works of Father Secchi, Tacchini, and Faye, he studied the theory of sunspots and the underlying relations among them, the faculae, and the flocculi. Since the little Kenwood Observatory was not sufficient for the development of his projects, after having founded Yerkes Observatory and mounted the 40-inch refractor, he had the "Rumford spectroheliograph" constructed, which, attached to the 40-inch refractor, has been one of the most efficient instruments of this kind. Dark flocculi of hydrogen and calcium have been discovered with it, which are nothing but the prominences seen in projection on the solar disk. The great dispersion obtainable with this instrument has made possible the separation of different levels of the flocculi and the discovery of the presence of the green band of carbon in the spectrum of the chromosphere. In 1872 Young had observed the widening of the Fraunhofer lines in the spectrum of the sunspots, which were then studied systematically by Maunder, Cortie, and Lockyer. Hale had realized that, in order to find the reason for this widening, it was necessary to have a spectrum with considerable dispersion. He therefore constructed a spectrograph of great focal length, which it was impossible to attach to a movable telescope because of its length. It has been coupled with a horizontal telescope furnished with a coelostat. This was the Snow telescope, used first at Yerkes Observatory, then at Mt. Wilson, where extensive research on the spectrum of sun-

spots was initiated. With a spectrograph attached to the 40-inch refractor, Hale, collaborating with F. Ellerman and J. A. Parkhurst,
studied in particular the stellar spectra of Secchi's fourth type (class
N of Draper) and identified numerous elements, in some spectra even
emission lines and certain characteristics which resembled the spectrum of sunspots. Successive studies with even more powerful means
have confirmed and extended these results.

The founding of Mt. Wilson Observatory gave Hale the opportunity to construct other instruments on a large scale for special
studies, rather than follow those studies which were suited to the
existing instruments. This is actually the point of view of the physicist, which he always followed. In fact, the Snow telescope was spe-
cially constructed so that different types of spectroheliographs of
varying great focal lengths could be applied to it. The 60-foot solar
tower was constructed to improve the visibility of the solar image,
and in the underlying well of almost constant temperature a spectrograph of great focal length has been mounted. The 150-foot solar
tower was constructed in order to obtain an even larger image of the
sun (about 16 inches in diameter) for the study of the polarity in the
spots. The 60- and 100-inch reflectors were designed to be used with
various focal lengths and for direct photographic use (nebulae, stellar
parallaxes, photometric work), and in conjunction with other spectrographs for the measure of radial velocities and the determination
of characteristics of various types of spectra.

One of the first important studies made by Hale at Mt. Wilson,
in collaboration with W. S. Adams, his successor and director at the
same observatory, and H. G. Gale, physicist at the University of Chicago, was the study of the spectrum of sunspots with the Snow telescope. This telescope made evident the differences between the
spectrum of the photosphere and the spots, and also the presence of
bands identified later by A. Fowler at the Imperial College of London
as belonging to titanium oxide and calcium hydride. Although in 1905
the classification of the temperatures of the spectral lines had not
been made, nor the theory of ionization developed, nor the dependence of spectra on energy levels quantitatively analyzed, nevertheless
following Lockyer's investigations the difference was known between
lines of low excitation and Lockyer's "enhanced" lines. Hale and his
collaborators were able to begin in the laboratory the study of the
effects of temperature on the spectra of various elements. They found
that the spectral lines which are much more intense in the spots

than in the photosphere are lines of "low temperature," whereas the opposite occurs with lines of "high temperature." A. S. King, also at Mt. Wilson, confirmed these results by studying the spectra of various elements with the electric furnace. In this way he made a classification of the spectral lines according to a scale of temperature, which made possible the analysis of the spectra in later years. On the other hand, the discovery of the weakening of the enhanced lines in the spectrum of the spots suggested that effects due to variation in density were combined with those of temperature, a fact which was explained later with the foundation of the theory of ionization.

While Hale was continuing his systematic work with the spectro-heliograph at Mt. Wilson in the violet lines of calcium, progress in photographic technique led to the manufacture and use of photographic plates sensitive also to the red regions of the spectrum (panchromatic plates). Hale and Ellerman were able to use the spectro-heliograph in the red line of hydrogen (Hα), in which a structure of hydrogen vapors very different from that of calcium vapors was revealed. The bright and dark flocculi of hydrogen often presented a vortex structure. Following this discovery, Hale wrote in 1908:

> In view of the fact that the distribution of the hydrogen flocculi frequently resembles that of iron filings in a magnetic field, it is interesting to recall the exact correspondence between the analytical relations developed in the theory of vortices and in the theory of electromagnetism.
>
> Double lines, which look like reversals, have recently been photographed in spot spectra with the 30-foot spectrograph of the tower telescope, confirming the visual observations of Young and Mitchell. It should be determined whether the components of these double lines are circularly polarized in opposite directions, or, if not, whether other less obvious indications of a magnetic field are present. I shall attempt the necessary observations as soon as a suitable spot appears on the sun.

In fact, in the summer of that same year, Hale was able to obtain a series of spectrograms of sunspots by using a polarizing apparatus made of a Fresnel rhombus and a Nicol prism with which he discovered the Zeeman effect in various lines, thus proving beyond all doubt that every spot is the seat of a magnetic field. The observations and studies for the determination of the polarities and intensities of these fields proceeded uninterruptedly from that time. Since a dispersion even greater than that given by the 30-foot spectrograph was needed to separate the components of the Zeeman triplets, Hale had the 150-foot tower constructed with a spectrograph of 75-foot focal length. Meanwhile, in 1913, when the sun was reaching a minimum of activity and there were no spots, Hale and his collaborators, among them A. van Maanen and F. Seares, devoted themselves to investigating whether a general magnetic field of the sun might possibly exist, like that of the earth. As the theory predicted, the problem was to discover not the separation of the spectral lines as in the magnetic fields of the spots, but, because of the weak intensity of the field, only small displacements of the lines, by means of suitable polarizers. Positive results were obtained in 1913. Because of the very small displacements, which even on the scale of spectra given by the 75-foot spectroheliograph amounted to only three- or four-hundredths of a millimeter, there was still some doubt about the reality of the phenomenon. Nevertheless everything pointed to the belief, which other methods of research later confirmed, that a general magnetic field exists on the sun. A few years later (1918) a new phenomenon of the polarity of the spots was discovered at Mt. Wilson and announced by Hale, F. Ellerman, S. Nicholson, and A. Joy. At the completion of a cycle, in the next one the polarity of the spots, which begin to appear at a high latitude, is reversed with respect to the polarity of the preceding cycle. Seven years later, with even richer observational material, the reversal of the polarity of the magnetic fields existing in the sunspots was fully confirmed. The length of a cycle of solar activity, with the same characteristics as the preceding cycle, was established at twenty-two years.

Toward the end of his scientific career, Hale invented also the "spectrohelioscope," an instrument adapted to a rapid examination of the solar disk and therefore to the observation of eruptions and other phenomena of short duration. Since he realized the necessity of a continuous observation of the sun, especially in the problem of the influence of solar phenomena on terrestrial phenomena, he had these instruments constructed in large numbers and distributed to various observatories in different longitudes. At the same time, and when his health was rapidly failing, Hale, always following with deepest interest the great rewarding work which was being done with the 100-inch telescope in the investigation of the structure of the universe, was thinking and writing about the possibility of larger telescopes, even making plans for one in collaboration with F. G. Pease.

We have seen how these plans were realized, for in 1929 he succeeded in obtaining from the Rockefeller Foundation the necessary funds for the construction of the 200-inch telescope.

Hale, like Father Secchi, understood from the beginning of his scientific activity the great importance of astrophysics for the investigation of the universe. His work is well summarized in the following words written by his faithful disciple and successor, W. S. Adams:

> Hale not only has founded the Mt. Wilson Observatory but he has left a profound impression of his personality in the life and works of that Observatory during the thirty-four years of its existence. Perhaps his greatest contribution has been his conviction that problems and methods must first develop within the science and that the instruments must be adapted to the problems, not the problems to the instruments. This is the attitude of the physicist in the laboratory; Hale has employed the same principle in astronomy with enormous advantage for progress in this science. He has always insisted on the close collaboration between physics and astronomy, and the extraordinary development of physical astronomy in the last thirty years has been greatly influenced by his vast knowledge and broad views. Hale's active years of research at Kenwood, Yerkes, and Mt. Wilson have led to extraordinarily rewarding discoveries on the physical constitution and nature of the sun. These in turn have found immediate application to the stars, and thus our horizon continually widens from year to year. He well appreciated this fact and was able to complete plans for the 200-inch telescope which was his last great tangible contribution to the vast field of his already remarkable research. If he did not live to see this new work of his finished, he surely saw enough of its progress to be sure it was in good hands, and in those best adapted to obtain rapidly the most notable results.

PROGRESS IN THE STUDY OF THE SUN

As we continue to relate the history of the progress of solar physics after the application of the methods of spectrum analysis, we recall that Vogel in 1871 demonstrated the possibility of determining the period of rotation of the sun by means of the Doppler effect, with greater precision and at higher solar latitudes than was possible with sunspots. But the first visual determinations, the most famous of which are those by Dunèr between 1888 and 1893, could not have been very accurate, for the displacements of the spectral lines to be measured were very small.

But with the advantage of photography and spectrographs of large focal lengths, in 1906 Adams began a classical series of measurements at Mt. Wilson which have since been continued there by C. St. John and other astronomers. Their results substantially confirm those obtained from the sunspots and extend them to higher latitudes up to ± 75°. They also show that the angular velocity of rotation of the various gases in the photosphere and chromosphere increases with increasing height above the lower levels, and at the same time the equatorial acceleration decreases. From later determinations, at Mt. Wilson, at Arcetri, and in other observatories, the existence of a possible variation of the period of rotation of the sun seems very doubtful, whether periodic with the movement of the eleven-year cycle, or secular.

The outermost envelopes of the sun, that is, the upper atmosphere and the corona, until a few years ago could be studied only during the brief moments of a solar eclipse. This fact explains why astronomers tried never to miss a single eclipse, traveling with appropriate instruments to the localities on the earth where they could observe the totality. Photography and spectrum analysis have remarkably extended our knowledge of the physical nature and constitution of these envelopes. It is possible to photograph the so-called "flash spectrum" in the brief moments preceding and following totality, that is, immediately before the second and immediately after the third contact. During the eclipse of 1898, visible in India, the first photographs of this kind were made by Lockyer and A. Fowler; they discovered many emission lines, enhanced in the flash spectrum, which we now know are due to ionized atoms. During the same eclipse W. W. Campbell, who was director for many years of Lick Observatory on Mt. Hamilton, used a new and ingenious method, placing a slit in front of the photographic plate along its entire length, so that the plate was impressed by a strip of the solar spectrum as large as the slit. Sliding the plate with uniform motion in a direction perpendicular to the slit during the critical moments of the flash spectrum, he registered the various phases of transformation of the spectrum on the photographic plate, from that of absorption to that of emission. His method was used in that eclipse and in many others following, with very interesting results concerning the constitution and physical conditions of the solar gases passing from the photosphere to the chromosphere.

S. A. Mitchell, director of the McCormick Observatory in Virginia, having had the opportunity to observe nine total eclipses, then wrote his famous book *Eclipses of the Sun*. Among other results he obtained some beautiful photographs of the flash spectrum with the prism objective, from which one can easily deduce, by measuring the amplitude of the various chromospheric monochromatic arcs along the whole spectrum, the various heights attained by the gases on the sun's surface. These determinations then made it possible to compare the results obtained from the solar rotation, in regard to the heights attained by the various elements, and those obtained from observing the so-called "Evershed effect." The English astrophysicist, J. Evershed, discovered in 1909 a radial motion of the vapors which leave or enter the sunspots, a motion which is superimposed on and is greater than the vortical motion. He made the discovery by systematically observing the spectrum of the sunspots at various longitudes in the course of the sun's rotation, and by determining the Doppler displacement due expressly to the inward and outward flow of the different gases. These measurements have enabled us also to establish and confirm the different levels of the solar atmosphere.

The highest level of the atmosphere, the corona, extends, as is well known, a great distance from the solar globe and changes its form periodically during the 11-year cycle of solar activity. This fact has been discovered during the brief moments of total eclipses of the sun, for it was impossible, until a few years ago, to observe it in any other way, or to photograph its spectrum and thus to obtain some knowledge of its physical nature. Some emission lines visible in the corona, which could in no way be identified with any lines reproducible in the laboratory, were attributed to a hypothetical element called "coronium." The progress of atomic physics and the possibility of observing at least the interior of the corona other than during total eclipses have brought new and important clarifications of these problems. The attempts made in the past to see the corona in full daylight, without waiting for the rare moments of a total eclipse, were numerous and fruitless. Secchi and Tacchini had already made some attempts in this direction, and knowing that it was necessary to have an especially transparent atmosphere to succeed in the undertaking, they thought of going to Mt. Aetna, where as Father Secchi says, "the sky is of admirable purity, while the sky of Rome in contrast seems dirty and cloudy." The project was resumed and effectuated years later by Hale and Riccò on Aetna itself, with special instruments, but without success. The difficulty lies in the fact that the corona, in comparison with the disk of the sun, is very faint. In the interior portions it shines no more than the surface of the full moon, which is six hundred times less luminous than the sun. Near the edge of the sun the light of the photosphere is so dominating that it becomes very difficult to photograph the corona in full sunlight.

B. Lyot, astrophysicist at the Meudon Observatory ingeniously discovered how to overcome the difficulty by devising and constructing a special, and at the same time simple, instrument which permitted him to photograph the entire corona under special conditions of clear sky. His first concern was to eliminate, as much as possible, the diffused light, which in all astronomical instruments is considerably greater than the light of the corona. This effect occurs mainly because of the small air bubbles usually imprisoned in the glass of the optical parts of the instruments, and because of thin, almost invisible, lines which are almost always present after the polishing, and the multiple reflections on the faces of the various lenses. With the construction of his "coronagraph" Lyot learned how to remove these inconveniences almost entirely. At the Pic-du-Midi Observatory in the Pyrenees, above the lowest and most unsettled parts of the terrestrial atmosphere, he was able in 1931 to obtain interesting direct photographs of the prominences and of the entire corona. Then by adding a spectrograph of wide dispersion to his coronagraph he was able to determine with fine precision the wave lengths of numerous emission lines, some of which had not even been discovered during the total eclipses. His method is applicable also to the study of the spectrum from green to infrared, when long exposures are possible.

On the basis of these results and of those which have been gathered during the total eclipses of recent years, the interpretation of the emission spectrum of the corona begins to make progress. W. Grotrian, of the Potsdam Astrophysical Observatory, having observed some forbidden lines of Fe VII in the nova RS Pictoris and coronal lines in RS Ophiuchi, formulated the hypothesis that they could be ascribed to forbidden transitions of repeatedly ionized iron. As a proof of his hypothesis he showed that the difference in wave number between the levels of the fundamental state of Fe X coincided with the wave number of the red line in the corona. Proceeding from this hypothesis,

Bengt Edlén, of the Physics Institute of Upsala, has succeeded in giving an interpretation which seems satisfactory, by identifying the various emission lines with those of iron, nickel, and calcium in various stages of ionization, from X to XVI. These results and others regarding the continuous spectrum and the variation of the form of the corona, have led to the formulation of various theories in attempts to explain the observed phenomena.

Another step has been taken by Lyot to facilitate and improve the observation of solar phenomena. In astrophysical research the use of filters is very important. They isolate a certain more or less extended region of the spectrum, so that certain radiations of a star can be studied by separating them from the others. The most common filters are the well known ones of glass or gelatin, colored with mineral salts or organic compounds. Though very practical, they have the disadvantage of letting through too extended a region of the spectrum, that is, of not being very monochromatic. It is with great difficulty that we can limit a region to less than 300 Å. Another type of filter, which permits us to isolate monochromatic radiations, is in a certain sense the spectroheliograph of Hale and Deslandres. Spectrographs in which there is sufficient dispersion and resolving power can eventually separate almost any region of the spectrum limited to about 0.3 Å. But this instrument has the inconvenience of rendering very little light because it successively photographs regions of the sun limited to the size of the second slit. For the very bright solar chromosphere this apparatus, ever since its invention, has given very important results, but for the study of the corona, whose luminosity is some hundreds of thousands of times weaker, it cannot be usefully employed.

In 1929 Lyot, while looking for a new type of filter, highly monochromatic and highly luminous, studied the interference patterns produced in polarized light by a set of crystal laminae. In later years he established their properties and the necessary elements for the calculation and production of a filter which could isolate in the green region of the spectrum a narrow band of 1 Å whose wave length could be varied within certain limits. In 1937 the Swede Öhman, of the Stockholm Observatory, thought of using polarized films, and he built a simpler filter, based on the same principle as Lyot's. This filter, however, isolated a spectral band of average width equal to 40 Å with a fixed wave length equal to that of the chromospheric radiation $H\alpha$, making possible the observation of the most luminous prominences with a simple telescope. A year later Lyot, proceeding in his experiments, also constructed a filter using polaroid sheets and reducing the band to 2 Å in the green and 3 Å in the red. By regulating the desired wave length with a thermostat, he obtained at Pic-du-Midi in 1939 movies of the chromosphere at the edge of the sun and the prominences, and the first monochromatic photographs of the corona in green (5303 Å) and in red (6374 Å). Lyot has subsequently perfected his monochromatic filter by substituting calcite for polaroid film; he obtained greater luminosity, at the same time doubling the selective power in the red and diminishing the diffused light. In this way he was able to observe at Pic-du-Midi the chromosphere in front of the solar disk and the corona in the green and red simultaneously. Then separating the various radiations, he succeeded in impressing three movie films simultaneously: the first shows the prominences in the line Hα; the second, the corona in the line 6374 Å; and the third, the corona in the line of 5303 Å. Finally in 1942 Lyot was able to reduce the width of the transmitted band to about 1 Å, by adding a supplementary lamina of calcite to the filter. He succeeded in observing and making movies (in the radiation Hα) of the movements of the chromosphere at the edge of the sun, the dark flocculi on the disk, as well as the evolution of the numerous chromospheric eruptions, showing their radial velocities with an analyzer for elliptical polarization.

In 1939 Lyot put the polaroid filter in place of the eyepiece of his coronagraph, with a diverging lens interposed between the objective and the filter. This lens sends to infinity the image of the disk which hides the sun in the coronagraph; and behind it an objective forms in the eyepiece, or on the photographic plate, the monochromatic image of the corona and the prominences distributed around the solar disk. The temperature being progressively increased at 15° C the bright prominences appeared on a dark yellow background because of the absorption of the polaroid in the D_3 radiation of helium; then at 19° C they were illuminated in blue in the Hβ of hydrogen. Near 17° C they presented an intermediate greenish color which borders on blue or on yellow at the points moving with radial velocities respectively positive or negative. Near 21° C they disappeared. With the new filter, provided with calcite polarizers, the images were brighter and better defined. Lyot was able to compare the images of the green and red corona, which differ from each other as the photographic images of the prominences differ in the light of hydrogen and calcium, respectively. A further result is the almost complete independence of the corona from the prominences. Instead, photographs of the corona taken during eclipses often show an evident correspondence between the prominences and the coronal streamers.

With this new means of observation it has been possible to study also the motions of the coronal matter, concerning which eclipses have until now given uncertain results. Lyot's photographs do not reveal any real displacements. Some parts are illuminated and others are extinguished periodically without our being able to follow the displacement of any particular part. The phenomenon must be analogous, aside from the conditions of excitation, to what happens in the upper terrestrial atmosphere in the northern aurorae, where we observe the rapid appearance and disappearance of the streamers and luminous clouds in different parts of the sky. In the corona, however, there may be more complicated motions—vortices, for example—which only a fast-moving movie camera would be able to reveal. This was actually done by Lyot, with the result that with an acceleration of twelve hundred times he could not detect any motion in the various parts of the corona, but only relative variations of intensity. As the prominences move very rapidly, the corona observed in monochromatic light, either in the green line or the red, remains entirely motionless. The arcs, the streamers, and the clouds are periodically illuminated, just like the northern lights, without any noticeable movement of material masses. In general these observations prove that the corona changes in form and aspect, like most of the prominences, not by relative movements of its various parts, but by the appearance and disappearance of luminous zones which change in intensity from one point to another. The streamers and coronal clouds which form the complicated patterns are born somewhere on invisible trajectories, which existed long before and whose origin and formation for the time being cannot be explained. On the other hand, the chromosphere does not appear as a homogeneous atmosphere, but as a multitude of tiny flames—the "flaming prairie" of Father Secchi—which rise up on the photosphere, sometimes vertically, sometimes obliquely. These flames are projected one in front of the other, giving the impression of a continuous fluid. If the wave length of the band transmitted by the filter is slowly diminished by the rotation of the last polarizer, the flames which approach the observer appear more intense than the others and the chromosphere becomes striated and more transparent.

The coronagraph and the monochromatic polarizing filter of Lyot, as we conclude from the results attained, are new powerful means of investigation, thanks to which we shall be able to discover other important characteristics of the constitution of the sun.

Before leaving the history of solar physics of these last years, we must recall the progress attained in the study of the relations between solar and terrestrial phenomena. We have already said how the first sugestions, that the former could be the cause of the latter, were made with the discovery of the variations of terrestrial magnetism, both periodic corresponding to the various phases of the 11-year cycle, and accidental because of the presence of sunspots and their passage across the central meridian of the sun. Ever-widening research on the upper terrestrial atmosphere, especially following the rapid progress of radio engineering, reveals many of its characteristics and their dependence upon solar phenomena. Thus we see how necessary it is for the astrophysicist to follow with the greatest possible continuity and regularity the phenomena which occur and develop on the sun. The geophysicists gather data on related terrestrial phenomena, or on what they think may be related. Such a task cannot be executed by a few isolated investigators, and many astrophysical and geophysical observatories scattered throughout the earth must collaborate, just as is done every day to establish meteorological elements in the various regions of the earth.

The International Council of Scientific Unions, founded after World War I (1914–1918), instituted in 1924 a committee of about a dozen members, astrophysicists, geophysicists, and radiotechnicians. Under the presidency first of S. Chapman and then of G. Abetti, it organized a collaboration to which the International Unions of Astronomy, Geodesy-Geophysics, and Radio Sciences have contributed. Up to 1939, when World War II interrupted its work, the committee had published five reports, which contain the relations between the observations made and the results obtained, both in astrophysics and geophysics. With the resumption of international co-operation (in 1948), the sixth report was published by L. d'Azambuja. This collaboration has made remarkable progress in the continuous observation of the sun; the stations being appropriately distributed in longitude and latitude, they can follow with various instruments the occurrences on the sun almost every hour of the day and in all seasons. Thus they can observe the solar tempests during their entire course on the visible hemisphere of the sun and note particularly the so-called "flares," which have been discovered to have an immediate response in the perturbations of the ionosphere. The ionosphere is in fact very sensitive to solar radiations, especially to the ultraviolet. When these are more or less intense we have real "ionospheric storms," which can be distinguished from other irregularities of the ionosphere and which show the well-known "fadings" in the transmission of radio waves, simultaneously or almost simultaneously with the chromospheric eruptions. In addition we have found that these radiations have some effect on terrestrial magnetism, producing variations of a special type. The influence of the solar perturbations on the production and frequency of the aurorae, according to recent investigations in Norway and Sweden, seems increasingly evident.

In the more or less near future it will be found necessary to gather the data of solar observations and to communicate them rapidly, as is done now with terrestrial meteorological observations. Today, however, they are published regularly in a quarterly bulletin by the Federal Observatory of Zürich, and by other observatories, including Arcetri, Coimbra, Greenwich, Meudon, and Mt. Wilson. These are compared with geophysical data compiled in other bulletins and periodicals.

PARALLAXES OF THE FIXED STARS

In the determination of the parallax of the fixed stars, photography has again completely replaced visual observation. One of the pioneers in this field was Frank Schlesinger, director first of Allegheny Observatory, then of Yale Observatory. He learned the art of celestial photography from Rutherfurd and made his first reduction measurements from Rutherfurd's plates. Later at Allegheny he began the determination of stellar parallaxes on a large scale, reducing the probable error in their values to $\pm0.008''$. At the same time he asked various American and European observatories to collaborate in the huge undertaking.

To extend the knowledge of the parallaxes to the Southern Hemisphere stars, in 1923 he set up a 26-inch photographic refractor near the University of Witwatersrand in Johannesburg, South Africa. There, in collaboration with the Observatory of the Cape of Good Hope, many determinations have been made. In 1935, after gathering all values of the parallaxes obtained by different methods, Schlesinger published a general catalog containing 7534 stars. At Yale Observatory, under his direction, many catalogs have been published of star positions photographed with a wide-angle astrograph on photographic plates 19 by 23 inches and embracing 140° square in the sky.

STELLAR PHOTOMETRY

To the field of stellar photometry photography has also brought remarkable progress, in both the precision of the results and the quantity and rapidity with which they are obtained. A pioneer in this field was Karl Schwarzschild, director first of the Göttingen Observatory, then of Potsdam. His well known and ingenious work in various branches of astrophysics was interrupted by his untimely death in 1916 at forty-three years of age. In order to diminish the systematic errors in the measurement of double stars, he had thought, even in the early years of his astronomical career, of placing a plate in front of the objective to make the first measurements of "effective wave lengths." Passing then to the study of variables, he thought of using their extrafocal images and determining the blackening which they produced on the photographic plate. This led him to his discovery of the law concerning the density of photographic images, and with this law he increased his precision by measuring the diameters of the focal images. The application of this method led him immediately to the discovery of the color variation, for he had proved that the photographic amplitude of the variations exceeded the visual amplitude. Photographic observations of the variable β Lyrae, compared with visual observations, gave him a proof that the velocity of light was independent of the wave length.

He continued his studies in stellar photometry with a new instrument devised by him, called *schraffierkassette*. Instead of photographing the little disks of the whole or extrafocal stellar images, he obtained the regular star traces; they were more or less large according to the more or less broad motion back and forth which he might effect, by means of appropriate clock movements, on the photographic plate placed in the *kassette* at the eyepiece end of the telescope. He measured the density of these traces, rather than of the little disks, and gained a great deal by thus extending the usable field. The "Actinometry of Göttingen," made with this instrument, contains the photographic magnitudes of 3500 stars brighter than 7.5 magnitude, which are found in the *Bonner Durchmusterung*, in the declination zone 0° to +20°. They are the same stars which constitute the photometric visual catalog of Potsdam. From comparison of the data contained in these two catalogs we can find for every star the "color index," that is, the difference between the photographic and visual magnitude.This very important element introduced by Schwarzschild into astronomy has proved, in the "Actinometry of Göttingen," to be in strict correspondence with the respective stellar spectra.

One problem of stellar photometry, difficult to solve precisely, has always been that of establishing a scale of magnitude invariable for different plates taken in different weather and under different conditions, and of comparing the results obtained by different instruments and by different observatories. Various methods are in use. Edward C. Pickering had the idea of utilizing, for the Northern Hemisphere, a field of stars in the immediate vicinity of the north celestial pole, and of determining with great precision the photographic magnitudes of the stars therein from the brightest to the faintest. The magnitude of the stars, in any region of the sky whatsoever, could be obtained by direct comparison with the so-called "north polar sequence" by including the two zones on the same plate. The sequence furnishes the exact photographic magnitude of 96 stars in the immediate vicinity of the pole, from the second to the twenty-first magnitude. F. Seares, astronomer at Mt. Wilson Observatory, by combining the photometric results obtained at Harvard, Greenwich, Potsdam, and Mt. Wilson, has established a polar sequence which has been adopted internationally.

The name of Schwarzschild will remain in the history of astronomy not only for his theoretical and practical contributions to celestial photometry, but also for his studies in various other fields. One of his theoretical studies concerned the pressure of light on small spherical particles which, under solar influence, are attracted in proportion to their volume and at the same time repelled by light pressure in proportion to their surface. At the appearance of Halley's comet in 1910 photographs adapted to photometric measurements were obtained by an expedition of the Potsdam Observatory to Tenerife. From these photographs Schwarzschild deduced the important result that the decrease in intensity of the comet's tail, with increasing distance from the head, could be explained by a corresponding decrease in density. In other words, the luminosity of the repelled particles is maintained along the tail, just as if the phenomenon were due to resonance of solar light.

Other methods independent of the naked eye or of photography have been devised for measurements of stellar magnitudes. In 1910 J. Stebbins of the Washburn Observatory of the University of Wisconsin applied the property of selenium (that it changes its electrical resistance under variations of luminous intensity) to celestial photometry. A selenium cell, contained in a receptacle with melting ice to maintain it at constant temperature, was attached to the eyepiece end of a 12-inch refractor and used to measure the intensity of the extrafocal images of the stars. The cell was enclosed in the arm of a Wheatstone bridge, and the intensities or the variations in intensity of the stars were determined with a galvanometer. With this arrangement Stebbins discovered in the variation of Algol the secondary minimum, which proves that at half the interval between the two principal eclipses there is a secondary eclipse, in which the combined light of the two components diminishes by only 0.06 of a magnitude, because the companion of Algol is not a completely dark body.

The selenium cell was soon abandoned by Stebbins when a year later J. Kunz, a physicist at the University of Illinois, suggested using a photoelectric cell instead of selenium for stellar photometry, and he succeeded in constructing one sensitive enough to be used for astronomical photometry. At almost the same time P. Guthnick, who later became director of the Babelsberg Observatory in Berlin, and H. Rosenberg, director of the Kiel Observatory, were thinking of the same application. This was derived, in fact, from the experiments of Elster and Geitel, who several years before had constructed cells of alkali metals which, when struck by luminous waves more or less intense, emitted more or fewer electrons (photoelectric effect). The improvement of photoelectric cells was so rapid that with the 100-inch reflector at Mt. Wilson it is now possible to measure stars to the sixteenth magnitude with a probable error of 0.04 magnitude. Stebbins estimates that even a star of 18.5 magnitude can be detected; compared with Jupiter, whose —2.2 magnitude caused no deflection at all on the galvanometer in the first experiments made with selenium, this shows a progress of more than 20 magnitudes with the use of the photoelectric cells. Of this progress, 4.5 magnitudes are due to the increase of power in the telescope and 15 or 16 magnitudes to the improvements in the technique and methods used. Also, in measuring the color of stars, photoelectric cells give good and important results. The use of two or more filters to limit the various regions of the spectrum has the advantage over photographic photometry of needing no reference scale of magnitude. The photoelectric cell has thus acquired an important place among the various instruments used to measure the quantity and quality of the radiations which come to us from the celestial bodies. It is important to note that the use of the photoelectric cell is independent of the magnitude of the image or of its form, as long as the image is not larger than the cathode.

The ability of the photoelectric cell to make a rapid and precise measurement of surfaces of low luminosity made possible, for the first time in 1932, the determination of the luminosity of the sky at Mt. Wilson and Mt. Palomar. It was then used for measuring the total light of the sky and the combined magnitude of more than a hundred extragalactic nebulae. The ability of the photoelectric cell to integrate the light which strikes it is particularly useful for comparing luminous points and surfaces. In photometry the photoelectric cell attains an accuracy superior to that of any other method. This accuracy depends on the gathering of the available light, that is, on the power of the telescope, and on the fact that the current is directly proportional to the intensity of the light. The accurate determination of the light-curves of eclipsing variables, obtained with photoelectric cells, has led to a better knowledge of the linear diameters of the stars and of their densities, as well as the degree of limb darkening. The measurement of the color of a large number of celestial objects can easily be done with photoelectric cells. In the color measurement of stars of Secchi's first type and of globular star clusters, the photoelectric cell shows the existence of a great quantity of interstellar dust which darkens and reddens the light of the most distant stars. With cells sensitive to various regions of the spectrum and with more monochromatic filters, we can make use of spectrophotometry in several wave lengths.

Experiments to measure stellar radiation by means of thermoelements and various types of radiometers were begun by Huggins, who used couples of bismuth and antimony at the focus of a refractor. Later the thermoelements were placed in a vacuum, and thus they became considerably more sensitive. W. W. Coblentz, at Lick Observatory, obtained results for about a hundred stars by using thermocouples made of an alloy of platinum-bismuth and bismuth-tin. To the Newtonian focus of the 100-inch telescope of Mt. Wilson, E. Pettit and S. B. Nicholson, between 1922 and 1927, successively attached twelve different types of thermocouples, provided with apertures covered with crystal, fluoride, quartz, and microscope slides.

The thermocouple was connected to a galvanometer, sensitive to 3×10^{-10} amperes per millimeter on a scale 25 feet away. Pettit and Nicholson were thus able to determine, for about a hundred stars, the total radiation, which leads to the knowledge of the "radiometric magnitudes." Subtracting these from the visual magnitudes gives the so-called "heat index," which is naturally positive and sometimes very great for the red stars. The absolute temperatures and the apparent diameters have also been found for these stars. These observations show that stars of low temperature do not irradiate like black bodies and that the long-period variables are quite different in their minima from those of a black radiator.

Although observations and investigations tell us the apparent magnitudes of the stars and their eventual variability, the astrophysicists have tried, by direct and indirect methods, to establish also their intrinsic luminosity or the so-called "absolute magnitude," that is, the magnitude that a given star would have at a given distance equal for all stars. In 1905 and 1907 the Danish astronomer Hertzsprung, who was then director of the Leiden Observatory, published two of his works in a German periodical on scientific photography. He disclosed a remarkable discovery, at which he arrived by considering another, made by Antonia C. Maury, of Harvard Observatory, while classifying stellar spectra for the Draper catalog. Since she had observed that the Fraunhofer lines in stars of the same class appeared with different characteristics of definition, she thought that this fact could be attributed to the different stages of stellar evolution. To explain this matter Hertzsprung tried to put the observed characteristics in relation to the proper motions of the stars, which, as is well known, are a function of their distance from the solar system. He found that the stars of type I of Secchi (white) are intrinsically very luminous, but those of type III (red) are divided into two groups: one of stars intrinsically very luminous, the other of very faint stars. Red stars of intermediate luminosity are almost completely nonexistent. From the white stars we pass by degrees across the yellow and orange (type II of Secchi) to faint red ones, but among these there also exist some very luminous stars which rank with the very bright red ones. In other words, he demonstrated that all the stars find a place in two "sequences." The "main sequence," starting from the white stars, advances rapidly to the weak red stars; the other sequence is also formed from white to red, but of stars of great luminosity. Since the white stars are all very bright they can be considered as belonging to both sequences. But the other stars diverge, the more separated one sequence from the other, the closer they come to the red stars, of which there are none, or almost none, of intermediate luminosity. Hertzsprung called the very luminous stars "giants"; the orange and red stars of the main sequence, "dwarfs." These names at once suggest what was better clarified when it was possible to establish the volumes and masses of both sequences.

The discovery of Hertzsprung, perhaps because it was published in a nonastronomical periodical, was not generally recognized. In 1914 it was independently discovered by means of another method by Henry Norris Russell, director of the Princeton University Observatory. Some years before, as a student at Cambridge Observatory in England, Russell, in collaboration with A. R. Hinks, had made photographic determinations of stellar parallaxes, and he deduced from these the absolute magnitude of fifty-five stars. These confirmed Hertzsprung's discovery, and Russell deduced, from the existence of two different types of red stars, some very luminous, others faint, the hypothesis that they represent two different stages of stellar evolution. Thus in a certain sense there was a return to an old theory of Lockyer, that the stars are born red and with increasing temperature take on a blue color; then as they revert to a lower temperature, they turn back to a red color.

The investigations of Hertzsprung and Russell led to the drawing of the so-called "Russell-Hertzsprung diagram," which gives the underlying relation between absolute magnitude and spectral class. As the most abundant observational data has accumulated in subsequent years, this distribution of the stars has been more and more confirmed, and the yellow and red stars separated into giants and dwarfs. To explain what principally causes the difference between giants and dwarfs, we must first gather data on their masses and volumes. The former are obtained by means of double stars through the application of Kepler's third law and other indirect means. The latter can be determined through knowledge of the diameters and densities. By elaborating a theory of eclipsing variables, Russell and Harlow Shapley, director of Harvard Observatory, in 1913 furnished methods of calculating, from the light-curves, the orbits described by the two components and, from the knowledge of the radii, also their density.

STELLAR SPECTROSCOPY

Meanwhile the progress of atomic physics and spectroscopy helped to explain stellar spectra. In the spectrum of the star ζ Puppis a series of Fraunhofer lines had been discovered at Harvard which closely resembled the Balmer series of hydrogen, and one might believe that it was the Balmer series displaced by a radial motion of the star. But laboratory experiments made in 1913 by A. Fowler, professor of astrophysics at the Imperial College in London, who was experimenting with condensed sparks in a mixture of hydrogen and helium, proved that the "Pickering series" present in ζ Puppis and other stars at high temperature was very probably due to helium. This surmise has been confirmed by subsequent investigations with vacuum tubes, in which there was only pure helium in a state of ionization, that is, having lost an electron. It therefore had properties similar to those of the hydrogen atom.

A year after Fowler's investigations, which were beginning to explain the presence of lines in the stellar spectra due to greater or less excitation of the atoms, at the Mt. Wilson Observatory, Adams and A. Kohlschütter, who was later made director of the Bonn Observatory, found a spectroscopic method for the determination of the absolute magnitude of the stars. We must recall that Lockyer had already observed certain characteristics of the intensely luminous stars, for instance, the low intensity of their ultraviolet spectrum. Next Hertzsprung had noticed that the giant stars generally presented spark lines, that is, the enhanced lines of Lockyer, more intense than those which are in the dwarfs, where the arc lines are predominant. The two astrophysicists at Mt. Wilson succeeded in distinguishing in the stellar spectra some pairs of lines whose relative intensity is a function of the absolute magnitude. At first they thought that the criteria derived from the variability of these lines could only serve to indicate which were the most distant stars, and the parallaxes could then be measured by known methods. But later, improving the method, Adams succeeded in determining the "spectroscopic parallaxes" of a great number of stars.

A new theory was devised in 1920 by the Indian Physicist, Megh Nad Saha, of the University of Calcutta, proceeding from the principle that ionization—that is, the decomposition of an atom into an ion positively charged and one or more negative electrons—is a phenomenon of the same nature as that of the reversible dissociation of a gas into two others, studied in physical chemistry. Then by applying the physicochemical laws of molecules to the particular case of atoms, Saha derived a formula which has been successfully applied to the interpretation of the physical characteristics of the stars. The formula relates the three quantities—percentage of ionized atoms, pressure, and temperature of the outer layers of the stars observable with the spectroscope—in such a way that by establishing two of the quantities one can determine the third. Saha's formula lends itself to a great many applications. Thus, for example, since it is now possible to determine with remarkable precision the intensity of the Fraunhofer lines, the degree of ionization of the gas which absorbs the given lines can be derived. The temperature can be determined by Planck's equation or by other methods, and then by Saha's formula the pressure at the levels of the star in which the absorption takes place can be calculated. The application of Saha's theory to the determination of the pressure in the outer stellar envelopes has been particularly studied by R. H. Fowler and by E. A. Milne, professor at Oxford University, and later by D. A. Menzel and Cecilia Payne, both of Harvard Observatory.

Thus we have come to have a clearer and more complete picture of the sequence of stellar spectra and of the various physical conditions which they represent, among them also the qualitative and quantitative composition of the elements which constitute the various types of stars. Of the 92 elements known on the earth, 61 have been identified in the solar atmosphere. This fact does not mean that the others may not exist on the sun, but rather that their lines cannot be observed. Our imperfect knowledge of the spectra of some of them, the fact that most of the important lines are to be found in inaccessible regions of the spectrum, and the scarcity of these elements on the earth, and probably also on the sun, may be the reasons why these elements seem to be lacking in the solar atmosphere. Investigations by Russell and Menzel have made known the percentage in volume of some of the more abundant elements in the solar atmosphere, and also the total amount of mass of each element as represented in an atmospheric column vertically extending from the photosphere and having a base of a square centimeter. The most remarkable result is the great abundance of hydrogen and helium. More than 80 per cent of the atoms of the solar atmosphere are hydrogen, a fact which explains why the hydrogen lines are visible in most of the stellar spectra of the various types of stars. By applying Saha's formula, Russell found that at temperatures a little lower than those on the sun the carbon compounds are very abundant. At still lower temperatures carbon monoxide is formed. He seeks to explain, as R. A. Curtiss suggested, that the sequence of stellar spectra in the more advanced classes may be derived from small differences in chemical composition.

The appearance of novae in relatively recent times and the possibility of studying them spectroscopically with powerful means at the moment of their greatest development and of following the various phases of decreasing luminosity have helped to explain, at least in part, the great and rapid phenomena which they present. On the evening of June 8, 1918, while E. E. Barnard, an astronomer of Yerkes Observatory, was in Wyoming to observe a total eclipse of the sun, he noticed a very brilliant nova in the constellation Aquila. In fact, because of its remarkable brightness, it was seen simultaneously, or almost so, in many parts of the world. It was possible to verify with photographs of that zone of the sky, taken three days earlier, that the star was then of eleventh magnitude, as it had been for at least thirty years before. Increasing in brightness on June 9 it reached —0.5 magnitude, almost as bright as Sirius and Canopus. After that date its luminosity rapidly decreased. This is the most outstanding nova of modern times, and it has been followed and studied in detail by many investigators with important results.

As we have already said, the phenomenon of novae had been recognized even in ancient times, but it is certain that the great astronomical interest in recent novae has, as it were, intensified the phenomenon, increasing its importance and frequency both in our galactic system and outside of it. It will be enough to say that between 1604, the year of the appearance of the nova of Kepler and Galileo, and 1901, when the nova Persei appeared, only five novae were observed, none of them exceptionally brilliant. In the present century eight novae of remarkable brilliancy have appeared, two greater than first magnitude, two of first, two of second, and two of fourth and seventh magnitude. Now if we do not wish to believe that this fact can be acribed to an intensification of the phenomenon in recent years, a highly improbable suggestion, we must conclude that the larger number of novae seen recently is due to a more efficient and continuous survey of the sky from all parts of the world. Furthermore, if some nova happens to be in any photograph made with the prismatic camera, its spectrum can easily be found at the moment or near the date of its appearance. On the plates taken at

Harvard for the Draper catalogue, Mrs. Fleming discovered two novae in 1893 and 1895. S. J. Bailey, another Harvard astronomer, from a statistical examination of the same plates, calculated that at least ten and perhaps twenty novae, reaching the ninth magnitude or brighter appear annually.

Among the most remarkable novae of recent times we shall cite the nova Geminorum 1912, whose spectrum was photographed during the phases of maximum brightness in many observatories, in particular in Cambridge (England) by F. J. Stratton, and in Allegheny, Pennsylvania. A rich series of spectrograms has permitted us to derive from the displacement of the emission and absorption lines the proof and confirmation that in the nova a real explosion of gas takes place, which rapidly increases the diameter and thus the luminosity. Three weeks after the discovery, the decrease in brightness of the nova Geminorum was interrupted, as in the case of the nova Persei, by periodic oscillations of brightness with notable variations in the spectrum. These can be explained by the motions of the various gaseous envelopes as they depart from the central nucleus of the star.

The nova Aquilae has also made a notable contribution to the complicated and interesting phenomena presented by the novae. Because of its great brilliancy it could be followed with wide-dispersion spectrographs, especially in the Mt. Wilson and Lick observatories. An important fact is that its spectrum, before the explosion, was similar to that of normal white stars. At the moment of explosion the absorption lines were displaced toward the violet by an amount corresponding to a velocity of expansion of the outer layers of about 900 miles per second. Immediately after the maximum there appeared large emission bands of hydrogen, which indicate that an important envelope of this gas separated itself from the central nucleus of the star with an even greater velocity, of the order of 1500 miles per second. Gradually as the envelope expanded and became more and more tenuous, the hydrogen bands disappeared and were replaced by new bands which are identified with the "forbidden lines" of oxygen and nitrogen, whose existence is possible only at extremely low densities. A year after the maximum the spectrum of the stellar nucleus was essentially continuous, with few forbidden bands. A year after that the bands disappeared. After the explosion the star must have suffered a collapse; it became less luminous than before the explosion, but its surface, with higher temperature and therefore greater luminosity, compensates for the contraction, so that its total luminosity is about the same.

A phenomenon rarely observed in novae occurred in the nova Aquilae. Some months after its maximum a tenuous circular nebulosity was seen around the star and it continued for some time gradually to expand. Since 1922 the nebulosity has increased by 2″ a year. Combining this information with the velocity of expansion furnished by the spectrum, we obtain a distance of 1200 light-years for the nova. At its maximum luminosity the nova Aquilae reached an intensity equal to 300,000 times that of the sun, the maximum observed until now for normal novae. Interesting observations on the nebulosity of this nova were made by J. H. Moore and C. D. Shane at Lick Observatory in 1919, as they succeeded in photographing the spectrum of the nebulous disk in different sections. The displacements of the spectral lines resulted in these differences, but not so as to be explained by a simple expansion. It seems that a kind of turbulence existed, superimposed on the expansion. In fact, from the measurements a remarkable symmetry results, which suggests the presence in the gaseous envelope of currents rotating simultaneously in opposite directions.

In May, 1925, the nova Pictoris, which increased in brightness rather slowly, was discovered in South Africa. It was possible to study in detail the variations of the spectrum during that interesting phase, especially at the Cape of Good Hope, where H. Spencer Jones, then Astronomer Royal at that observatory and later at Greenwich, made an extensive study of all the collected observational material. While the star was increasing in luminosity its spectrum remained unaltered, and thus the surface temperature must have remained unchanged. Consequently the increasing brightness must be ascribed solely to an expansion of the star. Spencer Jones was able to prove that, during the first two weeks of observation, the diameter of the star increased every day by an amount equal to about 14 times the diameter of the sun. At maximum luminosity, its diameter had reached 400 times that of the sun. Three years after the appearance of the nova Pictoris, W. H. van den Bos and W. S. Finsen, at the Union Observatory in Johannesburg, observed a nebulous disk around the nova. The disk was not round and symmetrical as in the nova Aquilae, but it consisted of two or three luminous nuclei. Later, and until 1930, the two observers noticed that the disk was definitely expanding, a fact which led to the determination of its distance. Immediately after the maximum, emission lines appeared in the spectrum of the nova, on the red side of the absorption lines, and they continued to become broader and more luminous. Furthermore, two series of absorption lines appeared one after the other, indicating the presence of two envelopes of gas erupting respectively at velocities of 90 miles per second and 200 miles per second. At the same time the continuous spectrum began to grow faint at a velocity corresponding to the general weakening in the luminosity of the star. Spencer Jones calculated that a contraction had taken place corresponding to about twelve solar diameters every day. After the nova Pictoris, two other noteworthy novae appeared, the nova Herculis 1934 and the nova Lacertae 1936, and still others of the recurring type.

The discovery of the nova in the constellation Hercules has an interesting history. The director of the meteor section of the British Astronomical Association, J. P. Prentice, was observing the Geminid meteors on the morning of December 13, 1934. He noticed in the constellation Hercules, not far from Vega, a nova of about third magnitude. He did not delay in assuring his discovery, and telephoned the Greenwich Observatory. There the astronomer, E. G. Martin, who was observing at the 36-inch reflector, confirmed the discovery and immediately began observations of the nova with his instrument, equipped with a spectrograph. This was one of the very few cases in which immediately after the discovery it has been possible to observe with a large instrument a nova in the most interesting moments of its appearance. The news was spread to observatories all over the world, and regular observations with various instruments were immediately started and continued. Research in the photographic archives of Harvard Observatory has shown that in the place of the nova a telescopic star of 15.5 magnitude previously existed. By comparison of the magnitude estimated at different times we might suspect that the star was variable, but so faint that it could be reached only by a telescope of aperture not less than 12 inches. Since the star passed rapidly from 15.5 to third magnitude, its luminosity increased by about 100,000 times and it remained thus for about four months, offering to astrophysicists an excellent opportunity to study in detail the spectrum and its variations. Then suddenly the star diminished in brightness, dropping in the course of a month to thirteenth magnitude; then it rose to seventh magnitude, where it remained over a year. In the course of these variations in brightness G. P. Kuiper, with the 36-inch reflector of Lick Observatory, discovered the first signs of a nebulous disk around the nova, or better, two luminous nuclei which soon were seen to separate from each other.

In 1885, in the great spiral nebula of Andromeda, a nova was discovered which attained seventh magnitude, thus reaching a tenth of the entire luminosity of the nebula. Little could be surmised about the circumstances of the phenomenon, but recent photographic observations, especially those of M. L. Humason, of Mt. Wilson, have led to the discovery of about twenty novae, all of them, however, weaker than the 1885 one, which had a maximum many thousands of times brighter than all the others. Such a nova must belong to another class of stars, which by reason of their tremendous luminosity can be called "supernovae." Novae and supernovae can appear in the same nebula but with different frequency. In 1936, after a systematic search of several years by E. P. Hubble, W. Baade, and F. Zwicky at Mt. Wilson Observatory, a supernova of 17.5 magnitude was discovered, sufficiently luminous for Humason to photograph its spectrum with a 17-hour exposure. It presented emission lines like those of a nova but enormously broader, indicating that the star was exploding with a velocity of about 4000 miles per second. Baade and Zwicky then initiated a systematic search for supernovae at the new Mt. Palomar Observatory with an 18-inch Schmidt telescope, discovering in 1937 three other supernovae. One of these was brighter than ninth magnitude, and Humason was able to obtain a detailed spectrum of a supernova with the 100-inch at Mt. Wilson. Since 1885, 40 supernovae have been discovered in 36 star systems, 22 of them since 1937, that is since the systematic search began, 300 nebulae having been studied whose total brightness exceeds fifteenth magnitude. These can be considered as a representative group of the region of the universe within the range of the largest telescopes, and thus we can derive a value for the frequency of supernovae.

In nebulae of any type whatsoever, without preference for one or the other, it seems that a supernova may appear every 600 years. Assuming for the nebula of Andromeda the appearance of 30 novae in a year, we conclude that the frequency of supernovae is 20,000 times less. With a new Schmidt-type telescope more powerful than the existing ones, we believe that about 20 supernovae a year can be spotted. The fact that these stars appear in nebulae of any type, that is, presumably without regard for a determined period in their evolution, makes us think that the instability, which is the cause of the explosions, is not connected with particular stages in the history of the life of star systems. We make the hypothesis that novae may represent explosions of dwarf stars; and supernovae, those of giants. In fact, the latter reach an absolute magnitude of −14 at the maximum of the explosion, that is, a brightness equal to a 100 million times that of the sun. The absolute magnitude of the supernovae is of the order of the mean absolute magnitude of the nebulae in which they appear, and thus the phenomenon may reveal something of their constitution. Since the average absolute magnitude of the novae is −7, we have also in this case a distinct separation between the two classes of stars, like that between the giants and dwarfs.

From these first investigations of supernovae it appears that they can be divided into two groups. In the first are those which present light-curves similar in general to those of the novae. Their luminosity increases at the moment of explosion a million times and more in the space of a few days. On the average the maximum, which is of the order of a 100 million suns, is comparable to the integrated magnitude of a star system of average dimensions. After the maximum the supernovae diminish rapidly in brightness, but after a few weeks more slowly, losing a third of their light every month. Typical of this group is the supernova discovered by Zwicky at Mt. Palomar in August, 1937, in the nebula IC 4182, which is a dwarf stellar system about 3 million light-years away. On August 22 the supernova reached its maximum brightness with an apparent magnitude of 8.2, equivalent, at the distance of the nebula, to −16.6 magnitude. It is the brightest of the supernovae observed until now; its luminosity equaled 600 million suns and was therefore 100 times brighter than the nebula in which it appeared. Its spectrum was first photographed August 30, and it was followed for nearly a year, so that we have a complete history of its spectral variations. The star was photographed until two years after the discovery, when it was about half a million times fainter than at its maximum. The exceptional phenomenon was of great importance when we think that the supernova irradiated in one day as much energy, in the regions of the photographic spectrum, as the sun has radiated in a million years.

In the second group are included those supernovae which reach maxima of the order of 10 million suns and present in the descending branch of their light-curve a noticeable halt, after which the decrease in light is resumed. The spectra resemble those of the novae but, like the whole phenomenon, on a much larger scale. A typical example of this group is the supernova which appeared in May, 1940, in the spiral nebula NGC 4725, which is a gigantic stellar system 5 or 6 million light-years away. At the maximum the supernova reached a luminosity of 30 million suns, about a seventh of the total brightness of the nebula. After the maximum the star began to decline, at first proceeding for several weeks more slowly than the stars of the first group, then more rapidly. Photographed at maximum light, the star showed the continuous spectrum of a high-temperature star of the first classes. The emission bands continued to appear four or five days after the maximum, as in the novae, and indicated an explosive velocity of the order of 4000 miles per second.

The supernovae belonging to our galactic system naturally offer better opportunities of study than those of the extragalactic systems, but because of their frequency, one in several centuries, not one has yet appeared during the eighty years in which the spectroscope has been in use, and not even during the three hundred years since the invention of the telescope. In the historical epochs it seems we can count among the supernovae the two stars which appeared in the years 1054 and 1572. The former appeared near the ζ Tauri and remained visible for several months. In this region of the sky is found the nebula of Cancer (Messier 1), which has a diameter of about 5'. Twenty years ago a noticeable angular motion of the cloud of gas which constitutes the nebula was discovered, as if it were expanding with constant velocity. The beginning of the expansion occurred between eight and nine centuries ago, and we suppose that this nebula represents only the remains of the supernova of 1054. Other documents, of Chinese and Japanese origin, confirm this supposition both on account of the place where it was seen and on account of its brightness, equal to that of Venus and visible even by day. The spectrum of the nebula tells us that the velocity of expansion is about 800 miles per second. Its distance from us is about 5000 light-years, and thus we can calculate that this supernova, probably belonging to the first group, reached at its maximum a luminosity of 300 million suns. At the center of the nebula we now find two faint stars. From its proper motion one evidently does not belong to the nebula itself, but the other is a blue star of apparent magnitude 16.6 and having spectral characteristics of the white dwarfs. It probably therefore is the supernova, now 400 million times fainter than at the moment of explosion in 1054. The other supernova is the famous Tycho Brahe supernova, so called because he carefully observed it as long as it was visible to the naked eye. Among the many faint stars near the position determined by Tycho, it has not been possible to find one of abnormal type which could be identified with his supernova.

SOLAR SYSTEM

The progress in the physical study of the surface of the planets has been considerable, because of the more perfect and powerful instruments for visual, photographic, and spectroscopic observation. We will mention the most important advances. Percival Lowell, founder of the observatory in Flagstaff, Arizona, which bears his name, was one of the most fervent admirers and followers of Schiaparelli in visual observations of Mars. In 1907 he was among the first to try to photograph the planet, and he even sent a special mission to Chile where it was visible almost at the zenith and thus was under the best conditions for observation. The comparison of the photographs with the drawings is very instructive. On the former the two polar caps are clearly visible, and also some gray shadings with barely perceptible traces of the "canals." It seemed then that here was almost a confirmation of the geometry of the configurations visible on Schiaparelli's maps. But successive visual observations by E. M. Antoniadi, made at the Flammarion Observatory in Juvisy and at Meudon, by V. Cerulli, founder of the Collurania Observatory in Teramo, and by M. Maggini at Arcetri and Teramo, as well as by many others, reveal that the curious network of geometric canals, which might seem manmade, really depends on an optical illusion caused by the imperfect visibility of the numerous details present on the surface of the planet. Antoniadi came to the conclusion that 70 per cent of the canals are dark, irregular strips, more or less continuous, wherein are scattered small spots of different widths and aspects; 21 per cent correspond to the irregular borders of diffuse gray spots; and 9 per cent are made up of isolated and complex nuclei. The more or less actual changes of the surface of Mars have been followed, the most outstanding being that of the polar caps. Astronomers have tried to interpret the substance there which melts and evaporates, when the temperature rises in spring, diffusing itself in the atmosphere of the planet and again precipitating when the surface becomes colder.

Photographs of the planet have been numerous, especially during the period of "favorable opposition." In the very favorable one of 1924 W. H. Wright, who was director of Lick Observatory on Mt. Hamilton, photographed the planet through filters, which transmit radiations limited only to certain groups of wave lengths, and with plates sensitive to these wave lengths. He obtained in this manner images of the planet in ultraviolet light, in the region of the visible spectrum, and in the infrared, and he noticed considerable differences among them. The disk of the planet comes out bigger in ultraviolet light and presents no detail, with the exception of the polar caps, which seem more extended. If a spot is present it is only of transitory nature. In orange light we see the well known visually observable details, which become better defined and darker in the infra red radiations. As is well known, something similar occurs also in photographs of terrestrial landscapes or in those taken from the air with equivalent filters and plates. We must therefore conclude that also on Mars there exists an absorbing and diffusing atmosphere with selective power. In the red images we see more deeply into the atmosphere of the planet, and the images probably represent the true aspect of its surface. From the difference between the diameters photographed in the longer and shorter wave lengths, Wright estimates the height of the atmosphere to be about 125 miles. He maintains that the polar caps are compact masses of clouds suspended in the atmosphere of Mars, which melt and evaporate under the sun's influence. Some bright prominences have also been observed on the rim of the planet's disk; they occur at more or less frequent intervals, and at times they are completely detached from the edge. Antoniadi, in the same opposition of 1924, observed among others one such protuberance on the configuration called Hellas, whose highest point seemed to oscillate for four days from 5 to 13 miles above the surface of the planet.

Interesting observations have been made by W. W. Coblentz and C. O. Lampland at Lowell Observatory, by Pettit and Nicholson at Mt. Wilson, on the surface temperature of the various planets, and by Lyot on the polarization of their reflected light. For Mercury measurements made with a very sensitive thermocouple in a vacuum at the focus of the 100-inch telescope at Mt. Wilson give a temperature varying from 420° C at phase angle 0°, to 230° with the smallest crescent visible (phase angle 120°). The period found by Schiaparelli has been confirmed by Antoniadi's accurate observations of the details presented by the surface of the planet. Father Secchi had already noted that Mercury was not very bright close to the edge, and recently Lyot has shown that just for this reason it is difficult to find the planet in full daylight near its inferior conjunction. With a very sensitive polarimeter Lyot determined the polarization curve of Mercury, which came out very similar to that of the moon and exactly like the curve between the first and last quarter. By comparing observations made in the observatories of Meudon and Pic-du-Midi under various conditions of visibility with those obtained in the laboratory, he confirmed the fact that the surface of Mercury is probably covered with dusts, similar to our volcanic ashes. Furthermore, the regularity of the variations in the polarization of the light from Mercury observed at different phases, and the perfect resemblance to the lunar variations, prove that its surface cannot be surrounded by clouds as on the earth. Lyot thinks that the white spots observed by Schiaparelli and Antoniadi, which are variable in intensity and position, must be constituted of dust particles, detached from the surface of Mercury, and of considerable dimensions compared to the wave lengths of visible light.

Concerning the interesting and unsolved problem of the rotation of Venus, the observations and discussions of Schiaparelli are still plausible. Although the spectrum at the edge of the disk has been photographed with considerable dispersion, no noticeable displacement of the Fraunhofer lines as a consequence of the Doppler effect has been revealed. This fact is therefore a confirmation of the visual observations of Schiaparelli, with the proof that the velocity of rotation is too slow to be measured with the spectroscope. It may be that the rotation takes place in less than 225 days but certainly not in less than 20, because in this case there would be a good measurable Doppler effect. Pettit and Nicholson find that the surface illuminated by the sun rises to a temperature of about 150° C, whereas the part in shadow is about 0° C. This temperature is what should result from a radiation emitted by cirrus clouds covering the atmosphere of Venus, so that the planet has an almost even temperature, on the illuminated hemisphere as on the darkened one.

Lyot has also made interesting studies of the planet directly and in the laboratory with his polarizer, from which he obtained the polarization curve of Venus in all her phase angles, having been able to carry out his observations even in broad daylight. This curve, which represents the variations of the proportion of polarized light observed under different conditions, proves that the atmosphere of Venus does not undergo as frequent perturbations as that of Mars. The laboratory experiments made by Lyot prove that the polarized light emitted from the planet must be produced from clouds in its atmosphere.

In fact, the many inversion points of the polarization curve would seem to resemble those made by rain clouds. The remarkable and uniform brightness of Venus is a confirmation that the planet must be entirely surrounded by clouds. Of the surface underneath we can have no indication. The surface of Mars is difficult to study with the polarizer because of the clouds which often cover it. Nevertheless Lyot, by watching for the moments when the sky was clear on the planet, finds that its polarization curve is almost identical with the moon's. He infers the existence on the "Martian continents" of a dust similar to that covering the lunar surface. The southern polar cap has often presented a polarization much stronger than that of terrestrial clouds, and its variability can be explained by the formation of frequent clouds in this region. Some white patches appearing at the eastern edge of Thyle II and Aonius Sinus might be formed by transparent particles like icycles. When examined very obliquely they present, like terrestrial snow, a very intense polarization by refraction. No polarization is presented by the clouds when examined obliquely. These observations confirm the fact that the atmosphere of the planet must be of low density; Lyot estimates it to be a fifteenth of ours.

Many new discoveries and results have been obtained in the study of the minor planets. Although there are about 1500 whose orbits can be calculated, W. Baade, from his observations with the Mt. Wilson telescope and on the basis of statistical considerations, estimates that the minor planets, down to the nineteenth magnitude, probably number around 45,000. Since 1906 the "Trojan group" of minor planets has been discovered, so called from the assigned names Achilles, Patroclus, Hector, which have periods and distances approximately identical with those of Jupiter. For celestial mechanics they are of great interest, presenting a particular example, already foreseen by Lagrange, of the problem of three bodies, in which the "sun-Jupiter-Trojan planet" always forms an equilateral triangle in a configuration of equilibrium. Of the Trojan planetoids, twelve have been discovered up to now and their orbits have small eccentricities and large inclinations.

In 1898, the year after Gill completed his arduous task of determining the solar parallax, a minor planet, only about 15 miles in diameter, was discovered photographically by G. Witt, director of the Urania Observatory in Berlin, to which the name of Eros was given. The calculation of its orbit revealed that it could approach a minimum distance from the earth of about 14 million miles, that is, a little more than half the minimum distance of Venus. It thus offered the possibility of more precise determinations of the astronomical unit of distance. At the time of its discovery Eros had already passed this minimum distance; nevertheless in 1901 when the planetoid came to a distance of about 30 million miles, many visual and photographic observations were made, with the international collaboration of fifty-eight observatories. Nine years later Hinks communicated the result, which increased by a few hundredths of a second of arc the value of the solar parallax calculated by Gill.

In 1931 the planet again approached the earth almost to the minimum possible distance, about 16 million miles. Since it described a huge arc in the sky from north to south, observations could be made in both hemispheres and thus a comparison between northern and southern observations was possible. The solar parallax could be derived from the parallactic displacements in declination in addition to those derived in right ascension by the usual method. At the general assembly of the International Astronomical Union in 1928 a commission was chosen for the solar parallax, with the Astronomer Royal of Greenwich, H. Spencer Jones, as president. They were to prepare a program of international collaboration to assure observations during the favorable opposition of the planet, and the consequent reduction and discussion. Forty-four observatories in all parts of the world made many visual and photographic observations that year, and ten years later when the long reductions, calculations, and discussions were completed, H. Spencer Jones communicated the final results to the Royal Society. The value of the solar parallax was given as 8.709″ ± 0.001″, that is, 0.010″ less than that adopted in the Ephemerides. This gives a distance of the earth from the sun of 93,004,000 miles with an uncertainty, more or less of 11,000 miles. This value, derived from the international studies and having such a high degree of precision as results from the mean error, was very unexpected, because the value formerly adopted was not believed to be so much in error. As the president of the Royal Society said when he bestowed the gold medal of the Society on Spencer Jones for his work: "The results from northern and from southern observatories, from right ascensions and from declinations, from photographic and from photovisual telescopes, and from four successive intervals during the opposition, all show excellent agreement, and so there is good reason to believe that every serious systematic error has been eliminated."

As an added result of this work, Spencer Jones also obtained a value, more exact than that known before, of the "lunar equation," and thus of the ratio of the masses of the earth and the moon, which came out 81.271 ± 0.021, that is, 0.3 less than the one formerly adopted. On the basis of these results the constant of nutation has been adjusted, as well as the degree of flattening in the shape of the earth.

Still in the field of the minor planets, one was discovered in 1936 whose orbit crossed that of Venus and the earth, passing at a distance of 1.5 million miles from the earth, that is, only six times the distance of the moon from the earth. To this minor planet of the same class as Eros, the name Adonis was given by its discoverer, E. Delporte, director of the Uccle Observatory in Belgium. Apollo, discovered in 1932, can reach a distance even closer to the earth, and it evidently belongs to the same family. The record of closeness to the earth was broken by a celestial object of about ninth magnitude and of very rapid motion, discovered by K. Reinmuth at the Heidelberg Observatory. After the announcement had been sent over the whole world, the minor planet was followed by many observatories, only for a few days, however, because it passed from one end of the celestial dome to the other in less than four days. On October 31 its motion through the stars reached 5° an hour, and thus it moved in the sky faster than the moon. The orbit calculated on the basis of the few available observations led to the conclusion that the planet moves only slightly inclined to the ecliptic and that it crossed it at a point very close to where the earth was immediately after the discovery. The closeness between the earth and Hermes, as the interesting object is called by analogy with its companions, was really extraordinary on the evening of October 30, when its minimum distance was about 440,000 miles. Its diameter is estimated to be little more than five-eighths of a mile; we are thus at the border line between minor planets and meteorites.

Returning to the major planets of the solar system, we must remember that visual and photographic observations of the surface of Jupiter have always been numerous, especially on the part of the Jupiter Section of the British Astronomical Association, directed for more than thirty years by Rev. T. E. R. Phillips, and in Italy after the earliest observations of Father Secchi, by Tacchini, Riccò, and L. Taffara of the Catania Observatory. Numerous currents, permanent or irregular, cross the disk of the planet, almost entirely longitudinally, with small occasional spots which present a vortical motion. Taffara, from his observations made in the opposition of 1928–1929, reveals that the durations of revolution of the stable spots visible at different latitudes do not differ much from one another. Therefore the average value of about 9^h56^m, which is the longest observed, can be considered as the probable value of the rotation of Jupiter. He observes furthermore how the spots are formed on the surface. As they thin out, they usually form a long band with the characteristic aspect of a column of smoke, which as it distends envelops the planet with long bands. There is some analogy to the eruptive pinnacles produced by terrestrial eruptions, which rise with a certain density so as almost to resemble solid bodies, and then exploding, spread out and disperse, carried away by the upper currents. From observations of the polarized light reflected by Jupiter, Lyot proves the presence above the clouds of a dense atmosphere having a high diffusion power, like that of the terrestrial atmosphere in clear weather. The strange polarizations which the polar caps present would be in accordance with the existence, underneath the clouds, of a dense and very diffusive atmosphere from which the bluish light derives.

In 1895 J. E. Keeler, then at the Allegheny Observatory and afterward director of the Lick Observatory, obtained spectroscopic proof that the outside rim of Saturn's outer ring turns more slowly than the inside one, as required by theory, but not as it would turn if the ring were constituted of a mass of continuous matter. In the inner rim of the ring Keeler's observations indicate a velocity of 12.5 miles per second, in the outer rim only 16, exactly the velocity which the satellites of Saturn would possess if they were at the same distance from the planet. At the edge of the planet the Doppler effect gives a period of rotation of 10.25^h, in good agreement with the value deduced by A. Hall at the Washington Naval Observatory, from observations of spots visible on the surface of the planet. From Keeler's observation we can conclude that the rings of Saturn are composed of thousands of tiny particles which revolve around the planet in their individual orbits. More or less noticeable spots appear on the surface of the planet. The most conspicuous is that which appeared in 1933 close to the equator under the rings. A year later it disappeared and in its place a white equatorial band was extended. Determinations of the temperature on the surface give $-150°$ C, about 30° higher than would result solely from the effect of solar radiation. Some information on the atmosphere of the planet and on the constitution of the rings has been deduced by Lyot from his measurements of polarized light. On one whitish zone, appearing in 1924 as a pale and very indistinct cloud, a polarization similar to that of Jupiter's clouds was observed. The polarization curve of the rings is very different from that of the moon and Mars. For the inner ring it is similar to that of numerous unpulverized minerals, as for example fragments of lava and granite. We might conclude that the inner ring is perhaps formed of more or less large blocks. The phenomena observed on the outer ring are very complex, and the differences presented by the two ends are remarkable.

Spectroscopic observations of the solar light reflected by the surfaces of the various planets have given us interesting results concerning the composition of their atmospheres. C. St. John and Nicholson, with the horizontal Snow telescope connected to a grating spectrograph of high dispersion at Mt. Wilson Observatory, were able definitely to establish in 1922 that no absorption lines or bands were present in the spectrum of Venus's atmosphere. The search was made during the periods when the velocity of Venus, relative to that of the earth, is sufficient to separate the lines due to the same substance, as for example water vapor, eventually present in the atmospheres of both planets. From these observations we can conclude that in the atmospheric level of the planet pierced by the solar light there cannot exist more than the equivalent of a meter of oxygen, that is, less than a thousandth of that existing in our atmosphere, or more than a millimeter of condensed water vapor. Later (1932) Adams and Th. Dunham, with a grating spectrograph applied to the end of the polar axis of the 100-inch reflector at Mt. Wilson, and thus with considerable dispersion, fully confirmed, by using the intense bands present in the infrared spectrum, the absence of oxygen and water vapor in the level of the atmosphere of Venus which we are able to investigate with the spectroscope. They discovered instead, on the spectrograms, two bands with their heads at 7820 Å and 7883 Å and another band at 8689 Å, well defined toward the violet and less so toward the red, similar in their general characteristics to the oxygen bands produced by carbon dioxide, as could be established by the theory of band spectra and then by experimental proofs. Dunham, by using the same spectrograph, succeeded in reproducing the bands in the laboratory, and by further research it was concluded that the amount of carbon dioxide existing on the visible surface of Venus is at least

2 miles high at atmospheric pressure. However, the whole quantity over the solid crust of the planet may be even greater. As a comparison, the whole terrestrial atmosphere under the same conditions rises 5 miles, and the oxygen in it, 1.3. Carbon dioxide is very scarce on the earth, and the corresponding level would have a height of only about 30 feet at atmospheric pressure.

We are now almost certain that the polar caps on Mars are composed of ice, because the temperature is too high to permit the existence of carbon-dioxide snow. The red color of the Martian surface suggests the presence of iron oxide in minerals, which might be caused by exposure to an atmosphere that once contained free oxygen. Nevertheless no such substance has yet been discovered with the spectroscope. A detailed study of the intensity and form of the spectral lines, carried out by Adams and Dunham in 1934 with the microphotometer, furnishes no sure evidence of the presence of oxygen. They indicate that the amount present in the Martian atmosphere is less than one per cent of that existing above an equal area on the earth's surface. Even water vapor and carbon dioxide seem to be nonexistent.

Fifty years after the discovery by Secchi and Huggins of the conspicuous bands present in the spectra of the major planets, their origin began to be explained. By means of the admirable photographs obtained at the Lowell Observatory by W. M. Slipher, R. Wildt established that the bands are produced by ammonia and methane. The fine structure of the bands in the spectra of Jupiter and Saturn has been photographed with high dispersion by Dunham (1933), and he confirmed Wildt's results with spectra obtained in the laboratory. A year later Slipher and A. Adel identified all the observed bands of methane in the spectrum of Neptune also. The ammonia bands are rather intense in Jupiter, weaker in Saturn, and absent in Uranus and Neptune. This fact can be explained by condensation at the very low temperatures of the outer planets. The methane bands, on the other hand, increase in intensity in the outer planets, possibly because the precipitation of condensed ammonia clouds permits us to see more deeply into the atmosphere of the planet. Dunham estimates that there are approximately 10 meter-atmospheres of ammonia and 40 meter-atmospheres of methane on Jupiter. He concludes that if the partial pressure of ammonia on the visible surface of Jupiter were equal to the weight of the quantity of this gas determined spectroscopically, the temperature could not be less than $-100°$ C. The presence of hydrogen compounds in the atmosphere of the major planets, of oxygen compounds in the atmosphere of the other planets, and the lack of atmosphere on the satellites and minor planets has been discussed and explained by Russell on the basis of physical and chemical principles, on the hypothesis that all these bodies were originally similar in composition to the sun.

The limits of the solar system were extended in 1930 by a discovery made by C. W. Tombaugh at the Lowell Observatory. On March 12 of that year a new planet was found near the star δ Geminorum in accordance with the position predicted in longitude by Lowell. He had calculated, in fact, the theoretical position of an extra-Neptunian planet which could explain the small residual motions observed in Uranus. The effects on Neptune could not be used, since the planet had not yet been observed for a long enough time to obtain a sufficiently precise mean orbit. The search in this case was more difficult than for Neptune, both on account of the uncertainty of the predicted position, and the faintness of the new planet, which was of thirteenth magnitude at the time of its discovery. After a laborious search with the so-called "blink" stereoscope by Tombaugh, who compared alternatively with the same eyepiece two plates taken at different intervals of time, "Pluto" was discovered. It was actually a body much smaller than Lowell had predicted. Its mean distance has been calculated as 39.5 astronomical units. Since its orbit is extremely eccentric, its effective distance from the earth varies from 4600 million to 2800 million miles. Its mass, according to the computations of D. Brouwer, director of Yale Observatory, and L. R. Wylie, should have a value between that of the earth and Venus, and its diameter should be four-tenths that of the earth.

COSMIC MATTER

The first mention of the presence of cosmic matter, eventually darkening the light of the more distant stars, seems to go back to Halley, about 1720. But the first person to formulate a mathematical theory of interstellar absorption was F. G. W. Struve in 1847. The work of this astronomer is based on the famous charting of stars in different parts of the sky made by Sir William Herschel with his gigantic telescopes. These charts gave the number of all the stars visible for each successive magnitude in a uniform field of the sky. The problem was to find the true distribution of the stars in space and to discover if there was any possible effect of absorption. We have already mentioned that during Herschel's systematic observations of the regions lacking in stars, near the pole, and of the thickly populated regions of the Milky Way, he happened to observe some darker regions which seemed completely devoid of stars, and he attentively examined them, without however arriving at a satisfactory explanation of their origin. Father Secchi published in 1877 a year before his death, his memoir on "Astronomy in Rome in the Pontificate of Pius IX," which can be considered his scientific testament. He speaks of the observations and discoveries of multinuclear comets whose disintegration in space he affirms, and thus he prepares the way for the discovery of Schiaparelli. Secchi writes:

> Now according to the well-confirmed theory of Schiaparelli, immense masses of these dark bodies can slowly be carried away into space from system to system. They are true wandering nebulae, whose fragments or condensed particles may last through years and centuries of traveling. They can be seen as dark masses in the depths of space, as if projected on a bright region of the sky. Thus to the dark stars which have already been shown to circulate around some stars, as for example Algol, our spectroscopic research adds the dark nebulae wandering in the great void of the universe.

Further, speaking of his observations begun in 1853, he is even more explicit:

> Among these studies there is the interesting fact of the probable discovery of dark masses dispersed in space, whose existence will be revealed by the bright background of the sky on which they are projected. Until now these masses have been classified as "black holes," but this explanation is quite improbable, especially since the discovery of the gaseous nature of the nebular masses, and it is much more probable that the blackness results from a dark nebulosity projected on a bright background which intercepts its rays.

After having spoken of Huggins's discovery of the spectrum of diffuse nebulae, consisting of emission lines with hydrogen among them, and of his corresponding studies in the southern regions of the Milky Way, including the nebula of Sagittarius, he continues:

> It was in these regions that we found those entirely dark spaces, so well defined and sharply terminated that they made us be-

lieve that instead of holes they were rather shadows of dark masses. The probability of the latter lies in the fact that many nebulae, although they have a continuous spectrum, are still gaseous, and therefore cannot present long interruptions in a straight line. This structure is found in the channels of the nebula in Andromeda, a structure which can be said to be impossible in an expanding mass, because the channels would soon be filled up.

On the basis of his splendid photographs of the Galaxy made with photographic objectives of great light-gathering power at Yerkes Observatory, many years afterward (1919) Barnard wrote in his paper "On the Dark Markings of the Sky":

> I did not at first believe in these dark obscuring masses. The proof was not conclusive. The increase of evidence, however, from my own photographs convinced me later, especially after investigating some of them visually, that many of these markings were not due simply to an actual want of stars, but were really obscuring bodies nearer to us than the distant stars. In this way it has fallen to my lot to prove this fact. I think there is sufficient proof now to make this certain. For some years I have tried to secure long-exposure photographs of as many of these bodies as possible. This has resulted in the location of a considerable number of them in different parts of the sky. Their apparent preference for the bright regions of the Milky Way is obviously due to the fact that they are more readily shown with a bright background. They are, however, not strictly confined to the Milky Way.

Among the first to look upon these dark places as real matter was A. C. Ranyard, whose lamentable death occurred December 14, 1894. Shortly before his death, he published a series of papers on the Milky Way and the nebulae in *Knowledge*, a magazine of which he was editor. In speaking of the dark lane south and east of θ Ophiuchi on a Lick photograph of mine which he reproduced, he says: "The dark vacant areas or channels running north and south of the bright star (θ Ophiuchi) at the center . . . seem to me undoubtedly dark structures, or obscuring masses in space, which cut out the light from the nebulous or stellar region behind them."

Father J. G. Hagen, who was director of the Vatican Observatory, after long and patient work compiled a general catalog of light and dark nebulae. In 1893 he began to observe the dark ones but, as he says, they are not the same objects as "the dark holes" of Herschel or the dark masses revealed by the photographs. The diffuse nebulosity found by Father Hagen is in a unique grouping which covers a large part of the sky and which he called the "Via Nubila."

Considerable progress in the knowledge of cosmic matter scattered in space has been made, thanks to the research by R. Trumpler at Lick Observatory on open star clusters, and by A. H. Joy at Mt. Wilson Observatory on the Cepheids. The former, by comparing the absolute magnitudes and the diameters of the galactic clusters, like the Pleiades, Hyades, and Coma Berenices, was able to find the existence of an interstellar absorption amounting to about 0.7 magnitude per thousand parsecs. The latter made a comparison between the radial velocities of the Cepheids located at different distances from the center of the Galaxy, and their absolute magnitudes. The theory of the rotation of the Milky Way implies that the rotational component of the motion of a star along the line of sight should be proportional to its distance from the sun. By forming the hypothesis that the individual motions of the stars are distributed at random, Joy considered the average velocities for groups of Cepheids divided according to their apparent magnitudes. He found a series of values, the ratio of which furnishes directly the distance of the various groups.

On the other hand, the Cepheids have a remarkable property, discovered by Miss H. Leavitt at Harvard Observatory in 1912 when she was studying the light variations of the Cepheids in the lesser Magellanic Cloud. For these variables the periods of light variation are in direct proportion to their intrinsic luminosity, so that once the periods are known we can immediately deduce the absolute magnitude and thus the distance. Joy, by considering the radial velocities of 156 Cepheids divided into five groups according to distances from 1400 to 6500 light-years, concludes that in various regions of the Milky Way the obscuring gases are not distributed uniformly. A better representation of the observations would be obtained by correcting all magnitudes for a total uniform absorption of about 0.6 magnitude per thousand parsecs, in good agreement then with Trumpler's result. In addition, Joy finds that the sun should have a rotational velocity, in a circular orbit around the center of the Galaxy, of about 190 miles per second, corresponding to a period of revolution of 207 million years. On the other hand, the examination and counting of the galactic objects in different parts of the sky led Seares to the conclusion that there must exist a diffuse absorbing layer which extends equally above and below the galactic plane. The zone in which there are no galaxies is of irregular form and is associated with the dark clouds of the Milky Way which give the well known irregular appearance to the star clouds.

The problem of the existence of a selective absorption began to have interest when in 1895 J. C. Kapteyn, who was director of the astronomical laboratory at Groningen, discovered that the average color of the stars in the Milky Way was bluer than outside of it. He thought that such a phenomenon was due to a selective absorption which makes the stars appear bluer wherever there is less absorption. Nine years later W. de Sitter, in an accurate study of the colors of the stars, concluded: "Real differences in the colors of the stars, or general absorption in certain spectral regions, or selective absorption by cosmic clouds or nebular masses are problems which can be proposed but not yet solved." Now we know that the latter intrinsically blue stars have a remarkable tendency to crowd together toward the galactic equator more than the less hot red stars. H. Kienle, director of the Potsdam Observatory, concluded in 1923 that the coefficient of selective absorption must be less than 0.1 magnitude per thousand parsecs, and Otto Struve, three years later, affirmed that the reddening effect is produced by the diffusion of light in the dark nebulae and calcium clouds.

The existence of nebulae which emit reflected light, that is, whose spectra are continuous and whose absorption lines are identical with those of the stars associated with the nebula, has been demonstrated by W. M. Slipher. Later Otto Struve and his collaborators investigated in detail the character of the light diffused by the nebula or by interstellar space, and they confirm the fact that the nebulae are illuminated by the light of the stars which accompany them.

In 1904 J. F. Hartmann, then astronomer at Potsdam and later director at the La Plata Observatory, discovered that the absorption lines of ionized calcium in the spectrum of the double star δ Orionis did not participate in the periodic oscillations of the other lines. He concluded that "in some region of the space along the line-of-sight sun-δ Orionis there must exist a cloud which produces the absorption, a cloud which is moving away with a radial velocity of 10 miles per second." Since then, other absorption lines have been identified, produced by atoms and molecules existing in interstellar space, like those found at Mt. Wilson by Adams and Dunham, of sodium, calcium, neutral iron, CN, and CH. It has been shown that the lines belonging to a neutral or ionized atom correspond to an electronic transition which originates from the lowest energy level of the atom. The measurement of the relative intensity of the lines of neutral or ionized calcium furnishes a way to determine the relative abundance of the atoms of neutral and ionized calcium. The structure of the interstellar lines is generally complex. C. S. Beals, of the Victoria Observatory in Canada, had noted that the famous intense lines of ionized calcium (H and K) were double in the spectrum of certain stars. Recent observations, made at Mt. Wilson with high dispersion, show that in a good percentage of the examined stars these lines are double or multiple, sometime up to five components. This tendency of the lines to be multiple varies very much according to the region of the sky considered. It is particularly accentuated in the constellations of Orion, Sagittarius, and Cygnus, and much less in Perseus and Scorpio. Observations prove that the absorption is due to some clearly defined interstellar clouds, each one possessing both a weak turbulence and a well-defined proper radial velocity.

The constitution of the matter diffused in interstellar space has been particularly studied at the Yerkes and McDonald observatories by Otto Struve and his collaborators. They have also investigated the Stark effect, that is, the effect of the electric field on the stellar atmospheres; and from the profiles of the absorption lines in the spectra of rapidly rotating stars Struve has deduced their period of rotation. The consideration of the spectra of single stars has made evident the characteristics of the mysterious eclipsing variable β Lyrae and the presence of extended atmospheres and envelopes of expanding gas around stars with special spectra like P Cygni. These studies are being intensified more and more, and show the importance of individual spectroscopic study of the stars, which present so infinite a variety.

NEBULAE

The mystery of the so-called "nebulium," the hypothetical gas which produces the two intense lines (N_1 and N_2) in the green region of the spectrum of the diffuse and planetary nebulae, was unraveled in 1927 by J. S. Bowen, director of the Mt. Wilson and Mt. Palomar observatories. After the discovery of helium there was no place in the periodic table for a new light gas like the gas which constitutes the nebulae. From what special excitation of already known atoms these lines could be derived had to be explained. Because of the particular nature of the physical conditions of the gases existing in those nebulae, Bowen thought that there could take place from the "metastable" levels of the atom those transitions which gave rise to the so-called "forbidden" lines, which would be better called "improbable." In the planetary nebulae, the electrons do not move with sufficient velocity to excite the atoms up to the normal levels; on the other hand, the free electrons move fast enough to excite the atoms from the normal level to the metastable levels, which are next to the fundamental level. Thus when an atom of oxygen finds itself in one of the metastable levels it has a small probability in one or two minutes of colliding with another particle, losing its energy and returning to the fundamental state. In such a way the majority of the atoms return to the fundamental level, with the emission of a forbidden line. Bowen has identified the lines of oxygen ionized twice (O II) and three times (O III), and in addition other forbidden lines of nitrogen, neon, and sulphur.

At almost the same time Hubble, who in 1916 had begun his studies of the most distant nebulae, was able to clarify the problem of the "island universes," that is, whether or not they belonged to the system of the Milky Way and could be compared in dimensions to it, constituting therefore other innumerable universes comparable to the one in which the solar system is immersed. The elliptic, spiral, and globular nebulae are giant systems outside of and very far away from our Galaxy. Only because they seem to lie outside our Galaxy had they been called nongalactic nebulae, to distinguish them from the diffuse and irregular nebulae which exist only at low galactic latitudes. Once their extragalactic character had been established, their particular distribution relative to the Milky Way became the real proof of the presence of absorbing cosmic matter in them. Making a vast systematic search for extragalactic nebulae with the 100-inch telescope of Mt. Wilson, Hubble was able to establish a scale of distance extended much farther than before. He went as far as a sphere of about 500 million light-years radius, and he discovered that most of the variables present in these systems were Cepheids, of which, with the known relation between period and luminosity, we can determine the distance. Furthermore, he established a classification of the extragalactic nebulae as different types: elliptical, irregular, normal, and barred spirals, which seem to form a true evolutionary sequence.

His studies of the great nebula of Andromeda (Messier 31) led to the establishment of its distance as 900,000 light-years and of its dimensions as comparable to those of our Galaxy. He also discovered many variables and novae. In 1929 Hubble found the well-known linear relation between the distances of 24 nebulae and their apparent receding velocities, which had been measured by Slipher. Recognizing the importance of such a relation, he extended his research, in collaboration with M. L. Humason, out to the distance of some 100 million light-years, confirming more and more the displacement toward the red of the spectral lines, increasing with increasing distance. It is known that the interpretation of these displacements, as being due to the Doppler effect, leads to the concept of the expanding universe. Further study in which the 200-inch telescope will give many results is necessary to clarify this problem. As Hubble wrote in his volume *The Realm of the Nebulae* (1936):

> The necessary investigations are beset with difficulties and uncertainties, and conclusions from data now available are rather dubious. They are mentioned here in order to emphasize the fact that the interpretation of red-shifts is at least partially within the range of empirical investigation. For this reason the attitude of the observer is somewhat different from that of the theoretical investigator. Because the telescopic resources are not yet exhausted, judgment may be suspended until it is known from observations whether or not red-shifts do actually represent motion.
>
> Meanwhile, red-shifts may be expressed on a scale of velocities as a matter of convenience. They behave as velocity-shifts behave and they are very simply represented on the same familiar scale, regardless of the ultimate interpretation. The term "apparent velocity" may be used in carefully considered statements, and the adjective always implied where it is omitted in general usage.

The distribution and number of the extragalactic nebulae, which in today's observable space amount to 100 million, have also been investigated by Hubble.

CEPHEIDS: THE GALAXY

In the field of variable stars Pickering's successor at Harvard Observatory, Harlow Shapley, in collaboration with his teacher H. N. Russell, in 1912 elaborated a new theory for the calculation of the orbits of "eclipsing variables." They considered the effects of limb darkening similar to what is observed on the sun, the reciprocal reflection, and the ellipticity of the components; and they succeeded in calculating the orbits of 90 systems. Later at Mt. Wilson Observatory Shapley began the study of Cepheids, which at first were believed to belong to the class of eclipsing variables. This interpretation soon had to be abandoned when it was proved that the light phases and the variations in the radial velocities of the Cepheids made it impossible. However, it was still believed that they were binary systems with light variations due to causes other than eclipses. But in 1914 Shapley proved that even this theory could not hold, because it was then certain that the Cepheids belonged to the class of giant stars and the orbits of the presumed binary systems would necessarily have had dimensions impossible for the smallness observed. He then formulated the hypothesis of "pulsation," that is, a periodic increase and decrease in the volume and thus in diameter of these stars, considered as single stars. They pass from a minimum to a maximum of light in a few hours or in several days, by an amount of about 10 per cent. Naturally temperature, radiation, and superficial density had to change accordingly, as was proved by observing the variations of the spectrum in the course of pulsation, and, theoretically, by the research of Eddintgon.

We have already mentioned Miss Leavitt's discovery. On this basis and on the assumption that the characteristics of the Cepheids are the same inside and outside our Galaxy, Shapley developed one of the most powerful means for fathoming the depths of space, making an extensive study of the color and magnitudes of the star clusters. For this also the "period-luminosity" relation of the Cepheids, along with other indirect methods, served to establish their distance from the solar system, to estimate their magnitude, and to mark the boundaries of the Milky Way.

The existence of planets not belonging to the solar system was discovered in 1943 during an investigation of the motion of the well-known double stars, 61 Cygni and 70 Ophiuchi. To the former is attached a component of mass 0.016, and to the latter one of 0.01

the mass of the sun. These planets are then at least ten times greater in mass than Jupiter, and their presence may indicate that others of smaller dimensions may exist, which cannot be discovered because of their slight effect on the motion of the visible components. Since these effects concern displacements on the photographic plate of the order of less than two microns we can understand how precise these measurements must be.

Since W. Herschel's studies of the form and constitution of the Milky Way, the knowledge of the structure and motion of our Galaxy has been remarkably increased by more numerous and more complete observations (at least as far as our modern methods of observation can reach) and by the possibility of determining with the spectroscope not only the angular motions of the stars in the plane perpendicular to the line-of-sight, but also their radial velocities in miles per second. In 1901 W. W. Campbell, director of Lick Observatory, from measurements of the radial velocities of about 300 stars, reduced the direction and velocity in miles per second of the sun in space. A few years later Lewis Boss, director of the Dudley Observatory in Albany, New York, published the first fundamental catalog of the proper motion of 600 stars, deduced by comparing the results given in many preceding catalogs and those obtained at Albany. In this observatory the work of observation and calculation continued on such a large scale that Benjamin Boss, director of the department of meridian astronomy at the Carnegie Institution in Washington, completed and published in 1937 the *General Catalog of 33,342 Stars for the Epoch 1950.*

With these and other data which are constantly increasing, in 1904 Kapteyn demonstrated a remarkable characteristic of the observed stars, that of apparently being arranged in two streams with well-defined directions. These streams are constituted, one of three-fifths of the observed stars, the other of two-fifths, moving in opposite directions. The first of the two streams is directed toward a point in the constellation Orion, and the second in the opposite part of the sky toward the constellation Scutum. The line connecting these two points is exactly parallel to the Milky Way. H. H. Turner, director of the Observatory of the University of Oxford, advanced the hypothesis that these stellar streams might be produced by a center of common gravitation, just as comets present two favored motions, one toward the sun, the other away from the sun, in their very eccentric orbits. He then thought that the stars of our Milky Way might all rotate around the galactic center in very elongated orbits. In this case the observations should prove whether the direction of favored motion is toward or away from the same center. In the meantime the hypothesis was advanced that the Milky Way was a system by itself and that other "universes" of the same type existed outside of it, of which we can see the various spirals and study their particular motions. This prompts us to find out if the motions of the stars in our Galaxy can be compared to those of the stars forming the spiral arms of the extragalactic nebulae.

Together with the discovery of the two streams by Kapteyn, we must note the discovery of Lewis Boss following his research on proper motions. He found that the group of the Hyades in the constellation Taurus are moving and all converging toward the same point in the sky. Such a convergence is naturally due to an effect of perspective, proving that the various stars of the stream should belong physically to a "cluster" of common origin; and Lewis Boss was able to determine its distance from the solar system. The discovery of similar clusters which possess a common motion followed rapidly in various constellations, as in Perseus, Scorpio, and Centaurus; thus the structure and size of the Milky Way are revealed more and more. Contributions were also made by the research of Hugo von Seeliger, director of the Munich Observatory, who continued the studies of W. Herschel. Proper motions, radial velocities, stellar magnitudes, and direct and indirect determinations of the distances gave to Kapteyn, Seeliger, Shapley, Strömberg, and Schwarzschild the elements for measuring the Milky Way and establishing its presumable boundaries. Schwarzschild was able to formulate his so-called "ellipsoidal hypothesis," which represented the observed favored motions better than the hypothesis of the two streams.

In the last twenty-five years there has been more and more talk about the hypothesis of the "rotation of the Galaxy" around a common center. In 1926 B. Lindblad, director of the Stockholm Observatory, expounded a theory according to which the system of the Milky Way would be constituted of a certain number of subsystems. Each of these would comprise all the stars belonging to a given class and would have the form of a flattened ellipsoid of revolution, for the axis and equatorial plane of all the subsystems would be the same as that of the Galaxy. The subsystems would all have the same extension in the galactic plane but different perpendiculars to this plane. In other words, they would have different flattenings. The subsystems would rotate around their common center with angular velocities decreasing in each subsystem the farther it was from the center, yet different from one system to the other. They would rotate the faster the more they were flattened. The most flattened would be those constituted of planetary nebulae and open clusters, and the least, of globular star clusters.

A year later J. H. Oort, director of the Leiden Observatory, as he was considering the radial velocities, discovered an effect of differential rotation which better clarifies the motion of the Milky Way. If the system rotated as a rigid body, the radial velocities of its components, determined from any point, would not be at all influenced by the effect of rotation. But if there is an orbital revolution around a center of mass, the velocities should decrease toward the outer edge, as in the solar system, instead of increasing as in a rigid body. Oort found the orbital effect in the radial velocities of the O and B stars, Cepheids, and planetary nebulae, and in addition he discovered that the center of rotation must be located in the direction of Sagittarius. Subsequent investigations with stars chosen among the most distant from the sun have confirmed the first results, especially those attained by Joy on Cepheids, which we have already mentioned in connection with the problem of cosmic matter.

ARTHUR S. EDDINGTON

In almost all the recent conquests of astronomy we find the personality of Sir Arthur S. Eddington, Plumian Professor of Astronomy and director of the Observatory of Cambridge (England), who was born in 1882 at Kendal in Westmoreland and died in 1944. As assistant at the Greenwich Observatory he published in 1914 his first book on *Stellar Movements and the Structure of the Universe,* in which he launched new speculations which were to serve as hypotheses for the work then in progress in the fields of both observation and theory. At that time the general opinion was that the spiral nebulae formed part of our Galaxy. Eddington, however, already thought that things were otherwise and he wrote:

> If the spiral nebulae are within the stellar system, we have no notion what their nature may be. That hypothesis leads to a full stop. If, however, it is assumed that these nebulae are external to the stellar system, that they are in fact systems co-

equal with our own, we have at least an hypothesis which can be followed up, and may throw some light on the problems that have been before us. For this reason the 'island universe' theory is much to be preferred as a working hypothesis; and its consequences are so helpful as to suggest a distinct probability of its truth.

The theory of radiation equilibrium, which already was beginning to supplant the very old ideas of convection currents, was applied by Eddington to the interior of the stars. His theory demonstrates that the transfer of heat from the interior to the exterior of the stars occurs almost exclusively by irradiation and that the distribution of temperature consequently is controlled by the flux of the radiation. This hypothesis, applied by Schwarzschild in 1906 to the equilibrium of the solar atmosphere, was generalized by Sir Arthur for all stars and was completed by the use of the investigations of R. Emden on gaseous spheres. His hypothesis was later applied to all the classes of stars in the Russell-Hertzsprung diagram, and it then permitted the development of the theories of the nuclear processes which liberate great quantities of subatomic energy, developed with so much success by Bethe, Weiszäcker, and Gamow. As early as 1929 Eddington wrote in his book *New Ways of Science*:

> I have referred to the practical utilisation of subatomic energy as an illusive hope which it would be wrong to encourage; but in the present state of the world it is rather a threat which it would be a great responsibility to disparage altogether. It cannot be denied that for a society which has to create scarcity to save its members from starvation, to whom abundance spells disaster, and to whom unlimited energy means power for war and destruction, there is an ominous cloud in the distance though at present it be no bigger than a man's hand.

From these studies he very soon arrived at the unexpected result that his theory could predict the absolute magnitude of all stars, giants as well as dwarfs. He found the explanation in the fact that highly ionized matter in the interior of the stars behaves practically like a perfect gas up to the highest densities. Thus he came to a new conception of stellar evolution based on the important relation which he derived between the "mass and luminosity" of the stars, having to admit by it an appreciable loss of mass. The later discovery that the companion of Sirius, belonging to the class of stars called "white dwarfs," had to have a density equal to 60,000 times that of water led Eddington to predict that a considerable "Einstein effect" must be measured in its spectrum because of the extraordinary mass of this exceptional star. The prediction was confirmed by observations made by W. S. Adams at Mt. Wilson.

The Internal Constitution of the Stars is the title of the book in which are collected these and other investigations of Eddington, as for example that of the importance of the hydrogen content in the stars, that of the periodic pulsation of the Cepheids which explains the "period luminosity" relation, in effect a relation between mass and density, and that of the effect of reflection in eclipsing variables. If the components are sufficiently close, the fainter component is illuminated on the hemisphere turned toward the more luminous component, producing a different brightness in the two hemispheres, which accounts for the observed variations in light between eclipses. In the study of matter diffused throughout interstellar space Eddington was able to bring to light the process by which the absorption lines of calcium, sodium, and other elements are observed in the spectrum of the most distant stars, lines due to the presence of the "cosmic clouds" scattered throughout the universe.

Besides explaining the "theory of relativity" in his writings, he well understood its importance and future applications. Together with other English astronomers he took part in the observations of the total eclipse of the sun of May 19, 1919, on Principe Island (equatorial Africa) for the principal purpose of verifying Einstein's predictions of the deflection, caused by the sun's gravitational field, of the rays coming from the stars which at the moment of eclipse are apparently close to the limb of the sun. The results obtained by Eddington and several other investigators at other eclipses fully confirm the prediction. Thus with this proof and the proof of the displacement of the spectral lines toward the red, measured in the spectrum of the companion of Sirius, the Einstein theory came to have full confirmation.

Eddington has been called a "modern Archimedes." Like Archimedes in the field of geometry, he in the field of physics tried to elaborate a fundamental theory with which he might bind all the physical sciences into one synthesis, from astrophysics which investigates the macrocosm to modern physics which studies the microcosm. Combining Newton's theory of gravitation, the "quantum" theory of Planck, and the theory of relativity, he tries to show that the constants of nature can be deduced, for the most part, on the basis of mathematcal considerations derived from the unification of the said theories and of others of lesser importance.

Sir Arthur was also a true ambassador of science for international scientific co-operation. Opening one of his lectures on the "expanding universe" at the General Assembly of the International Astronomical Union at Cambridge, Massachusetts, in September, 1932, he prophetically warned:

> This is an International Conference and I have chosen an international subject. I shall speak of the theoretical work of Einstein of Germany, de Sitter of Holland, Lemaître of Belgium. For observational data I will turn to the Americans, Slipher, Hubble, Humason, recalling however that the vitally important datum of distance is found by a method which we owe to Hertzsprung of Denmark. As I must not trouble you with mathematical analysis, I have to pass over Levi-Civita of Italy whose methods and ideas we employ. But I must refer especially to the new interest which arises in the subject through its linkage to wave-mechanics; as a representative name in wave-mechanics I mention that of its originator, de Broglie of France.
>
> My subject disperses the galaxies, but it unites the earth.
> May no "cosmical repulsion" intervene to sunder us!

Two years after the death of Eddington, English astronomy lost another brilliant physicist and astronomer, Sir James Jeans, born in Southport in 1877. Secretary of the Royal Society, he published in 1917 his well known work *Problems of Cosmogony and Stellar Dynamics,* which followed his other works in physical theory. In his *Astronomy and Cosmogony* he mathematically examined the stability of pear-shaped liquid rotating masses, giving a complete picture of stellar evolution. He demonstrated that gravitational instability in a chaotic mass of gas could give birth to the spiral nebulae and that the same instability could lead to the formation of stars in the outer regions of the spiral nebulae, as is actually observed. Furthermore, he proved that the normal effect of an increase in rotational velocity due to contraction is that of breaking a body in two and forming a binary system. Following the planetesimal hypothesis of the Americans T. C. Chamberlain and F. R. Moulton, Jeans attributes the origin of the solar system to the reciprocal forces of the fields of two stars which at one time passed relatively close to each other. Such a passage would have produced a stream of gaseous matter which has broken into fragments and has condensed into the present planets. Jeans, like Eddington, is very famous for his clear and at the same time profound books of explanation, not only for the purely astronomical part, but also for the philosophic deductions which both of them were able to derive.

It is impossible to mention individually the discoveries and works of all the astronomers throughout the world who are contributing actively through important theoretical and practical research to the progress of astronomical science. But we wish to close this chapter by recalling another astronomer of the English school whose activity is very close to that of Eddington and Jeans, in that he developed and integrated his results into the loftiest speculations of human thought.

E. A. Milne, professor at Oxford, with R. H. Fowler applied Saha's theory to the determination of the pressure prevailing on the outer layers of the sun and the stars, finding that the pressure is very low. His theoretical research on the conditions of equilibrium of the uppermost part of the solar chromosphere, constituted principally of ionized calcium, led him to conclude that the gas must be sustained by the pressure of radiation. In accordance with Milne's theory is the possibility from time to time of a collapse of the chromosphere over the reversing layer, and its successive reconstitution. When the atoms are expelled and move away from the sun, by the effect of the perturbations which are revealed at the sun's surface, he calculates that their velocity of escape is of the order of 1000 miles per second, which is in perfect accordance with observations of the beginning of magnetic storms on the earth resulting from solar eruptions.

Milne has developed interesting theoretical work in his search for various possible models according to which the stars might be formed, and he came to the conclusion that their luminosity may depend on various proportions of "degenerate" and "perfect" gases contained in them. This result led him to consider the phenomenon of novae and to elaborate a theory which seems to receive confirmation from the observed facts. By making the great phenomenon depend on a general evolutionary process, he can explain both qualitatively and quantitatively that in their manifestations novae and supernovae all reach a certain determined stage at the climax of their explosion.

In two recent lectures at the Royal Astronomical Society on the

"Nature of Universal Gravitation" (1944) and "Natural Philosophy of Stellar Structure" (1945), Milne expounds new and bold ideas which will find other important developments through him and in his school.

Among the important treatises in theoretical astrophysics on the structure of the atmosphere and the internal constitution of the stars, published in the last twenty-five years, we will mention those of S. Rosseland, director of the Institute of Theoretical Astrophysics at the University of Oslo, of A. Unsöld, director of the Observatory of Kiel, of S. Chandrasekhar at Yerkes Observatory, and of Bengt Strömgren, director of the Copenhagen Observatory.

20 : the International Astronomical Union and astronomy's future

AT THE RESUMPTION OF INTERNATIONAL RE-
lations after world War I, the International Astronomical Union
was instituted by the International Council of Research, together
with other scientific unions. Its purpose is to facilitate relations
among the astronomers of the various nations where international
co-operation is necessary and useful and to promote the study of
astronomy in its various branches.

The Union then comprised thirty nations, and it held its first
general assembly in Rome in 1922. It is organized in a certain number
of commissions, which take up different topics and problems of interest to the various branches of astronomy, each commission being
composed of a certain number of astronomers of different nationali-
ties with specific competence in their fields. We shall give the titles
of the commissions and a brief summary of their activities, as gathered
from the triennial general assemblies of the Union. These assemblies,
after the one in Rome, took place in cities of different nations and
there were six up to 1938. The seventh, which was to have been
held in Zürich in 1941, had to be postponed until 1948.

COMMISSIONS OF INTERNATIONAL ASTRONOMICAL UNION

Notation, Units, and *Economy of Publications.* One can well
understand the importance of international unification of notations

and units in astronomy; this commission takes care of such work.

Ephemerides. Collaboration and division of work among the various nations which publish annual ephemerides, like the *Nautical Almanac*, the *American Ephemeris*, the *Astronomisches Jahrbuch*, the *Connaissance des Temps.*

Analysis of Bibliography. Organized for the publication of ancient and classical astronomical works and for the collection of abstracts of astronomical works, which for years have been published in the *Astronomischer Jahresbericht.*

Telegrams and Astronomical Circulars. News of discoveries and most outstanding astronomical facts are communicated by the individual observatories to the central office in Copenhagen, from where they are directed to everyone interested or to whoever subscribes to this service.

Meridian Astronomy. Revision of the fundamental catalogs and of the constants to be adopted; distribution of assignments for the observation of the fundamental stars.

Astronomical Instruments. Study of new types of instruments, visual, photographic, and spectroscopic.

Solar Physics. Four commissions are concerned with solar physics. The first gathers observations and statistics of sunspots and of the so-called "characteristic numbers," which give information day by day about the activity and state of disturbance of the sun. These international observations are published in a quarterly bulletin edited by the Zürich Observatory. The second commission gathers and coordinates chromospheric phenomena, like the flocculi, the flares, and the prominences which are present with varying frequency and characteristics on the sun. This is done by means of spectroheliograms and visual observations made with the greatest continuity possible, by observatories well distributed throughout the earth both in longitude and latitude. The third commission deals with radiation and solar spectroscopy. The measurement of the "solar constant" is made regularly in different parts of the earth, especially by the Astrophyiscal Observatory of the Smithsonian Institution, which was directed for many years by C. G. Abbot. In 1940 an important photometric atlas of the solar spectrum was published at Utrecht by M. Minnaert, G. F. Mulders, and J. Houtgast. The fourth commission co-ordinates the work of preparation and observation of solar eclipses, for which expeditions from different nations meet in the zone of totality. They agree also on the programs to be developed and on the problems which are of interest for the study of the outermost layers of the solar atmosphere, like the chromosphere and the corona.

Fundamental Wave Lengths and Tables of Solar Spectra. The standard wave lengths, primary and secondary, have been established after long labor and by international agreement and are published by the Union for all astrophysical uses.

Physical Study of the Comets. Spectroscopic observations of comets with instruments of various types and photographs made during their apparition have led to the knowledge of their physical constitution and the variations which they undergo in their approach and departure from the sun.

Physical Observations of Planets and Satellites. Observations of the planetary surfaces are made with care and regularity, especially during favorable oppositions, that is, when the various planets come closest to the earth. Notable discoveries have been made about the constitution of their atmospheres.

Motion and Form of the Moon. Research on the motion of the moon and its form. Nomenclature of the details visible on the surface.

Longitudes by Wireless. For the determination of longitude over the entire earth, this new and precise method naturally implies the co-operation of the various nations, with the purpose also of establishing whether variations in longitude differences occur in time.

Variation of Latitude. For this problem of astronomical-geodetical character, seven stations at the same latitude and well distributed in longitude over the earth have continually determined, by now for more than fifty years, the variable position of the terrestrial poles caused by the motion of the axis of rotation in the interior of the mass of the earth. All the numerous observations made are collected and discussed in a central office, which in the past was in Japan, then in Naples, and is now in Pino Torinese.

Position and Movements of the Minor Planets, Comets, and Satellites. The determination of the position and consequently the orbits of the minor planets requires special international work, from which a more precise knowledge of the solar parallax may be obtained, as was mentioned for the favorable opposition of Eros.

Meteors, Zodiacal Light, and Similar Problems. These are of interest to astronomy as well as to geophysics for the study of the upper terrestrial atmosphere. The organization for the observation of meteors from various points on the earth is of vast proportions and gathers a steadily growing body of important data.

The Map of the Sky. We have already mentioned the international work for the mapping of the sky, which still must be completed. This work concerns catalogs, the above-mentioned maps, and the discovery of proper motions.

Stellar Parallaxes and *Proper Motions.* The use of photography and instruments of large dimensions, and the division of the work among the different observatories of the world, have made possible the determination of numerous trigonomctric parallaxes of the fixed stars and a better knowledge of the relative and absolute proper motions.

Stellar Photometry. The co-ordination of the various methods used to determine the apparent magnitudes of the stars, the search for the "zero point" of photographic magnitudes, and homogeneous systems of "color index" concern this commission, along with many other problems.

Double Stars. Statistics and compilation of the visual and photographic observations of the binary and multiple systems. A general catalog, which is a sequel to the famous one of S. W. Burnham, has been published by R. G. Aitken, of Lick Observatory.

Variable Stars. The organization for the observation of variable stars has expanded all over the world. Various institutes and societies divide among themselves the task of the preparation of the ephemerides, the observation of different types of variables, and the publication of the observations. To facilitate the work an atlas has been published with the various constellations arranged according to arcs of hour circles and parallels of declination.

Extragalactic Nebulae. Perfecting the fundamental stellar magnitudes, especially in the blue, for stars fainter than seventeenth magnitude, and also in the red. Publication of research programs for a division of the work. Development of a special technique for the measurement of the surface luminosity of the nebulae. Discussion of the dynamical problems which concern the structure of the Galaxy.

Stellar Spectra. The nomenclature of the stellar spectra is always a problem and no satisfactory solution has been reached. Nevertheless the sequence of the stellar spectra is now well defined, and the interpretation of their true characteristics, by means of many observations made with powerful instruments, has led to considerable progress.

Radial Velocities of the Stars. The measurements, now very numerous, of the radial velocities of stars of various types and magnitudes have been accomplished by international co-operation. They have led to the compilation of important catalogs for better knowledge of the individual motions of the stars and of their motions as components of binary systems and as members of groups. In addition, radial velocities are useful for the study of differential motions in the atmospheres of certain stars, like the Cepheids and other variables, whose spectra present emission lines. A list of stars whose velocities have been well determined by many observatories can serve as a standard, both for the examination of systematic errors and for the testing of new instruments.

Bureau de l'Heure. In 1919, coincident with the institution of the international unions, an "International Commission of Time" was established in Brussels, for the purpose of unifying the time by wireless signals of high precision. Then a "Bureau international de l'Heure," dependent on this Commission, was established with its seat at the National Observatory of Paris. The determinations of time are made in the principal observatories, which maintain the time with great precision by means of pendulums at constant temperature and pressure and with quartz clocks. From these observatories the time is transmitted by radio in hourly signals, which are collected in the International Office, where a *Bulletin Horaire* is published regularly under the auspices of the Union.

Selected Areas. Kapteyn's project of selected areas for exploring the entire sky has been developed in several observatories, which have divided the work of observation and publication among themselves.

Stellar Statistics. Counting, radial velocity, photometric and spectral research of stars of faint magnitude, proper motions, and statistics of stellar motions constitute the general program of this commission.

Interstellar Matter and Galactic Nebulae. The constitution and distribution of interstellar matter and nebulae present in the Milky Way and the recent discoveries afford material for discussion of the possible developments of current research in this field, so interesting for better knowledge of the Galaxy.

Constitution of the Stars. The progress of theoretical study of the constitution of the stars is principally made by individual studies, and thus the commission has only the task of presenting and collectively discussing the new theories.

Spectrophotometry. This science embraces one of the problems which most actively concerns the distribution of energy in the various stellar spectra. It implies the calibration and the testing of the instruments used in the various laboratories and observatories, and measurements of the intensity of the continuous spectrum, the profiles of the lines, and their equivalent widths.

Star Clusters. Research on the form, distribution, and other physical characteristics of these celestial objects.

Exchange of Astronomers. Arranges and facilitates the visits and exchange of astronomers in the different observatories of the various nations.

International Observatories. In collaboration with UNESCO, that is, the organization of the United Nations for education, science, and culture, the International Astronomical Union is making studies for the establishment of observatories and astronomical laboratories in localities adapted for furthering international collaboration.

Radioelectric Observations. The recent great development of radio engineering has permitted the capture of radioelectric waves coming from the sun, the Milky Way, and interstellar space. For the study and accumulation of these important data international agreement is needed.

Two other commissions which are concerned with the development and co-ordination of research are:

History of Astronomy.

Photoelectric Double Stars.

After the serious interruption of international relations and the suspension of the general assemblies from 1938 on, because of World War II, communications were easily and quite rapidly re-established at the cessation of hostilities. In March, 1946, the executive committee of the Union was able to meet at Copenhagen with a restricted number of delegates from various countries, who have re-established connections, brought everything up to date, and resumed the projected work. It was then established that the next general assembly should take place in Zürich in 1948.

ASTRONOMICAL RESEARCH IN THE FUTURE

The work of the International Astronomical Union, despite the damaging interruption, has great scientific value, and at the same time it indicates the way for the future work and progress in the various branches of astronomy. The general tendency is perhaps that of collecting rich and important observational material, which is gathered in the relatively few observatories equipped with powerful telescopes. The material obtained can be discussed by many astronomers, who may obtain many important results from it. We must not exclude the fact that also the individual work of astronomers provided with modest means, or of amateurs, sometimes makes a notable contribution. The huge programs of international collaboration will continue to be developed more and more, extending the known limits of the universe. We will come to know better the physical characteristics of the sun and the planets, and also of the island universes and especially the Milky Way in which our solar system is immersed. Recent discoveries about cosmic matter, scattered in space, and research on cosmic rays confront us with other interesting problems. We can foresee the possibility of recognizing some new element in the initial formation of the stars. The first indication has been revealed of the possibility of atomic energy as the source of their immense, and for us inexhaustible, radiation, and it has opened the way for the production of atomic energy on the earth, with all the scientific and practical consequences which will follow. We can easily predict, as has happened already in many other problems, that the solutions and new discoveries will be the fruit of the combination of astronomical, physical, and chemical research, with all the sciences co-operating for a mutual and rapid progress.

In the field of solar physics, modern observational means will surely attain other noteworthy results important not only for better knowledge of the star closest to us but also for its effects on the earth. This study is of great interest to the astronomer as well as the geophysicist, because information can be obtained on the character and method of propagation of the matter which leaves the sun, on its transmission through space, and on the conditions and constitution of the higher levels of the terrestrial atmosphere. The possibility of sending radio signals beyond the atmosphere as far as the moon and perhaps to some planet suggests other consequences and interesting results to astronomy.

The use of powerful instruments together with wide-dispersion spectrographs has shown what neither Donati nor Father Secchi, with the very modest means at their disposal, could imagine. The discovery of the "dwarf stars" and "giants" has enabled us to distinguish in these stars, apparently of the same type, certain small differences which naturally would have escaped the first observers. But after the improvement of instruments and theoretical research, they have been well explained and have made possible the determination of the real dimensions of such stars, and hence of their distances. By modern investigations the sequence of the stellar spectra has been extended, giving rise to a classification which still does not satisfy astrophysicists, but which little by little will be clarified and completed. The principal characteristic of the problem is the unending discovery of many varieties of spectra of the same sequence, which leads, if not to the necessity of an individual study of each star, at least to the investigation of a great many stars, always finding in their spectra new and interesting particulars, some explainable, and others still wrapped in mystery. Now with the very large telescopes to which spectrographs of great focal length are connected, it is possible to photograph the most luminous stars with spectra comparable to the spectrum already obtained for the sun. It is then possible to compare their spectra down to the last detail with that of the sun and to classify the eventual differences depending on the dimensions or other characteristic causes of the different stellar atmospheres.

The study of the stars belonging to the category of eclipsing variables has led to knowledge of interesting systems of various form and magnitude. In some of them there have recently been discovered tenuous rings of hydrogen and other gases, which envelop and rotate generally around the component of higher temperature and greater mass. These cosmic formations which the spectroscope makes known to us gradually follow the phases of the eclipse during the orbital motion of the two components. They show how great is the variety of the stars scattered in the universe, and they have opened new horizons on the origin and nature of binary and multiple systems. Even in the "Cepheids," whose study has just begun, a great variety of stars is revealed, quite different from the ones which constitute the great mass of other stars. They are similar, in fact, to the variables which can be called "cataclysmic," that is to novae, whose variations of light, spectrum, and temperature are still more rapid and tumultuous, of truly explosive character. In the class of the white dwarfs and the class of binary systems which present such perturbations of their motion as to permit the discovery of invisible stars, of true "planets," we have typical cases. They show what vast work remains for astronomers in the near future with discoveries of ever new worlds of different age, species, and dimensions, from the tenuous globes of enormous dimensions to the solidified ones with a solid crust, similar to our earth, on which forms of life similar to ours may be developed.

In conclusion, from the epoch of the invention of the telescope to that of the introduction of spectrum analysis and other physical methods for the study of the sky, the progress in the knowledge of the world outside the earth has been very remarkable. We can now easily predict that the history of astronomy will be enriched in future years by new discoveries and new results. The credit is due to the increased number of astronomers who with ever more powerful means are investigating the sky, to the possibility of a rapid and extended collaboration, and to the assistance which the related sciences in the theoretical and experimental fields lend to astronomy in increasing measure.

Appendix : development and aims of the world's astronomical observatories

BEFORE THE INVENTION OF THE TELESCOPE there existed in the world only a few rare observatories, though we can hardly apply the name in the modern sense. One of the most famous of these was the observatory of Tycho Brahe, constructed through the munificence of King Frederick II of Denmark on the island of Hveen in the strait of Sund. The instruments which he used in his long series of observations, that led Kepler to his discovery of the laws of planetary motion, he devised and built himself. They can be regarded as truly exceptional for that time, considering that they were not equipped with a single optical part. There were large sextants, equatorial armillae, and wall quadrants installed in the various sections of a huge building or on the large terraces, and crude timekeepers, with which the stellar co-ordinates were measured.

Galileo never had a fixed place which could be called an "observatory" because his marvelous telescope of such modest dimensions could be directed toward the sky from any place whatsoever, from a window or a garden, perhaps with the help of some crude tripod (of which, however, no trace remains), but without the need of a special locality or particular accessories. We know that several decades had to pass, from the time Galileo with his students made his first astronomical discoveries from the house in Borgo dei Vignali in Padua and then continued and completed them at the Villa delle Selve and the Villa Segni in Bellosguardo on the outskirts of Florence, before a real and genuine astronomical observatory existed in Europe.

Furthermore, the duties and tasks of the first observatories were not confined to the astronomical field, but extended to other fields, principally those of meteorology and geodesy. The meteorological service with its daily records and the astronomical geodetical operations for the measurements of the earth were mixed with genuine astronomical observations and investigations.

The rapid and enormous development of the various scientific branches has led, in comparatively recent times, to a complete separation of the various tasks, so much so that today an astronomical observatory may be dedicated exclusively to the study of the stars, whether of interest to humanity from a purely speculative point of view or as serving practical or instructive purposes. Astronomy as such has been developed more and more into specialized theoretical and practical branches; in the former, particularly in mathematical and physical fields, in the latter in observational and experimental fields. Although important observatories do exist in which all the branches are treated, other lesser ones specialize in this or that research or even only in instruction.

The main duties of the modern astronomical observatories are essentially two, well defined and at the same time integrated: that of scientific research as an end in itself, for greater knowledge of the distribution and physical constitution of the stars and hence the universe; and that of instruction. Nowadays, for the former, costly and ponderous instruments are needed, placed in suitable localities; for the latter, modest instruments, even without the most modern perfection, can serve the purpose, and the locality where the observatory is erected should be reasonably accessible to those desiring to learn. Galileo's first telescope of 1609, with an objective aperture of 1½ inches and with an area sixty times greater than the pupil of the naked eye, revealed half a million stars in contrast to the few thousands visible to the naked eye alone. The largest telescopes today gather thousands and thousands of times more light than does the naked eye, and thousands of millions of stars can be photographed. Between these two extremes we find telescopes of all sizes, and it is natural that the astronomer desiring to fathom the universe at ever greater distances should have called upon optical and mechanical engineering to help him obtain perfect instruments of the largest dimensions possible. A century ago telescopes with objectives 12 to 16 inches in diameter, like those built by Amici in Florence and by other opticians in Europe, were considered "large"; today the reflectors have grown to 200 inches in diameter. Of "large telescopes," with apertures greater than 40 inches, there now exist several in various parts of the world; if it be questioned whether there are not already too many, we would make immediate reply by comparing their number to the immensity of the universe to be investigated. In the course of this *History* we have tried to explain on broad lines the discoveries and results achieved in the various observatories of the world. In this appendix we are trying to give some brief information about the development and direction of the largest astronomical observatories throughout the civilized world, which are collaborating, as we have said, in the International Astronomical Union.

In Holland, where flourished the school of Willebrord Snell and Christian Huygens in physics, optics, and astronomy, six years after the death of the former, in 1632, an observatory was founded and built on the roof of the University of Leiden. An azimuthal quadrant was mounted under a revolving roof. The founding of this observatory, following after that of Tycho (which belongs to the sixteenth century and can be considered the first in Europe), with instruments provided with optical parts, is certainly a remarkable event. In 1860 the observatory was moved, still in the city of Leiden, but into a more appropriate building where it stands today. The development and achievements of this observatory are well known in astronomical history; it will suffice to mention the names of the most recent directors: W. de Sitter, who has been concerned with problems of relativity and of the structure of the universe; E. Hertzsprung, who discovered with Russell the giant and dwarf stars; and J. H. Oort, who with Lindblad has discovered and studied the rotation of the galactic system.

We have already mentioned in the preceding pages the founding of the Paris Observatory which, together with the Greenwich Observatory a little later, marks the beginning of systematic work, extensive and continuous, for greater knowledge of the positions and motions of the bodies of the solar system, and later of the fixed stars, whose number grows larger as the power of the observational means increases.

The problem of the determination and adoption of a "universal time" has been solved with the rapid progress of wireless telegraphy. At the Paris Observatory the International Astronomical Union instituted the Bureau de l'Heure which collects time signals from the major observatories of the world, averages them, and issues the

Bulletin Horaire. From classical positional astronomy we have had to pass to the study of the physical constitution of the stars. The Paris Observatory has been modernized in the sense that it founded, through the work of J. Janssen in 1876, an astrophysical observatory in the park of Meudon on the outskirts of Paris, and more recently the "Institut d'Astrophysique," which stands close to the original Paris Observatory.

The founding of the Royal Observatory of Greenwich traces its origin to the problem of the determination of longitude at sea, at that time an unsolved problem which, as we have seen, had troubled astronomers even before Galileo's time and for whose solution striking rewards had been offered.

The story is well known that Amerigo Vespucci, on his first voyage to the West Indies, made a determination of longitude near the coast of Venezuela by measuring the distance between Mars and the moon with reference to their preceding conjunction of August 23, 1499. The account is in a letter of Vespucci dated July 18, 1500, addressed to Lorenzo di Pier Francesco de' Medici in Florence.

John Flamsteed, champion of the method of "lunar distances," was named by Charles II "our astronomical observator" with the title of "Astronomer Royal" and a salary of one hundred pounds a year. The Royal Warrant for building the Observatory ran as follows:

> CHARLES REX. *Whereas,* in order to the finding out of the longitude of places for perfecting navigation and astronomy, we have resolved to build a small observatory within our park at Greenwich, upon the highest ground, at or near the place where the Castle stood, with lodging rooms for our astronomical observator and assistant, our will and pleasure is, that according to such plot and design, as shall be given you by our trusty and well beloved Sir Christopher Wren, Knight, our surveyor-general of the place and site of the said observatory. . . .

We have had occasion to mention the Astronomers Royal following Flamsteed, and some of the most important accomplishments and discoveries made at the Greenwich Observatory. This observatory, like the others which were founded in Europe inside city walls and on rooftops, eventually found it necessary to move outside the populated centers.

Among the first to mark the inconveniences of city observatories there comes to mind Tommaso Perelli, professor of astronomy at the

University of Pisa, who in 1751 advised the Tuscan government against founding an observatory inside the walls of Florence, for it was better "to make use of some of the very pleasant suburban hills which surround Florence . . . the best of all sites adapted to the purpose; if the choice were left to me, I would be inclined to the hill of Arcetri, a place ennobled by the observations and long residence of the great Galileo. For this very reason the place is worthy to serve, even in the centuries to come, that science which recognizes a large part of its important achievements as deriving from the labors and genius of that truly incomparable man." But fifty-six years were still to pass before an observatory was founded in Florence, and even then, despite the wise counsel of Perelli, inside the city. Not until 1872 did G. B. Donati succeed in moving it outside the city and to Arcetri.

But to proceed in chronological order, the oldest observatory in Italy worthy of the name is that of Bologna. Not long after the death of Galileo, the Bolognese Senate called to the chair of astronomy at the University of Bologna G. D. Cassini, who made the celebrated observations and discoveries for which he was called to France. But only much later in 1712, was a tower actually constructed on the university building so that a certain number of instruments could be erected for making regular observations and preparing the Bolognese ephemerides. The city branch of this ancient observatory is still in the same place, but an auxiliary station has been constructed on the Apennines at 2600 feet above sea level on the Bologna-Florence national highway.

In the second half of the eighteenth century there arose in the major Italian cities and especially in the university towns observatories made famous by the astronomers who worked there. After the Bolognese Senate, the Venetian Senate in 1761 began the construction of an astronomical observatory on top of a square tower which had served to defend the ancient castle of Ezzelino III and as a state prison in 1242. Father Boscovich, in 1767, recalling the story of this monument, wrote in Latin the following epigraph which we still see today carved on the entrance to the tower: "This tower which once led to the shades of hell now under the auspices of the Venetian Republic opens the road to the heavens." The Observatory of Padua, particularly renowned for its school which has trained so many Italian astronomers, now has a substation at Asiago on the lower Alps at 3428 feet above sea level, with a 49-inch reflector. The Jesuit Fathers founded the observatory at the Brera College in Milan, which rose to fame in 1777 after the arrival of Bernabas Oriani. The Brera astronomers are particularly engaged in calculating and publishing the Ephemerides of Milan, which have existed for a century. Oriani developed the theory of the new planet Uranus, calculating a first orbit which was the beginning of an enormous work of observation and theory, completed in the following years. The Brera Observatory, which now has a dependency at Merate in Brianza, was made still more celebrated by the work of G. V. Schiaparelli, who was its director from 1862 to 1900.

Rome had its observatories, that of the Jesuit Fathers being located in the great building of the Roman College, where observations had already been made at the time of Galileo by Father Clavius, Father Scheiner, and others. Father Angelo Secchi, resuming a project of Boscovich, had a new observatory erected in 1849 on the pillars prepared for the dome (which was never erected) of the Church of St. Ignatius, incorporated in the building of the Roman College. He soon made this observatory famous with his discovery of "stellar types" and other discoveries about the sun. At the same time the University Observatory was erected on the roofs of the Campidoglio palace. These observatories were combined and recently were transferred to the hills of Mt. Mario.

The observatories of Palermo and Naples must also be remembered in the history of astronomy. The former was constructed in 1790 by the Abbot Giuseppe Piazzi on the roofs of the Royal Palace in Palermo, and it was soon recognized by the astronomical world for the discovery of the first planetoid, Ceres, by Piazzi. On the hill of Capodimonte in Naples King Murat in 1812 instituted an observatory, completed later by Ferdinand I, who called Father Piazzi to direct it under the title of "director general of the observatories of the kingdom," meaning those of Naples and Palermo. At the Naples Observatory were discovered the short-period variations in latitude, and until 1948 the observatory was the seat of the international office for variations in latitude, an office now transferred to the observatory of Pino Torinese near Turin.

In most of the European nations, as in Italy, observatories have been multiplying and continuously perfecting their instruments in order to achieve greater precision in the determination of the positions of the celestial bodies. However, these observatories were all in the Northern Hemisphere, and the necessity of developing systematic research in the Southern Hemisphere also became more and more evident. After the expeditions sent by the Paris Observatory and by Halley to St. Helena (1676–1678), we reach 1750 before finding a serious project for the study of the southern celestial hemisphere. In that year the Abbot of Lacaille, under the auspices of the Academy of Science in Paris, went to the Cape of Good Hope, the southernmost point which he could conveniently reach, in order to erect an observatory. The determination of the longitude of the Cape with the greatest possible precision was also very important for navigation, and Lacaille proposed to make such a determination through observations of the eclipses of Jupiter's satellites, comparing them with corresponding observations in Europe. We have mentioned, on preceding pages, the work done at the observatory of the Cape of Good Hope and its great development, especially under the direction of Sir David Gill. Writing in 1913 the history of the Cape observatory, he recalls in the preface the story of another famous observatory, the "Central" of Pulkovo, founded by Emperor Nicholas I of Russia under the direction of F. W. Struve in 1830. Sir David Gill speaks of Struve's work in this way:

> There is inspiration to be found in nearly every page of it, for its author had the true genius and spirit of the practical astronomer—the love of refined and precise methods of observation and the inventive mechanical and engineering capacity—these qualities in him being stimulated to the highest degree by the unique opportunity offered by Emperor Nicholas, viz., the command to design and erect, almost regardless of cost, the most perfect and complete observatory that Struve could devise.

In truth the instrumental equipment with which the best German technicians furnished the observatory, and the ability with which it was employed by Struve and his successors, led to remarkable results, especially in positional astronomy, in astronomical constants, double stars, and so on.

Following Father Secchi, the Jesuit Fathers did not forget the study of the sky and they have today, through the munificence of Pope Pius XI, a modern observatory built on the pontifical palace of Castel Gandolfo in the vicinity of Rome. Besides the modern astronomical instruments, there is a very well equipped astrophysical laboratory which has published, among other things, important spectroscopic atlases.

Meanwhile the desire and ambition to promote scientific research with large funds provided in great part by generous benefactors was spreading through the new world, and in 1839 the Harvard Observatory was established by an official act of the corporation of Harvard University. The work of the new observatory was soon directed into many branches of astronomy, a large staff availing itself of the new research methods then coming into use, particularly photography and spectral analysis. J. W. Draper, in whose honor the present classification of stellar spectra is named, obtained in 1840 the first photograph of the moon, with an exposure of 20 minutes. Daguerrotypes were also used as early as 1842 on total eclipses of the sun, and the sun itself was photographed in 1845.

A very considerable development was added to the observatory by its fourth director, E. C. Pickering, who, as a physicist, gave a great impulse to astrophysical research. He did not, however, forget positional astronomy which, with the meridian circle, had kept astronomers and calculators occupied for nearly forty years. In 1921 he was succeeded by Harlow Shapley, whose work is very well known.

In the search for better sky conditions, for calmness and transparency of the atmosphere, Lick Observatory was inaugurated in 1888 on Mt. Hamilton, Santa Clara County, California. James Lick was an organ- and piano-maker, a pioneer California businessman and landholder. He provided a sum of $700,000 for building an observatory to contain the most powerful telescope in the world, to be connected with the University of California. His body now lies in the base of the pier of the 36-inch refractor. From the time of its foundation and with the addition of many other instruments, Lick Observatory has risen to great fame through the work of well known astronomers, from E. S. Holden, who was its first director, to J. E. Keeler, S. W. Burnham, E. E. Barnard, and W. W. Campbell, director from 1900 to 1939 and president of the University of California. Succeeding him were R. G. Aitken and W. H. Wright; the observatory is now directed by C. D. Shane. At Mt. Hamilton there is now under construction a reflector with a 120-inch mirror, which will be the second largest in the world.

The inventions and discoveries of G. E. Hale in the United States and of H. Deslandres in France made ever more evident the importance of research on solar physics. How Hale, from his first observatory at Kenwood near Chicago, seized an opportunity to obtain glass disks for a 40-inch objective and to plan for the large Yerkes

Observatory has been told in Chapter 9. Photographic determinations of parallaxes and spectrographic and spectroheliographic observations have been made and are being made with the 40-inch refractor and with other instruments. The dependent station, McDonald Observatory in Fort Davis, Texas, was built by Otto Struve II.

Meanwhile in Washington the Carnegie Institution was founded, devoted exclusively to the furtherance of research. Hale immediately took advantage of it to establish an observatory exclusively for the study of the sun. Scrupulous care was taken in selecting a suitable location, and the choice fell on Mt. Wilson, on the Sierra Madre near Pasadena in southern California. In 1904 the Carnegie Institution furnished the means to send there an expedition composed of Hale and his faithful collaborators, W. S. Adams and F. Ellerman. First the horizontal Snow telescope was erected, equipped with a spectroheliograph; later two solar towers, a 60-inch reflector, and the Hooker 100-inch reflector. With these powerful instruments and with a complete astrophysical laboratory, partly at the observatory at Pasadena and partly on Mt. Wilson, research was no longer limited to solar physics but spread to other fields, such as the study of the structure of our Galaxy and the visible universe.

The great and rapid development of these scientific institutes in California, the foundation of the California Institute of Technology ("Caltech"), at Pasadena, the opportunities offered by the Rockefeller Foundation, stimulated the initiative and genius of Hale to increase still further the power of optical and mechanical means for the investigation of the sky. At Mt. Wilson astronomers and engineers were prepared to undertake the planning of a new telescope, a reflector with a 200-inch aperture.

Perhaps the most important fact to emphasize about the two observatories, Mt. Wilson and Mt. Palomar, the former under the auspices of the Carnegie Institution, the latter under the auspices of the Rockefeller Foundation, in that they operate jointly under the same direction, availing themselves of the collaboration of the noted astronomers of Mt. Wilson and of the astrophysical laboratory of Caltech. The astronomical and lay worlds await the results which certainly will be forthcoming from the persevering work of these two observatories, results as important as those achieved with the 100-inch telescope in the period from 1918 to the present. We can say that if the name of Galileo has been linked for more than three centuries to the first telescope, the name of Hale will always be connected with the telescope of Mt. Palomar. In fact, at the entrance to the great dome which houses it, on a bronze tablet under the bust of Hale, we read: "Two hundred inch telescope—named in honor of George Ellery Hale, 1868–1938. His vision and leadership made it a reality."

index